FOR ANDREW AND SIMON

Breasts, Bottles and Babies

who first aroused my interest in
infant feeding, and provided
invaluable practical
experience

BREASTS, BOTTLES AND BABIES

A History of Infant Feeding
by Valerie A. Fildes

EDINBURGH UNIVERSITY PRESS

© Valerie A. Fildes 1986
Edinburgh University Press
22 George Square, Edinburgh

Set in Linotronic Ehrhardt by
Speedspools, Edinburgh, and
printed in Great Britain by
The Alden Press Ltd, Oxford

British Library Cataloguing
in Publication Data
Fildes, Valerie A.
Breasts, bottles and babies:
a history of infant feeding
1. Infants — Nutrition — History
I. Title
649.3'09   RJ216
ISBN 0 85224 462 2

CONTENTS

PART ONE

Infant Feeding from Antiquity to the Renaissance:
Sources for a Study

Chronology c. BC 3000–1500 AD: The ancient Near East: Ancient India, the medical literature: Greece and Rome: Byzantium, the medical literature: Islam: Medieval Europe: The paediatric incunabula

PART TWO

Infant Feeding 1500–1800

Neonatal mortality: Maternal mortality: Maternal–infant relationships: Summary

Incidence in different parts of society: Reasons why mothers did not breast-feed: Contraceptive effect of breastfeeding: Acceptable reasons for not breastfeeding: Medical and religious ideas and recommendations: Reasons for preferring maternal breastfeeding: Technique of breastfeeding: Time and frequency of suckling: Quantity of breast milk: Summary

Insufficient breast milk (Internal remedies; Local applications; Sucking or drawing breasts; Other remedies): Too much milk: Drying up breast milk: Problems with breasts and nipples: Instruments connected with breast-feeding (Sucking glasses or breast pumps; Nipple shields and caps): Summary

LIST OF FIGURES

I WISH to thank the Wellcome Trust and the Nestlé Company Ltd for financial support during the writing of this book; this enabled me to investigate some aspects of infant feeding further than would otherwise have been possible. In the research and writing of the thesis on which Part 2 of this book is based, I received much encouragement and guidance from my supervisor, Professor Peter Davis of the University of Surrey. Professor Roger Short was responsible for encouraging me to write this book and suggested additions and alterations which have served to improve the final result. Mr Archie Turnbull of Edinburgh University Press has been helpful and encouraging throughout, and suggested several improvements to the original manuscript.

Many people from a variety of institutions have given freely of their time and expertise; some going to considerable trouble to clarify points within their own specialties which I wanted to relate to my own research. Some allowed me access to their own unpublished work and others provided helpful references and possible lines of enquiry. I am particularly indebted to Dr William Bynum; Dr Dorothy McLaren; Dr Roger Finlay; Dr Richard Palmer; Dr Richard Wall; Professor John Knodel; Dr Roger Schofield; Dr Fiona Newall; Dr Jane O'Hara May; Dr Johanna Geyer-Kordesch; Dr Debbie Dwork; Dr Faye Getz; Dr Jean Donnison; Dr Jonathan Shaw; Dr Adrian Wilson; Dr Roy Porter; Dr Michael MacDonald; Dr Carol Dickerson; Dr Patricia Crawford; Dr D. Dixon; Mr and Mrs Colin Hickman; Ms Sandra Cavallo; Mr A. Jones; Dr Harry McGurk; Professor Dickerson; Mrs Pallawela; Dr Rosalind Marshall and Dr Linda Pollock.

For tracing illustrations, and discussion of their relevance and the caution with which they should be interpreted, I am indebted to Dr Renate Burgess; Dr Elizabeth Sears; Dr E. Langmuir; Mrs Ginsberg; Dr Wolfgang Eckart and Dr K-D. Fischer. For photographic provision and assistance I am grateful to the staff of museums and art galleries all over the British Isles, all of whom dealt with my queries with interest and expertise. In particular, the Wellcome Institute for the History of Medicine, London; The Museum of London; The Fitzwilliam Museum, Cambridge; The Museum for the History of Medicine, Academy of Medicine, Toronto; The Howard Dittrick Museum, Cleveland, Ohio; Ashmolean Museum, Oxford; and the Victoria and Albert Museum, London. Two individuals merit my special thanks: Mr William Schupbach and Mrs Joan Drage. In addition I am grateful to the Clergy of numerous parishes who allowed me to photograph and/or make rubbings of memorial brasses and monuments in their particular church; especially those of Brampton, Norfolk; Blickling, Norfolk; Deal, Kent; Edwardstone, Suffolk; and Kimbolton, Cambridgeshire.

For information about feeding vessels I am indebted to those concerned with cataloguing and arranging the Wellcome Collection at the Science Museum, particularly Drs C.Lawrence; R.Driscoll; R. de Peyer; A.Ineson; and J.Shepherd. I also received much help from Mr R.Opie and Mr Gunnee of Cow and Gate Ltd; from Mr R.Hutchings who was responsible for building up the Cow and Gate Feeding Bottle Collection; and from Mr Raffé and Mr Hendey of the Nestlé Company Ltd.

For translation from French and German I must thank Mr Robert Brettell and Mrs Birgit Baldock, whilst Mrs Babs Crickett magnificently organised the chaos of my notes and indexes at a time when they threatened to overwhelm me.

My research into infant feeding would have been impossible without the facilities offered by the libraries of the following institutions, and the interested assistance given by their staff: British Library, London; Cambridge Group for the History of Population and Social Structure, Cambridge; Hertfordshire County Record Office and Local Studies Library, Hertford; Institute for Child Health, London; London Borough of Harrow Libraries, Grant Road Branch; Royal College of Obstetricians and Gynaecologists, London; Royal College of Physicians, London; Society of Friends, London; University of London, Senate House; and particularly the Wellcome Institute for the History of Medicine, London.

For permission to use quotations from published works I am grateful to the following publishers: Academic Press, New York; Allen & Unwin, London; Blakiston Company, Philadelphia; Cambridge University Press; Cassell, London; Charles Thomas, Philadelphia; Clarendon Press, Oxford; Collins, London; Constable, London; Duckworth & Co, London; Harper & Row, New York; Heinemann, London; Irish Manuscripts Commission, Dublin; John Murray, London; Johns Hopkins Press, Baltimore; Little Brown & Co., Boston; Oxford University Press, Oxford; Paul Hoeber, New York; Penguin Books, Harmondsworth; Routledge & Kegan Paul, London; Souvenir Press, London; Thomas Nelson & Sons, London; Virago, London; Ward-Ritchie, New York; Weidenfeld & Nicolson, London. Also the editors and publishers of the following journals: *American Journal for the Diseases of Children*; *Annals of Medical History*; *Archives of Disease in Childhood*; *Canadian Medical Association Journal*; *Journal of Pediatrics*; *Population Studies*. In particular the *Journal of Biosocial Science* in which the substance of chapters 2 and 15 of this book first appeared; and *Nursing Mirror* and *Nursing Times* in which part of chapters 16 and 17 first appeared.

In selecting illustrations for this book, every effort has been made to consult the owner of copyright; any error or omission is unintended. For permission to reproduce photographs I am grateful to the following: Annenmuseum, Lübeck, Germany; Ashmolean Museum, Oxford; British Museum, London; Canterbury Museum, Kent; Castle Museum, York; Colchester Museum, Essex; Cow and Gate Ltd, Trowbridge, Wiltshire; H. Dittrick Museum, Cleveland Medical Library, Cleveland, Ohio; Dover, New York; Drake Collection, Academy of Medicine, Toronto; Fitzwilliam Museum, Cambridge; Friedrich Pustet, Regensburg; Louvre, Paris; Museum of London; Nestlé Company Ltd, London; Oxford University Press, Oxford; Roger Dacosta, Paris; Reading Museum, Berkshire; Staatliche Museen, Berlin; Thomas Coram Foundation for Children, London; Victoria and Albert Museum, London; Wellcome Institute Library, London.

I was able to undertake the necessary research for this book only because of the willingness of friends and family to assist with childcare. I particularly wish to acknowledge the help of my late mother, and the active help, advice and interest of my husband, Brian. He has lived, somewhat uneasily, with infant feeding for several years; has been a sounding board for my ideas; played devil's advocate to my theories; and provided a critical review of all I have written. Without him this book would never have been written.

THE FIRST PART of this book is a descriptive review of source material on infant feeding in ancient and mediaeval societies. It is intended to be a general, and much less detailed, introduction to the main body of the book, which examines in depth the methods of feeding infants during the period 1500–1800; an era of which there has been no detailed examination of infancy (as opposed to childhood).

The year 1500 was chosen as an approximate starting date because the late 15th century marked the beginning of printed books, and many of those coming from the early presses were popular medical texts. Significantly, the very first book of this type printed in the vernacular (Latin would have confined its use to the scholarly) was a treatise on paediatrics and childcare (Metlinger 1473). The 16th century also saw the beginning of detailed records of baptisms, marriages and burials in parish registers (1538), and the publication of Bills of Mortality for the capital city which, however crude, made possible some estimation of infant morbidity and mortality (1529). The survey in Part 1 shows clearly the source of many of the ideas used by 16th- and 17th-century physicians and midwives.

1800 was selected as the finishing date because it marked the approximate end of the pre-industrial period of European history. While including the early changes of industrialisation, some of which were relevant to infant care (e.g. the mass production of feeding bottles by the Staffordshire potteries) it preceded the major medical discoveries of the 19th century related to infant feeding (particularly those of Liebig and Pasteur).

Today, infant feeding is primarily the province of the mother, assisted by midwives, health visitors, and, to a much lesser extent, the general practitioner and paediatrician. But the consequences of infant feeding must interest not only professional nurses, midwives, paediatricians, nutritionists and surgeons, but the physical anthropologist (concerned with growth and development); the psychologist (who relates it to emotional and physical development); the sociologist/social worker (who is interested in the general welfare of infants in the context of the family and the community); the social anthropologist (investigating differences between cultures); and the medical statistician or demographer (interested in questions such as fertility in breastfeeding mothers and the morbidity and mortality of infants). Thus, a notable feature of studies of infant feeding is their inter- or multi-disciplinary nature. Any study of its history must also involve this variety.

The principal area here studied is the British Isles, although the mass of evidence relates to England. In the 18th century, many of the physicians and surgeons whose writings are referred to in this book had lived and/or been trained for several years in Scotland, particularly in Edinburgh, and they refer to Scottish examples and case histories as well as to those from England. Throughout the whole period, English and Scottish physicians largely gained their medical degrees, experience and ideas from European Universities such as Padua, Montpellier, Rheims and, especially, Leyden. Thus medical ideas relating to young children were more frequently cosmopolitan than parochial. In contrast, literary sources, such as letters, diaries and memoirs relate to the strictly local or regional customs and practices; but among the upper classes, who travelled between London and their country houses in all parts of the British Isles, the care of infants related to the social class of the parents rather than to where they lived.

In some aspects of infant feeding there were major differences between Britain and other regions and nationalities (for example, in artificial feeding and wet nursing), and in such cases evidence of French, German, other European and American Colonial practices has been employed for comparison, and to illustrate and clarify the differences. Differences between social classes within Britain are also detailed.

In the three centuries under review, infant feeding was of such common concern that reference to the subject is commonplace in novels, plays, painting and sculpture. Such a large body of potential material has enforced a selection of detail in each aspect of feeding. Some topics have been chosen for greater attention than others, particularly those which have not yet been investigated by any published writer; for instance, neonatal feeding, the foods used for mixed feeding, and the age of weaning. Some of the problems associated with infant feeding from the woman's point of view (for example, the physical problems of breastfeeding) have also been highlighted.

In the interpretation of the historical data, particularly in identifying possible trends and changes, attention is focused on three main points: the concern for, and effect on, the child; the concern for, and effect on, the mother; and the concern for, and effect on, the mother-child relationship. Modern research on infant feeding and associated care from all parts of the world, published predominantly in the specialist fields of paediatrics, nutrition, social anthropology and developmental psychology, has been used to aid interpretation, against the background of current ideas in historical demography, and social and family history.

A proper understanding of infant feeding practices in the past requires an up-to-date knowledge of different feeding habits, and their relationship to infant disease and mortality. The aim of this book is to discover and demonstrate how mothers did manage to feed their infants in a pre-industrial society, and to relate this information to current practice in pre-industrial societies today.

The evidence: From historical sources, two main types of information were sought and analysed: 1) medical and other educated opinions and recommendations written during the period 1500–1800; 2) the opinions and practices of people living at the time. The following is a brief resumé of the type of materials and sources used in the present volume. For a critical survey of previous literature on this subject, readers are referred to my thesis, *The history of infant feeding 1500–1800* (University of Surrey) which formed the original draft of Part 2 of the present work.

The books and manuscripts: In the period 1500–1800 infant care was thought to be the province of the midwife rather than of the physician, and most midwifery texts contained chapters on childcare and/or diseases of children. For this reason midwifery texts and manuscripts were examined in addition to treatises on paediatrics and general medicine. A small sample of relevant theological and educational works were also included.

Some books ran to about 20 editions during a period of 200 years, so it was clearly impractical to look at every book published. The first available edition of each book written in English has been examined, unless there was a definite reason for looking at a later edition (for example, a new supplement on hand-feeding). The aim of reading every author writing in English on the topic of infant nutrition between 1500 and 1800 was further modified by the availability of their books. Only those which could be found in the following London libraries were studied: Library of The Wellcome Institute for the History of Medicine; The Royal College of Obstetricians and Gynaecologists; The Royal College of Physicians; The British Library; The University of London, Senate House.

The first English translation of European books on midwifery and paediatrics were included, on the grounds that, if they were on sale in the English language, they could have influenced feeding practices in Britain and America. In addition, they provide material for comparison between countries.

Where a text was written in Latin in the 16th century and was not translated into English until the 18th century, it was regarded as a work of the century in which it first appeared, on the grounds that it reflected the practices and opinions of that century and that all educated people could read the Latin in which it was originally written. In a few instances, where a European text contained a first statement of importance in the history of infant feeding and no English translation was published, the short translations contained in Still's *History of paediatrics* (1931) and

Ruhrah's *Pediatrics of the past* (1925) were used.

The list of works analysed fell into eight general categories and are shown here in descending order of importance; that is, the largest number and the most comprehensive publications for this study were *Paediatric texts* (1), and the lowest number and least comprehensive were *Theological texts* (8).

Categories of books and manuscripts analysed.

Publications/manuscripts	Principally written by	Intended readership
1. Paediatric texts	physicians, apothecaries	medical and/or general public
2. Midwifery texts	man-midwives, mid-wives, occasionally physicians	midwives, physicians, general public
3. General medical works (which included information about infant care)	physicians, apothecaries, surgeons	physicians, apothecaries surgeons
4. Popular medical works (including some dietaries of the 16th century)	physicians, non-medical authors	general public
5. Advice books on child rearing	physicians, apothecaries, midwives	general public, particularly mothers and nurses
6. Manuscripts of notes taken at midwifery/infant care lectures in Edinburgh and London	student physicians, trainee man-midwives	
7. Educational texts	paedogogues, educated men	general public, particularly parents
8. Theological texts (including printed sermons and domestic conduct books)	puritans, protestant clergy, archbishops of Canterbury	general public, particularly married couples

The medical and other learned books: In the study of each work the chapters directly concerned with infant feeding were examined, in addition to any case histories or references to nurses, breast care, and infants and their diseases in the remainder of the text. It early became apparent that the subject matter divided naturally into five major areas: maternal feeding; wet nursing; mixed or supplementary feeding; artificial feeding; and weaning. These are considered in turn in Part 2. Each topic was analysed separately in order to find : i) recommendations of writers; ii) practices said by writers to be common; iii) some 'actual' examples from case histories.

Literary sources: The aim of including non-medical sources was to find examples of actual feeding practices, and opinions about them, from contemporary literature. Apart from some manuscript letters in the

Friends' House Library, London, only printed sources were used, which were available from the following libraries: The British Library, University of London Library, Senate House, The Public Library System.

The literary sources of information examined fell into six categories: letters; memoirs; diaries; autobiographies and biographies; newspapers/journals; novels and plays. These provided information about the feeding of particular children (often named) which were added to those obtained from medical and learned books. They were also used to discover supplementary information about attitudes to infant feeding, and statements from foreigners about what they observed to be common practice in England.

Pictorial evidence: Pictorial evidence of feeding practices was sought throughout. In addition to prints and figures in medical books, an attempt was made to find as many different types of pictorial evidence as possible; including woodcuts, sculptures, wood carvings, monumental brasses, church monuments, paintings and drawings. Again, these gave some information about the feeding practices of people in this period.

Data on feeding vessels: This investigation was approached initially by examining specialist books about nursery antiques, antique medical ceramics and surgical instruments, and archaeological publications. The two major collections used were those of The Wellcome Museum for the History of Medicine (now at the Science Museum, London) and the Cow and Gate collection of feeding vessels. Published material of items in other important collections (particularly that of T. G. H. Drake at Toronto) were used for comparison and verification. These artefacts were compared with the pictorial evidence of feeding vessels in use, and the information from the medical and literary sources, to provide a comprehensive study of the development of the infant feeding bottle.

Additional sources: For the comparison of feeding practices in Britain with those of other parts of the world, most notably France, Germany and Colonial America, published sources were used. But, for reasons of finance, time, geography, and linguistic ability, some parts of this investigation rely upon lengthy correspondence and discussion with scholars who have conducted research into specific areas. I am grateful for the time and expertise of demographers, social historians, anthropologists, psychologists, nutritionists, paediatricians, and museum staff. They helped me immensely in making a general study of infant mortality from 1550; the history of the family; the history of childhood; history of nutrition; psychological theories about breastfeeding; and information about infant feeding in pre-industrial societies today; all of which were necessary for applying my research to problems concerned with infant mortality, maternal-infant bonding, and general maternal and infant health.

Critique: There are several drawbacks inherent to this type of history, some of which should be considered when reading the detailed history in part 2. Books on the subject of infant feeding and paediatrics written in Greek and in Latin (the language used by all educated people in the 16th and 17th centuries) were omitted from the analysis. It is not known whether these would have altered or confirmed the findings. Similarly, it is not known how many people read the books of medical authors or, if they did so, whether they followed the recommendations or heeded the opinions of the author. Neither can we tell how typical were the views of medical authors compared with other medical opinions of the day.

In the case of printed literary sources, some relevant material could have been 'edited out' as being of no interest to the general reader. This is particularly applicable to material published in the 19th century, when intimate details of childbirth and women's health were sometimes thought unsuitable for inclusion. Letters and memoirs, especially, tend to be confined to the upper social classes, so that the care of their infants, and their opinions about this, may be quite different from those of the rest of the population. It is hoped that, by employing as many different types of sources as possible, and analysing them quantitatively as well as qualitatively, a truer picture has been obtained than if a very narrow group of sources was used descriptively.

Tables and figures: As will be immediately apparent, there was a great difference in the number of texts studied in each century. This does not reflect the interest in the subject of infant feeding but is a function of the total number of books published in Britain during the period 1500–1800. Publication of books in English increased during the 17th century and escalated in the 18th century so that, by the second half of the 18th century, almost as many texts were available for consideration as the total number studied in the preceding two hundred and fifty years. In order to make comparisons, the number of published writers discussing infant feeding in each period has been taken as representative of views in that century, although the conclusions drawn from a smaller number of writers necessarily must be more tentative.

Because of this great discrepancy in the number of texts, and the differences in period, background and daily lives of both writers and the population as a whole, as well as the nature of the data, it was not considered valid to apply statistical analysis to the figures obtained. Therefore, except in the rare cases where large numbers of reliable figures were available (e.g. infant mortality rates) all findings are presented in the form of the proportion of writers in each century who made particular observations or recommendations. Except where a table is necessary to the fullest understanding of the written text, all the tables have been collected together in the statistical appendix at the end of the book. In many instances, writers gave two or more opinions about a particular food or feeding practice, thus the proportions in some tables do not add up to 1.00. The aim is to show quickly and concisely the views held by physicians, surgeons and midwives in each century, and to identify any gross changes which might have occurred during a 300-year period. Although the different sizes of the samples in different centuries does reduce the validity of comparisons made between them on some topics, this method is useful in identifying general trends, and apparently sudden changes.

In many tables, which contain the opinions of up to 50 authors, it would be unwieldy to list these on each occasion; if the reader wishes to obtain a detailed breakdown of the evidence given in a table or figure, he/she is referred to the above mentioned thesis or to other published papers of the author which will be quoted in the bibliography and reference list at the end of the relevant chapter.

Bibliographies and references: A comprehensive bibliography and reference list is included at the end of each chapter. The aim is to present each subject area as a complete study in itself, in the hope that this will prove useful for those requiring detailed knowledge of one particular aspect of infant feeding.

The references noted in the narrative have been cut significantly to facilitate easy reading. If only one author is quoted or referred to in the text, it should not be assumed that this was the sole author to discuss the subject. For extensive and detailed references the reader is again referred to the thesis on which part 2 of this book is based. All references given in a table or chapter refer to the bibliography at the end of the chapter in which it appears. Whether quoted in the text or not, every author that wrote about a particular subject is listed in the bibliography at the end of the relevant chapter. This makes it possible to discover quickly and easily which specific topics in infant feeding were discussed by any given author or publication.

In the bibliography and reference lists the following conventions are used: 1) Anonymous works are listed under the first word of the title, excluding the definite and indefinite article; e.g. The *practice* of midwifery; The *English* midwife; 2) The name of the author is that given in the edition used. Known alternative spellings are given in brackets; 3) The date immediately following the author is normally the date of original publication in Latin or English. Dates given at the end of an entry denote the date of the edition or translation used; 4) Modern translations of pre-renaissance writers are listed under the name of the author of the original work; 5) Diaries, memoirs, letters and autobiographies are listed under the name of the original author; 6) Biographies are listed under the name of the biographer; 7) Hospital reports are listed under the first name of the institution, e.g. the *Found-*

ling Hospital; 8) Parish documents are listed under the name of the parish.

Abbreviations used: where there are alternative spellings (e.g. Paediatrics / Pediatrics) the spelling is that used by the publication itself.

Acta Paediat. Scand. = Acta Paediatrica Scandinavica
Adler Mus. Bull. = Adler Museum Bulletin
Am. J. Dis. Child. = American Journal for the Diseases of Children
Am. J. Orthopsych. = American Journal of Orthopsychiatry
Ann. Demog. Hist. = Annales de Démographie Historique
Ann. Med. Hist. = Annals of Medical History
Anon. = Anonymous
Archs Dis. Childh. = Archives of Disease in Childhood
Archs Pediat. = Archives of Pediatrics
Aust. Paed. J. = Australian Paediatric Journal
Br. Med. Bull. = British Medical Bulletin
Br. Med. J. = British Medical Journal
Bull. Cleveland Med. Libr. = Bulletin of the Cleveland Medical Library
Bull. Hist. Med. = Bulletin of the History of Medicine
Bull. Inst. Hist. Med. = Bulletin of the Institute for the History of Medicine
Bull. Med. Libr. Ass. = Bulletin of the Medical Librarians Association
Bull. Soc. Med. Hist. Chicago = Bulletin of the Society of
    Medical History of Chicago
Bull. Soc. Soc. Hist. Med. = Bulletin of the Society for the
    Social History of Medicine
Bull. Wld Hlth Org. = Bulletin of the World Health Organisation
Can. Med. Ass. J. = Canadian Medical Association Journal
Chemist Drugg. = Chemist and Druggist
Clin. Orth. = Clinical Orthopaedics
Clin. Pediat. = Clinical Pediatrics
Clio Med. = Clio Medica
DHSS = Department of Health and Social Security
Econ. Hist. Rev. = Economic History Review
Ed. = Editor or edition
Eng. Hist. Rev. = English Historical Review
French Hist. Stud. = French Historical Studies
Glasg. Med. J. = Glasgow Medical Journal
Hants = Hampshire
Herts = Hertfordshire
Hist. Childh. Quart. = History of Childhood Quarterly
HMSO = Her Majesty's Stationery Office
HRO = Hertfordshire Record Office
Hum. Biol. = Human Biology
Ind. J. Hist. Med. = Indian Journal of the History of Medicine

J. Adv. Nurs. = Journal of Advanced Nursing
J. Am. Acad. Psychoanal. = Journal of the American Academy of Psychoanalysis
J. Am. Diet. Ass. = Journal of the American Dietetic Association
J. Am. Med. Ass. = Journal of the American Medical Association
J. Biosoc. Sci. = Journal of Biosocial Science
J. Fam. Hist. = Journal of Family History
J. Hist. Behav. Sci. = Journal of the History of the Behavioural Sciences
J. Hist. Ideas = Journal of the History of Ideas
J. Hist. Med. = Journal of the History of Medicine
J. Hum. Nutr. = Journal of Human Nutrition
J. Interdisc. Hist. = Journal of Interdisciplinary History
J. Pediat. = Journal of Pediatrics
J. Psychohist. = Journal of Psychohistory
J. Soc. Hist. = Journal of Social History
Loc. Popul. Stud. = Local Population Studies
Maryland St. Med. J. = Maryland State Medical Journal
Maternity Child. Welf. = Maternity and Child Welfare
Med. Hist. = Medical History
Midwife, Hlth Vis. & Comm. Nurs. = Midwife, Health Visitor and
    Community Nurse
MS(S) = Manuscript(s)
New Engl. J. Med. = New England Journal of Medicine
Nurs. Mirr. = Nursing Mirror
Nurs. Times = Nursing Times
Perspect. Biol. Med. = Perspectives in Biology and Medicine
Popul. Stud. = Population Studies
Proc. R. Soc. = Proceedings of the Royal Society
Proc. R. Soc. Med = Proceedings of the Royal Society of Medicine
Proc. Soc. Med. = Proceedings of the Society of Medicine
Psychohist. Rev. = Psychohistory Review
S. Afr. Med. J. = South African Medical Journal
Soc. Hist. = Social History
SRO = Somerset Record Office
Trans. = Translated
Trans. Stud. Coll. Phys. Philad. = Transactions and Studies of the College
    of Physicians of Philadelphia
WHO = World Health Organisation

3000–c.1000 BC	Old Testament c.23rd C. *Egypt* (Hebrew) Code of Hammurabi. *Mesopotamia* Ebers Papyrus c.1550. *Egypt* Lesser Berlin Papyrus 16th C. *Egypt*	*Feeding vessels discovered in* Egypt, Cyprus, France
c.1000–900 BC	Protogeometric pottery. *Greece*	Greece, Cyprus
c.900–c.700 BC	Homer *Iliad* and *Odyssey*. *Greece* Rome founded c.753 BC. *Rome*	
c.700–c.500 BC	Assurbanipal 7th c. *Mesopotamia*	
c.500–c.300 BC	Herodotus 484–424. *Greece* Socrates 470–399. *Greece* Hippocrates 460–370. *Greece* Aristophanes 450–388. *Greece* Plato 429–347. *Greece* Aristotle 384–322. *Greece*	Greece, Cyprus, Phoenicia, Egypt, Sudan, Southern Italy, Germany, Austria
c.300–c.1 BC	*Susruta Samhita* 4th–2nd C. *India*	
c.1–200 AD	Pliny the Elder 23–79. *Rome* Plutarch 50–120. *Greece* *Caraka Samhita* c.1st C. *India* Tacitus c.55–c.119. *Rome* Soranus fl.98–117. *Rome* Galen 130–200. *Rome* Aulus Gellius 2nd c. *Rome*	Rome and the Roman Empire, England, Italy, France, Hungary, Germany
c.200–c.700 AD	Oribasius 325–403. *Byzantium* Aetios of Amida 6th c. *Byzantium* Paulus Aeginata 625–690. *Byzantium* *Astangahrdaya Samhita* 7th C. *India*	
c.700–c.1200 AD	Rhazes 850–932. *Persia* Haly Abbas d.994. *Persia* Avicenna 980–1036. *Persia* Trotula of Salerno d.1097. *Italy* Averroes 1126–1198. *Spain* (Moslem) Maimonides 1135–1204. *Spain* (Hebrew)	Iran, Germany, France
c.1200–c.1500 AD	Aldobrandino of Siena 13th C. *Italy* Gilbertus Anglicus d.c.1250. *England* Bartholomaeus Anglicus d.c.1291. *England* Bernardus Gordonius fl.1285–1307. *Scotland* Arnold of Villanova c.1240–1311. *Spain* John of Gaddesden ?1280–1361. *England* Heinrich von Louffenberg d.c.1458. *Germany* Michele Savonarola d.1462. *Italy* Bartholomaeus Metlinger d.1491. *Germany* Paulus Bagellardus d.1492. *Italy* Cornelius Roelans 1450–1525. *Belgium*	France, Germany, England

PART ONE

Infant Feeding from Antiquity to
the Renaissance: Sources for a Study

CHAPTER ONE

Infant Feeding from Antiquity to the Renaissance: Sources for a Study

"And Naomi took the child, and laid it in her bosom,
and became nurse unto it." Ruth, 4, 16

a) *The Ancient Near East*

IN THIS SURVEY of infant-feeding practices in pre-industrial societies, it is appropriate to begin with the peoples of that fertile cradle of civilisation, the ancient Near East. That term describes the civilisations of Mesopotamia (Sumer, Babylon, and Assur); Egypt; and the Bible lands of the Levant. From about 3000 BC onwards there is sufficient evidence – material, pictorial, and epigraphic – to show how infants were fed and cared for. Despite differences of language, culture, and economy, the ways in which these societies regarded young children, and the methods of nurturing them from birth, appear to have been similar, and relatively constant over several millennia.

Children were welcomed and cared for by the matriarchal societies of Babylonia and Egypt [10,17]; and by the Hebrews, who regarded the ability to bear and suckle children as a gift from God [35]. There is no evidence in these societies of exposure of unwanted babies – a practice to which, in other cultures, females were particularly subject. The family structure of the Sumerians, the pre-Semitic peoples of Mesopotamia, where women rarely had more than four children, and frequently more girls than boys, argues against selective infanticide, while indicating the practice of birth control, probably by prolonged suckling and *coitus interruptus.*

High regard for lactating women is implied in the wealth of images of mother goddesses, usually shown holding or suckling an infant. In ancient *Sumer,* the power of the goddess Inanna [the semitic Ishtar] (plate 1.1a) was believed to protect the child before, during, and after birth [17,32,36]. In ancient *Assyria,* the infant's health and safety were thought to be in constant danger from the female demon, Labartu, and incantations were recited, to protect baby, mother (plate 1.1b), and wet nurse. An example is:

3

a

b

c

d

Plate 1.1. a) Babylonia, 6th C. BC.
 Ishtar suckling.
c) Egypt, 6th to 3rd C. BC.
 Isis suckling Horus.

b) Babylonia, 6th C. BC. Woman suckling.
d) Egypt, 9th to 7th C. BC. Hathor
 (with cow's ears).

I implore you, by [   ] and his son,
That you don't come back to this house,
That you don't sit in the chair I sit in now,
That you don't breastfeed the baby as I do,
That the sleeping one shall not awake till the sun rises. [32]

In ancient *Egypt,* Isis (plate 1.1c) nursing the infant king Horus is a common representation [26]. Isis was his mother, and was worshipped by the populace as the goddess of magic who had protected her son Horus from predators and other dangers, and would protect mortal children also. In most such representations of breastfeeding, the child is held in the mother's left arm, sucking at the left breast, nearest to the mother's heart; a custom which lasted late into the Christian era, as *Virgo lactans* [41]. The Egyptians also worshipped the cow as a sacred animal of Hathor, goddess of heaven, and it was later associated with Isis. It was seen as a symbol of motherhood and the continuity of life. Hathor is sometimes depicted in human form, with the head of a cow, sometimes as a cow giving suck both to calves and to children [26] (plate 1.1d).

Evidence of Egyptian practices survives in two medical papyri of the 16th century BC: the *Lesser Berlin,* and the *Ebers.* Spells, potions and incantations were recommended, as means to increase the milk supply of the mother who had difficulty in breastfeeding; to protect her milk; and to recognise and to remedy bad milk. Examples include:

To get a supply of milk in a woman's breast for suckling a child: warm the bones of a *Xra*-fish in oil and rub her back with it.

Again:

Let the woman sit cross-legged and eat fragrant bread of soured *Dourra,* while rubbing the parts with a poppy plant [7].

And:

To recognise milk which is bad: thou shalt perceive that its smell is like *snj* of fish. To recognise milk which is good: its smell is like powder of manna . . . [7].

If a woman experienced pain while nursing, it was not suggested that she should stop suckling, but ointments and incantations were recommended:

Remedy for a breast (mamma) which is ill: Calamine, gall of ox, fly's dirt, yellow ochre, are mixed together, and the breast is rubbed therewith for four days [7].

The Ebers papyrus also demonstrates the high value put on human milk; particularly that of a woman who had borne a male child. Breast milk was included in many oral remedies and local applications for a variety of conditions, including retention of urine in a child; for expelling noxious excrements in the belly of a man; cataract; burns, erisipelas, and eczema [7].

5

¶ If the mother's milk failed to 'come in', or if she died in childbirth, or if for some other reason she was unable to breastfeed her child, then a wet nurse was sought. Wet nursing appears to have been well-known in ancient civilisations, although it was possibly used less among the Hebrews than in Egypt [18] or Mesopotamia [40]. A Sumerian lullaby, almost certainly composed in the late third millennium BC, has the wife of Shulgi, ruler of Ur, sing her son to sleep:

Come sleep, come sleep,
Come to my son,
hurry sleep to my son
put sleep to his restless eyes . . .

She then promises him a wife:

In my song of joy, I will give him a wife,
I will give him a wife. I will give him a son!
The nursemaid, joyous of heart, will sing to him;
The nursemaid, joyous of heart, will suckle him.

This must be among the earliest recorded references to wet nursing.

In ancient *Mesopotamia*, nurses were carefully chosen, and legal contracts were drawn up to safeguard the arrangements between parents and nurse [36]. The *Code of laws* of Hammurabi, Amorite king of Babylon (c.1728–1686 BC) includes a safeguard against nurses illegally substituting babies for those who had died at the breast. The fact that it was thought necessary to include such a clause suggests the prevalence of the act:

When a man gave his son to a nurse and that son has died in the hand of the nurse, if the nurse has then made a contract for another son without the knowledge of the father and mother, they shall prove it against her and they shall cut off her breast because she made a contract for another son without the knowledge of his father and mother [12].

If it were the nurse that died whilst suckling, this was thought to endanger the life of the child. A Sumerian lullaby pleads with the ghost of a deceased nurse not to let harm come to the child, and refers also to the various qualities of milk [32]. The difficulty of feeding weak and premature infants was recognised because 'an untimely birth sucketh not the breast of its mother' [36].

Parents in financial difficulties were allowed to sell their children. A mother could place her baby with a wet nurse for a term of two or three years at a stipulated price and, if the mother were unable to pay the nurse in full, the child could be sold to the nurse, usually at a price higher than that owed by the mother, so that the mother gained a sum of money from the transaction [36]. At least one Babylonian document records such an incident. Royalty, particularly kings, claimed that they were suckled by divine wet nurses. An inscription of about 2750 BC records that the king of Uruk was 'the provider for Inanna (Ishtar), the child of Nisaba, nourished with the milk of Ninhursag' [36].

In ancient *Egypt* also, the practice of wet nursing was widespread. In the pharaonic period legal contracts between parents and a nurse appear to be unknown, but they are common in Ptolemaic and Roman Egypt (304 BC to 4th century AD) [10,24,25]. At the time of the pharaohs, wet nurses were used almost exclusively by the highly-born and by royalty [18]. The royal wet nurses were selected from the harem of senior officials of the royal palace and enjoyed a high status. When a queen gave birth to a child, the baby was apparently immediately put to the breast of a wet nurse. Illustrations of royal confinements often include a second child, with one in the process of being born while the other is at the breast of a wet nurse. Each royal infant had several wet nurses. Some would actually suckle the child for a period of time, but others who were designated wet nurses needed only to put the infant symbolically to the breast for a short time [18].

The status of the Egyptian wet nurses was such that they appear in guest-lists of funeral feasts of royalty. In addition, the child of a royal wet nurse was allowed to call herself 'milk-sister' to the king [18]. The mother of Qenamūn had the title 'Great Nurse, she who brought up the god' (i.e. Pharaoh Amenophis II) [30]. In Egyptian illustrations, a wet nurse might appear in human form but wearing a distinctive headdress; or as the goddess Hathor, in human form but with the head of a cow [26].

Mention of Egyptian wet nurses brings us to the *Old Testament* story of the discovery of the infant Moses and the subsequent search for a wet nurse among both Egyptians and Hebrews [15,35]. Although the tale was probably embroidered with time, it shows that, in the ancient Levant, the idea of wet nursing an abandoned infant was regarded as essential for its survival.

The specific word used to describe Deborah, the nurse of Rebecca, makes it clear that she was a *wet* nurse [1]. After weaning, she remained with Rebecca until she was a young woman, accompanied her when she married, and remained highly regarded until her death [15]. Wet nurses are referred to elsewhere in the *Old Testament* and in the *Apocrypha* [34]. In the Book of *Ruth*, it is related that Ruth gave her son to her mother-in-law Naomi to nurse. At one time this was thought to be a gesture symbolic of caring, but since it is now known that grandmothers, and adopting mothers who have never been pregnant, are capable of promoting and continuing lactation, it is possibly a true record of a mature woman wet nursing her grandchild. In *Genesis*, it is related that Sarah, wife of Abraham, gave birth to a son in her old age, but it was emphasised that this was no bar to her breastfeeding her own child [34,35]. There are also references to nursing fathers. Though there are legendary accounts of lactating males, here the word is probably used in the sense of nurturing rather than nourishing [35].

There appear to be no laws in the *Old Testament* concerning wet nursing, although, much later, the *Talmud* and *Midrash* specified that it was a mother's duty to her husband to breastfeed, and:

> If a child recognises his mother and will suck from her alone she is forced to nurse him for three months.

Also, as long as the baby refused to suck the breast of another woman, his mother was expected to suckle him. If twins were delivered, then one was to be fed by a wet nurse. If a husband forbade his wife to suckle her baby, she had a legal right to make her own decision, since the labour and trouble would be hers alone. If, however, the wife wished *not* to breastfeed, then the decision was made according to the custom in that particular family. No wife could be forced to suckle her neighbour's child [27].

In *Greek and Roman Egypt*, however, the status both of wet nurses and of the children they suckled were different from what we have so far described. When the customs of Greece and Rome were superimposed on Egyptian life, exposure of infants, especially reflecting the low value of female offspring, became common [3,25]. Unwanted children were often exposed on rubbish heaps. People requiring an inexpensive slave could visit such places, choose an abandoned baby, and then select a wet nurse to feed it for periods of up to three years [10]. This practice is inferred in the naming of such infants *Coprus* or *Coprise* (i.e. picked off a dunghill) [3].

At this period, wet nurses were frequently, but not always, slaves. Contracts between employer and wet nurse, as well as receipts for payment of wages, survive in papyri. These were very often explicit with regard to the period of breastfeeding, supplies of clothes and oil for lamps, in addition to payment in money. The following relates to the engagement of a wet nurse in Egypt, in 13 BC:

> To Protarchus from Isidora . . . and from Didyma daughter of Apollonius, Persian, . . . Didyma agrees to nurse and suckle, outside at her own home in the city, with her own milk pure and untainted, for a period of sixteen months from Pharmouthi of the current 17th year of Caesar, the foundling infant slave child . . . called [. . .] which Isadora has given out to her, receiving from her, Isadora, as wages for milk and nursing, ten silver drachmas and two cotyls of oil every month. So long as she is duly paid she shall take proper care both of herself and of the child, not injuring her milk nor sleeping with a man nor becoming pregnant nor suckling another child . . . Didyma has forthwith received from Isidora by hand from the house oil for the first three months . . . She shall not cease nursing before the end of the time, and if she breaks the

agreement in any way she shall forfeit the wages which she has already received and those which she may have received besides, increased by one half, with damages and expenses, and shall moreover pay 500 drachmas and the prescribed fine, Isidora having the right of execution upon the person of Didyma and all her property as if by legal decision, all assurances which she may produce and all resort to protection being invalid. If she fulfils every condition, Isidora shall deliver to her the monthly wages as stated above for the remaining thirteen months and shall not remove the child before the end of the time, or she herself will pay the like penalty. Didyma shall visit Isidora every month regularly on four separate days bringing the child to be inspected by her . . . [24].

That some of the infants suckled were the bastards of a master and a female slave is shown in the following receipt for a nurse's wages in the 2nd century AD:

Thenkebkis acknowledges the receipt from . . . Isidorus . . . of 500 drachmas of silver, being the residue of payments for nursing and oil and other expenses during the three years in which Sarapias, the slave of Thenkebkis, suckled and nurtured Eudaemon surnamed my [. . .], the male child born to Isidorus by his slave [. . .] which child he has forthwith received back weaned and otherwise in good health . . . [39].

Some contracts specified how long the child should be breastfed whilst remaining with the nurse. One example specifies that the nurse should suckle for six months, and for the following eighteen months should feed the child with cow's milk, undertaking regular daily delivery of 'the best cow's milk' [10]. At this time a variety of feeding vessels was available for administering milk or other liquids to the child. In Greek and Roman Egypt, wealthy women also employed wet nurses, both slaves and freedwomen, but the majority of women breastfed their own infants.

¶ Once the child was several months old he was fed other foods also, particularly animal milk and eggs: even after weaning, his principal food was the milk of animals such as camels, goats, sheep and cows. Additional foods were introduced into the child's diet quite late, and these were almost exclusively of fruit and vegetable origin. Melons, cucumbers, leeks, roots and papyrus shoots were plentiful in Egypt and Mesopotamia, and corn and pulses are also mentioned in the Old Testament [14,30,35].

If no wet nurse could be found for a child, it is probable that some form of artificial feeding was used. As in the case of older infants, the main food was almost certainly animal milk [5], particularly that of sheep, goats and cows [35]. Although there are many portrayals of children sucking directly from a cow, the image is a symbolic one, and a child rather than an infant is depicted [18]; it is not known whether young babies were put to the udders of domesticated animals or whether the animal was first milked and the milk given to the child using some form of feeding vessel. Since direct suckling from animals is well-attested throughout history and in many parts of the world, and survived in Europe up until the 20th century (see chapter 11), it may well have been employed in the early civilisations of the Near East. However, Egyptian vessels depicting women holding or suckling infants (plate 1.2a), or portrayed holding a horn [18,23], were possibly used as feeding vessels, especially as some terracotta horns survive from the same period (plate 1.2c) [23]. Some authorities believe that these small-capacity anthropomorphic vessels were used to hold animal milk; and, possibly, were a luxury form of drinking horn for administering the fluid to the child [32]. Another view is that the women represent the wet nurses of goddesses and that the shape of these containers was intended to provide the contents with magical healing or protective powers (plate 1.2b) [5].

The horns of sheep, goats and calves were easily obtainable, and it is probable that when no other method was available, they were used to administer milk to infants, as well as during the weaning period. The more sophisticated feeding vessels, widely manufactured in the Roman Empire [21], would almost certainly have been used in Egypt also, in the Greco-Roman period. They will be described fully in chapters 13 and 14.

There is a possible reference to artificial feeding with cows' milk in the records of the Assyrian king Ashurbanipal, in the 7th century BC. It is in the form of an answer by the god Nabu to a prayer:

You were little,
Ashurbanipal
When I left you with the Queen of Nineveh,
You were weak
Ashurbanipal,
When you sat on the knees of the Queen of Nineveh.
From the four breasts that were put into your mouth
You sucked from two,
In the other two you hid your face. [32]

The Queen of Nineveh is the mother goddess in the form of a cow, who feeds the young god-king. One other method of feeding an older infant is shown in a relief from the palace of Ashurbanipal at Nineveh. It shows a woman walking with a young child on her shoulders; in one hand she carries a bottle and in the other a small stick with which she feeds the infant [32].

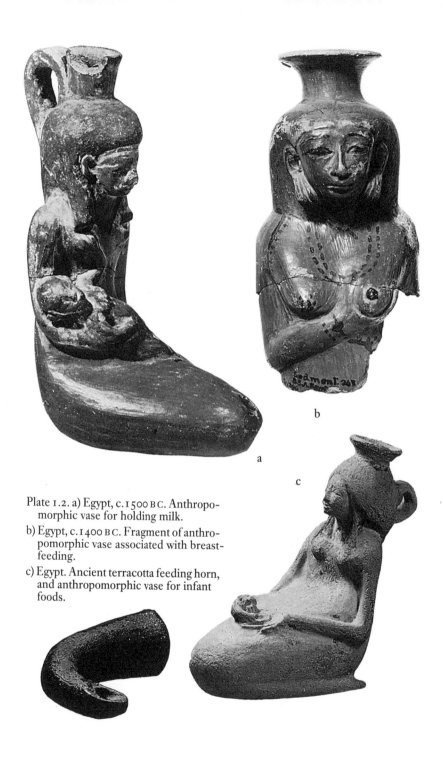

Plate 1.2. a) Egypt, c. 1500 BC. Anthropomorphic vase for holding milk.

b) Egypt, c. 1400 BC. Fragment of anthropomorphic vase associated with breastfeeding.

c) Egypt. Ancient terracotta feeding horn,
and anthropomorphic vase for infant
foods.

¶ Babies were usually breastfed from two to three years [1]. An Egyptian papyrus states:

> When in due time you were born she still carried you on her neck and for three years she suckled you . . . [30].

In Mesopotamia, records from Babylonia contain agreements with wet nurses [36] which specified nursing for two years; others specified three years. Mothers who fed their own infants suckled for the same period [40]. The Hebrews weaned their children after a similar length of time [1]. Three years was said to be the common age of weaning completely from the breast, and denoted the transition from infancy to childhood, when the child was old enough to enter the Temple. Hannah breastfed her son, Samuel, for three years (1 Sam. 1.23), whilst Isaac, son of Abraham, was weaned at the age of two (Rashi, Gen. 21.8). Later – about 200 AD – the period of nursing was laid down in the *Talmud*:

> A baby nurses for twenty-four months . . . the nursing period should not be cut down for the baby may die of thirst [27].

In some ancient societies, sexual intercourse was forbidden during lactation for fear that the mother's milk would be harmed [1,35]; but it was also recognised that lactation prevented conception. The wife of the prophet Hosea weaned her daughter in order to become pregnant and give birth to a son (Hosea 1.8). The long period of suckling has also been suggested as the main contraceptive device of the ancient Egyptians [5]. The *Talmud* decreed that:

> A woman may not marry while nursing a baby for she may become pregnant which will spoil her milk and the child may die of hunger [27].

Should this problem occur, the woman was advised to feed it with eggs and cows' milk [27]. Thus it appears that pregnancy was a justified reason for early weaning.

From the medical papyri of Egypt and from examination of mummies it is known that infant mortality was high, and that gastro-enteric conditions and eye diseases, both of which can be caused or exacerbated by poor nutrition, were common. A long period of breastfeeding in a hot climate would protect the young infant from the problems of contaminated food which accompany weaning. It is notable that although the deficiency disease, rickets, is known to have existed in antiquity, no trace of rachitic deformity has been found in the remains of ancient Egyptians [11,37]; a fact that has been attributed partly to the absence of swaddling and leaving young children naked, and thus exposed to sunlight [6,14].

When medicines were given to a suckling, they were either put on the nurse's breast for the child to suck, or were administered to the nurse, since it was believed that the medicine was transmitted through her breast milk to the child. Similarly, the diet of mothers and nurses was regulated so that the milk would not be spoiled or unsuitable for the child [34].

Plate 1.3. NW India. Medieval 'mother and child'.

b) *Ancient India: the medical literature*

Paediatrics was a well-developed medical speciality in ancient India [1]; the earliest known paediatricians practised there [6], and child-care and children's diseases merited one or more chapters in the four principal works of medicine which survive. The first dates from the Ayurvedic period (1500–800 BC) [5]; the other three from the Brahmanistic period, written between 400 BC and the 7th century AD. The precise date at which each was compiled is unclear, but the surgical document *Susruta Samhita* and the medical treatise *Caraka Samhita* were contemporary with the height of Greek and Roman medicine, while the Vagbhata's *Astangahrdaya Samhita* of the 7th century AD was a summary of both.

On the subject of infant nutrition there was little disagreement between the authorities. What follows is taken chiefly from the *Susruta Samhita* of the 4th to the 2nd centuries BC, in which a chapter is devoted to care of the pregnant and nursing mother and her infant [7], and from the *Caraka Samhita* of the 1st century AD, which had a chapter on the care of neonates and young infants [1,2].

Before the cord was cut, the mouth of the new-born baby was cleaned with ghee (clarified butter) and rock salt. Then, as part of the immediate post-natal rites, it was given an electuary of honey, clarified butter, and the expressed juice of Brahmi leaves and Anantá, mixed with a little gold dust, and given with the ring finger of the feeder [7] – a custom which survives today in some parts of the Indian sub-continent. Since the mother's milk does not appear for three to four days, the infant did not receive milk but was fed three times (morning, noon and evening) on the first day with clarified butter and honey, mixed with Anantá roots which had been sanctified with mantras (sacred chants). On the second and third days it was fed on clarified butter prepared with Lakshana root. On the fourth day the child was given its own handful of honey and clarified butter in the morning and at noon; and in the evening his mother expressed a quantity of her milk and then gave the child her right breast. Expression of her breasts was always to be performed before allowing the child to suck [7]. The *Caraka Samhita* advises that mother's milk and honey both be given from the fourth day.

If the mother were unable to breastfeed, then here, also, a wet nurse was selected, and there exist detailed instructions on the choice of a suitable woman and her milk. For the health of the child she was to be selected from women of its own caste, and of good parentage; of middle height, of middle age, of sound health and good character (not irascible or easily excitable); not fickle or greedy, neither fat nor thin, with unprotruding lips; her breasts should not be pendulant or drawn up, and should contain abundant healthy pure milk. Her skin should be healthy and unmarked, she must be innocent of crimes such as gambling, sleeping in the daytime, or debauchery. She must be affectionate, and all her children must be living [7]. The *Caraka Samhita* specifies that she must have living male children. Warning was given that nursing at the breast of a woman with upturned or flat nipples would deform the child's features, while large and flabby breasts might suffocate the child by covering its mouth and nose.

¶ Having chosen a suitable nurse, on an auspicious day the infant was laid in her lap with its face towards the north, while the nurse looked to the east. After expressing a small quantity of breastmilk, the breast was washed and consecrated with the following incantation:

> O, thou beautiful damsel, may the four oceans
> Of the earth contribute the secretion of milk
> In thy breasts for the purpose for improving
> The bodily strength of the child.

> O, thou with the beautiful face, may the child
> Reared on your milk, attain a long life, like
> The gods made immortal with drinks of nectar. [7]

The child was then put to the right breast. If for want of a good wet nurse the child was fed by several women, it was thought to be a likely prey to many diseases, as it would not be receiving milk suited to its physical needs. If the nurse or mother did not express some milk before feeding, the child might develop a cough, difficulty in breathing, or vomiting. Therefore the infant should never be given this initial milk.

Insufficient breastmilk was attributed to absence of natural affection for the child, or to anger, grief and other passions. To improve her milk supply, the woman must needs have her equanimity restored, and should follow a diet of rice, cereals, meat soups, wine, sesamun-paste, fish and garlic, together with various plant roots [7]. The *Caraka Samhita* says that, for good lactation, the mother or wet nurse should include wine in her diet, the flesh of animals living in marshy places, cows' milk, and plants with a milky juice. All these have clearly to do with sympathetic medicine. Overproduction of breastmilk was thought to be due to overuse of such foods, and also to excessive joy, contentment, peace of mind, absence of exertion, and the use of fattening foods [1].

To test for good breastmilk, a little should be expressed and cast into water. The ideal milk should mix easily with water, not form froths, float or sink, and should appear thin, cold, clear, and of the colour of a conch shell. It should have natural colour, smell, taste and touch [7]. A baby would thrive on such milk. Infants were never to be suckled with 'vitiated milk'; that which was abnormal in colour, taste or smell, because they would easily become diseased. Similarly, no infant should be fed by a hungry, aggrieved, fatigued, too thin, too fat, fevered, pregnant, or otherwise unhealthy woman. The nurse and her milk must in this case be treated with suitable medication, since treating the child alone was regarded as being inappropriate [2,7].

When a suckling infant was suffering from any disease, the breast of the mother or wet nurse was to be plastered with ointments advised by the physician for the particular malady, and then the child was put to the breast [7]. Alternatively, the nurse was given the medicine and the child suckled, since it was believed that the potion was transmitted through the breastmilk [7]. Occasionally an infant at least one month old could be given a pinch of medicine. An infant who was solely breastfed could be given a small dose by mouth, mixed with milk and clarified butter, in addition to the mother or nurse taking a dose. A child on a mixed diet of breastmilk and a solid, such as rice, could be given a decoction of various plants boiled with clarified butter, the whole not larger than a plum stone. Children on solid foods only were given a dose the size of a plum stone and the nurse was treated [2]. A child who was feverish was not to be breastfed at all in case 'the symptoms of thirst might develop' [7].

15

¶ The medical texts of ancient India have differing instructions on when the infant should be given its first solid food. The *Susruta* says 'in the sixth month of its birth the child should be fed on light and wholesome boiled rice' [7]. The earlier Ayurvedic text prescribes milk as the sole food for babies until the end of the first year; milk and solid food until the second birthday; then, weaning from the breast onto solid food only from that time [5]. Again, an infant could be allowed solid food when he began teething. Hindu families mark the giving of the first solid food to babies with a ceremony known as Annaprasana (i.e. initial eating of solid food by a baby) usually synchronised with the onset of teething [5]. The staple given in all cases was rice.

Artificial feeding is specifically mentioned in the ancient texts:

If human milk cannot be obtained, the milk of a healthy cow or a healthy she-goat should be given, in as much quantity as would be necessary for its satiety. Cows' milk is . . . heavy and is a good elixir. It is cold and sweet, both in taste and reaction. It subdues *vayu* (wind) and *pitta* (bile) and is accordingly one of the most efficient vitalising agents. The milk of the she-goat possesses properties similar to those of a cow. It is curative in all diseases [*Caraka Samhita*].

The *Susruta Samhita* states:

Milk is congenial to the organism of a child, it is its proper food. Hence in the absence of sufficient breastmilk, the child should be given the milk of a cow or of a she-goat in adequate quantities [7].

No indication is given as to the method of administering animal milk to a very young infant; neither direct suckling by the animals nor feeding vessels are mentioned.

c) *Greece and Rome*

Ancient Greece provides a significant body of evidence on infant feeding in antiquity. Extant medical texts and extensive mythology apart, there are artefacts such as feeding vessels, images of mother goddesses, wall paintings, vase paintings; opinions of philosophers and dramatists, family letters, wet nursing contracts, and epitaphs. The evidence ranges in time from feeding vessels of the Protogeometric period of about 1000 BC, down to the Hellenistic period. Most of our information comes either from the era in which the Homeric poems were shaped into their present form (perhaps covering the 9th/8th centuries), or from the 5th and 4th centuries, from which date the Hippocratic writings.

The earlier period is less satisfactory in terms of detail, and in its portrayal only of the wealthy aristocratic classes. Nor can the non-specialist decide, in regard to references to child-rearing, whether the practices recall the Mycenean period of the late second millennium BC (the historical setting), or describe the habits of the later age when Homer gave the *Iliad* and *Odyssey* their ultimate form. All we can say is that, in the poems, the infants of the nobility (Achaean and Trojan alike) were breastfed, and usually by the mother. In the *Iliad,* Hecuba suckled her son Hector, while the mother of Achilles 'nurtured him in wrath'. In the *Odyssey* there is a reference to Penelope as a young bride with 'an infant boy at her breast'. Although the custom was apparently less common than it later became, some children were wet nursed. 'Why do you wish to destroy me? You did nourish me at your breast', Odysseus asked his aged nurse Eurycleia [19].

Wet nurses in the early period were slaves, either captive or purchased, and their role was not confined to suckling, for a Greek nurse was responsible for the total care and early education of her charge. She occupied an important place in the household and remained within the family after the child was weaned [42,43]. Eurycleia remained with the family of Odysseus into old age, and she alone recognised him when, after twenty years' absence, he returned home in beggar's rags. As in all periods of history, the close ties of affection established at the breast during infancy were acknowledged, and lasted until death [19,43].

There is no mention in the Homeric period of the later diet of infants, nor how long they were breastfed. It is possible that, as in other civilisations of the first millennium BC, weaning was undertaken at 2–3 years. Nor is artificial feeding referred to, although infant feeding vessels of the period have been found in Greece [5,12,20,22] (plate 1.4). As in Egypt, direct suckling of children by animals is manifest in Greek myth. At a time when unwanted infants were exposed at birth, the myth of abandoned children adopted and suckled by other animals was pervasive. Zeus was said to have been suckled by the goat Amalthea, and an

Plate 1.4. Athens, c.1000 BC. Protogeometric feeding vessel (approx. 10.5 cm
high) from grave of a baby girl.

abandoned son of Herakles was reared by a deer, and given the name
Telephus, 'suckled by a hind' [45] (plate 1.5). The founding of Rome in
the 8th century BC by Romulus and Remus, the foster children of a she-
wolf, illustrates how firmly the possibility of animal suckling was held in
antiquity. Mythical tales these may be, but the belief that children could
be nourished on milk other than that of a woman remains an important
concept.

¶ In the classical period (5th–4th century BC), medical works, such as
those of the Hippocratic corpus, refer to infants only in passing, and
these texts contain no teaching or detailed description of infant nutrition. The Hippocratic *Aphorisms* include:
Infants endure fasting least easily.
Growing bodies have the most innate heat, they therefore require
the most food, for otherwise their bodies are wasted [18].
Teething in infants, which was closely related to the administration of
foods other than milk, and with weaning, received attention in *On
Dentition*:
Those who teethe in winter, all things being equal, come off best.
Those that eat solid food while being suckled bear weaning more
easily.

Plate 1.5. Herculaneum, Italy. Mural
painting of Telephus suckled by a doe.

They also made some general observations about sucklings:
> Children who are naturally well-nourished do not suck milk in
> proportion to their fleshiness.
> Children with voracious appetites, and who suck much milk do not
> put on flesh in proportion.
> Children at the breast that take much milk are generally drowsy.
> Children at the breast that are ill-nourished [and thin] also pick up
> strength with difficulty [18].

At this time it was principally the philosophers and dramatists who
wrote about and referred to the nurture of children. In Aeschylus,
Arsinoe, the nurse of Orestes, saved him from the fate that had befallen
his father Agamemnon.

Aristotle (384–322 BC) paid some attention to methods of infant
feeding. In his *Historia animalium*, he discussed the properties of different milks, lactation, and the human infant. He described the excrements
of the first day:
> [Meconium] resembles blood, extemely dark and pitch-like, but
> later on it becomes milky, for the child takes at once to the breast
> [2].

This indicates that breastfeeding ideally began on the first day of life,
rather than waiting until the third or fourth day after birth; but it is not

stated whether the mother's milk or that of another woman was given at first. Aristotle noted that the first of the milk [i.e. colostrum] was saltish, although he stated also that:

> Milk produced earlier than the seventh month is unfit for use; but as soon as the child is fit to live the milk is fit to use.

He considered that:

> In woman, milk of a livid colour is better that white for nursing purposes; and swarthy woman give healthier milk than fair ones, but milk with a scanty supply of cheese is the most wholesome for children [2].

Referring to dentition, he stated that:

> Children begin to cut their teeth in the seventh month ... And the warmer the nurse's milk so much the quicker are the children's teeth to come.

Describing how milk comes into the breasts after childbirth, he outlined the duration of lactation and its connection with menstruation. His teaching on this point was referred to by writers on breastfeeding and wet nursing until well into the 18th century:

> Women continue to have milk until their next conception; and then the milk stops coming and goes dry ... so long as there is flow of milk the menstrual purgations do not take place, at least as a general rule, though the discharge has been known to occur during the period of suckling ... when the animal is pregnant, milk is found, but for a while it is unfit for use, and then after an interval of usefulness it becomes unfit for use again [21].

Because of these ideas, together with the belief that breastmilk was formed from the menstrual blood which was not shed during pregnancy [2], it was advised for centuries that women were never to be employed as wet nurses if they were menstruating or pregnant; because their milk would be 'spoiled' and/or insufficient for the child.

¶ In this period wet nurses were frequently used, especially by the wealthier classes. As in the Homeric age, they had a high status within the household, often responsible for supervising servants and for certain domestic tasks. The wet nurse came into the home to suckle the child whilst an infant, but remained with her charge until he or she reached adulthood. The nurse of a female would stay with her until she was married, and often went with her to her new home in the role of a privileged servant [43]. The Greek nurse, who was only allowed to suckle one child at a time, was rarely portrayed as unkind or neglectful to her nurselings. Although Aristophanes referred to nurses who robbed their nurselings of their food, she was not commonly portrayed as anything other than a kind, loving and caring woman, devoted to her charge, who loved her in return [42,43].

Many epitaphs, statues and grave *steles* survive, erected by grateful or mourning adults to the memory of their beloved nurse. The following is from 4th century BC Athens commemorating a nurse from the Peloponnese:

Apollodorus the immigrant's daughter Melitta, a nurse.
Here the earth covers Hippostrate's good nurse;
And Hippostrate still misses you. 'I loved you
While you were alive, nurse, I love you still
Now even below the earth, and now I shall
Honour you as long as I live. I know that
For you below the earth also, if there is
Reward for the good, honours will come
First to you in the realm of Persephone and Pluto.' [21]

In *The Republic*, Plato (429–347 BC) gave Socrates' views on family life, modelled on that of Sparta:

As soon as children are born, they will be taken in charge by officers appointed for the purpose, who may be men or women or both, since offices are to be shared by both sexes. The children of the better parents they will carry to the crêche to be reared in the care of nurses living apart in a certain quarter of the city. . . . These officers will also superintend the nursing of the children. They will bring the mothers to the crêche when their breasts are full, while taking every precaution that no mother shall know her own child; and if the mothers have not enough milk, they will provide other wet nurses. They will limit the time during which the mothers will suckle their children, and hand over all the hard work and sitting up at night to nurses and attendants. That will make childbearing an easy business for the Guardians' wives [35].

Wet nurses in Periclean Athens were not always slaves. Free women, often in straitened circumstances, resorted to nursing other peoples' children, to earn wages. Answering the reproach attached to his mother of having been a nurse, Euxitelos said that his father had gone to the war, leaving his mother with two small children to support, and she was obliged to take in Cleinias to nurse. He admitted that it was mean employment, but said that he could give the names of freeborn women who like his mother, were compelled by stress of poverty to become nurses [43]. Inscriptions give evidence of free women becoming wet nurses for wages during this period:

Good Theoxene, wet nurse . . . Good Paideusis, wet nurse . . .
Good Pynete, wet nurse . . . Philyra wet nurse . . . [25,43]

Enslaved nurses could earn their freedom. Inscriptions recording the final process of manumission in 4th-century Athens include several whose profession is stated to be wet nurse:

Onesime, sesame-seed seller . . . Lampris, wet nurse . . . Eupithe,

Plate 1.6. Greece, c.440 BC. Red-figure vase.

her child, wet nurse . . . Thraitta, groceress . . . Atta, pulse-vendor
. . . [25]

Not all well-to-do mothers necessarily employed wet nurses. A vase
dating from 440 BC shows a rare scene of a relatively wealthy mother,
the legitimate wife, breastfeeding her child while her husband looks on
[39] (plate 1.6). The orator, Lysias, describing the trial of a husband
who killed Eratosthenes, his wife's lover, gives us a behind-the-scenes'
glimpse of domestic life in Athens about 400 BC. The husband speaks:

> Now first of all, gentlemen, I must explain that I have a small house
> which is divided into two – the men's quarters and the women's –
> each having the same space, the women upstairs and the men
> downstairs.
>
> After the birth of my child, his mother nursed him; but I did not
> want her to run the risk of going downstairs every time she had to
> give him a bath, so I myself took over the upper storey, and let the
> women have the ground floor. And so it came about that by this
> time it was quite customary for my wife often to go downstairs and
> sleep with the child, so that she could give him the breast and stop
> him from crying.
>
> This went on for a long while, and I had not the slightest
> suspicion. On the contrary, I was in such a fool's paradise that I
> believed my wife to be the chastest woman in all the city [25].

As in many later societies, wet nurses gradually became something of a status symbol for wealthier families. The type of woman to look for was outlined in a letter from Italy of the 3rd or 2nd century B C to a new mother, on how to hire a wet nurse.

Myia to Phyllis, greetings. Here is my advice to you now that you have become a mother. Choose a proper and clean wet nurse, a modest woman who is inclined neither to drowsiness nor to drunkenness. Such a woman can make the best judgements about how to care for children appropriately, particularly if she has milk to nourish them and is not easily persuaded to sleep with her husband, for it is in this that she has an important part, foremost and prefatory to the whole of the child's life, in her nursing, as concerns his being raised well, for he will do everything well, at the proper time. The nurse will give him the nipple and breast, not at his whim, but after due consideration. In this way she will encourage the baby's health. She will not succumb to sleep when she is tired, but when the newborn wants to rest. She will offer the child no small relief.

The wet nurse should not be temperamental or talkative or uncontrolled in her appetite for food, but orderly and temperate, practical, not a foreigner, but a Greek. It is best if the baby is put down to sleep when it is well-filled with milk. Such rest is sweet for little ones and such feeding most effective. If other food is given, it should be as simple as possible. One should stay away from wine completely because it has such a powerful effect, or mix it sparingly with its evening meal of milk. . . . This much then I think it is useful to write at present – my hopes based on nursing according to plan. With the gods' help, I shall in future provide the possible and appropriate reminders about the child's upbringing [50].

¶ The reference to simple food other than breastmilk is a rare instance. Little is known about the foods given to children as supplements, or during weaning from the breast, although the simple milk and cereal dishes later mentioned by Soranus [44] and Galen [13] were probably employed. After weaning, children were said to have been fed on milk and honey and apparently young children thrived on the shoots of figs [43]. There are references to nurses chewing food before giving it to the child, and Atheneus told of a man who had his nurse chew his food for him all his life [43].

An allusion to artificial feeding was made by Antiphanes, who considered the Scythians the wisest of men because they fed their children on mares' milk and cows' milk and did not entrust them to nurses as did the Greeks [43]. This is probably a reference to the Amazons, who scarred the breasts of girls at birth, so that they would not be hindered

a

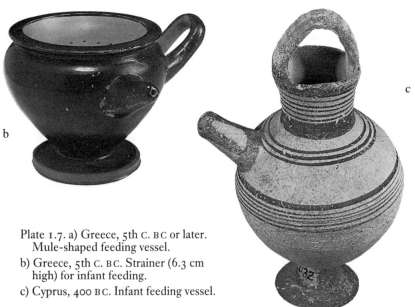

b

c

Plate 1.7. a) Greece, 5th C. BC or later.
Mule-shaped feeding vessel.
b) Greece, 5th C. BC. Strainer (6.3 cm
high) for infant feeding.
c) Cyprus, 400 BC. Infant feeding vessel.

by them when at war in adulthood. These infants were brought up by
the men on milk and other foods suitable to their tender years. It is uncertain here whether the animals were milked and food administered in
feeding vessels, many of which survive from this period [5,20], or
whether the infants sucked directly from the animal.

The age at which children nursed in their own homes were weaned
is uncertain; although wet-nursing contracts from Egypt, in the Greek
period, mention suckling from the breast for six months and then giving
cows' milk for 18 months [14]. The large numbers of feeding vessels of
different design, found especially in child graves all over Greece and
Italy, may indicate that weaning began relatively early, so that a special
vessel was necessary for feeding infants (plate 1.7a, b, c). On some
vases, or *Chous*, infants are occasionally portrayed holding what appears
to be a feeding vessel. On two feeding bottles in the British Museum an
inscription has been roughly scratched. One bears the word *Mamo* (i.e.
the breast), and the other reads, in Greek, *Drink, don't spill*. There can
be no doubt that these vessels were intended for weaned or partially
weaned infants to drink from.

As epilogue to this account of Greece, here is a funerary inscription
of the early Christian period from Athens:

> Good Athenodora, wife of Thaumasius, filled with God's influ-
> ence. She bore children and nursed them when they were infants.
> Earth took this young mother and keeps her, though the children
> need her milk [25].

Plate 1.8. Italy. Romulus and Remus.

Rome. The first medical works to pay significant attention to paediatrics come from Rome in the 1st and 2nd centuries AD. Although some non-medical sources refer to aspects of feeding, notably Pliny (AD 23–79) [36] and Plutarch (AD 50–120) [38], the most significant surviving text is the *Gynecology* written by the Greek physician Soranus of Ephesus (fl. AD 98–117) [44]. This is one of the first accounts in antiquity of paediatrics. It deals with the management of infants and the more-common children's diseases, as well as the care of the newly-delivered mother. It has the added interest that Soranus refers to current practice in infant care, and to the opinions of other physicians whose works have not survived. It is not known exactly how typical Soranus' views were of the medical opinion of his day, but the existence of an Ephesian school of medical thought and practice is attested by the body of writing of a contemporary of Soranus, Rufus of Ephesus. Among his books was a *Peri komides paidiu (On the upbringing of children).* The Greek original has perished; but parts of it survive in the works of Oribasius (see below); and much more in an Arabic translation, by al-Baladi, of about AD 1000 [50a].

The influence of Soranus on later writers of Byzantium and the Arabian school is given in table 1.1, which summarises medical opinion on different aspects of infant nutrition. It is arguable that Soranus was the single most important authority on infant feeding in the pre-industrial world. The other important medical writer of the period was Galen (AD 130–200), whose *De sanitate tuenda* covers the management of infants and children [13]. His views on this subject are often similar to those held by Soranus.

26

The first food recommended to be given a newborn child was boiled honey, or honey and goats' milk. Soranus' preference was to give nothing at all for two days, but, if the baby appeared hungry, then these were the best substances, since honey had a purging effect and helped to expel the *meconium* (black bowel contents) from the intestines before proper food was given. After this the child should be fed by a wet nurse:

> As for twenty days the maternal milk is in most cases unwholesome, being thick, too caseous, and therefore hard to digest, raw, and not prepared to perfection. Furthermore it is produced by bodies which are in a bad state, agitated and changed to the extent that we see the body altered after delivery when, from having a great discharge of blood, it is dried up, toneless, discoloured, and in the majority of cases feverish as well. For all these reasons, it is absurd to prescribe the maternal milk until the body enjoys stable health [44].

Soranus attacked the views of certain other physicians who obviously held differing opinions:

> One ought to censure Damastes, who orders the mother to give the newborn the breast immediately, contending that it is to this end that nature too has provided for the production of milk beforehand so that the newborn may have food straightaway. And one must also blame those who follow his opinion in these things . . . for by plausible sophistry they attempt to confuse clear evidence [44].

Just as occurs today, physicians held widely differing views, and practised paediatrics according to their own beliefs. Galen, for instance, does not seem to have shared the view that mothers' milk was unsuitable for twenty days after birth. In the event that another lactating woman was unavailable to feed the child, then he recommended that for its first three days it could be fed on honey alone, or honey mixed with a little goats' milk. Thereafter the mother could breastfeed it, providing that the 'first milk' had been sucked out by a 'stripling' or expressed by hand [44], since this milk was thought to be too thick and unsuitable for a neonate.

¶ Roman philosophers and moralists were against the employment of wet nurses. Pliny, Plutarch, Tacitus, and Aulus Gellius, all of the 2nd century AD [36,38,49,15], wrote strongly in favour of mothers of all classes feeding their own babies (plate 1.9), perhaps nostalgically reflecting the sterner sentiments of Republican Rome. Mothers' milk, they thought, was the most suitable and healthiest food and, the physiological advantages of maternal breastfeeding apart, they emphasised that if children were given to a wet nurse, then the bond of affection and love between mother and child would wither, possibly building up problems in later life. Writers referred to the fact that poor women had to endure

Plate 1.9. Taranto, Italy, 4th to 3rd C. BC. Suckling mother.

the burden of feeding their own children, whilst wealthy women employed slaves or 'purchased nurses'.

The mother was to be excused breastfeeding only if she were ill or if she wanted to have more children. Plutarch, for example, wrote:

> If [mothers] listen not, because they would have plenty of children, then . . . they should take honest and convenient nurses [38].

It is certain that the association between lactation and conception was known [2], but not clear whether it was recognised that breastfeeding had a contraceptive function, or whether they were referring to the widespread custom of banning sexual intercourse to suckling women. All writers of the period believed that wet nurses should abstain from sexual relations, in case this provoked menstruation and resulted in pregnancy, but whether or not wealthy women were also to abstain is unclear.

Medical writers were less insistent than were the moralists on mothers feeding their own babies. Soranus said that if there were a choice of who should suckle, then the best person should be selected, 'not necessarily the mother, unless she also shows the attributes characteristic of the best nurses' [44]. If the mother were not suitable or healthy enough, then a good wet nurse should be found,

> lest the mother grow prematurely old, having spent herself through

the daily suckling: for, just as the earth is exhausted by producing crops after sowing, and therefore becomes barren of more, the same happens with the woman who nurses the infant; she either grows prematurely old, having fed one child, or the expenditure for the nourishment of the offspring necessarily makes her own body quite emaciated. Consequently, the mother will fare better with a view of her own recovery and further childbearing, if she is relieved of having her breasts distended too [44].

Even if a mother had commenced suckling, Soranus and Galen advised changing to a wet nurse if she became unwell or pregnant – both conditions were thought to harm the milk and thus the child.

Wet nurses were extensively used in Roman society [25,39]. There seems to have been a preference for Greek nurses, but this may be because those who advocated them, though addressing a Greco-Roman audience, were themselves Greek. Soranus twice makes the point:

She should be self-controlled, sympathetic and not ill-tempered, a Greek, and tidy [44].

and again:

She should be a Greek, so that the infant . . . may become accustomed to the best speech [44].

Of all the Greeks, the Spartans were the most highly valued. It has been suggested, above, that Plato's views on child-rearing were influenced by Spartan practice. Plutarch, in his *Life of Lycurgus* (the legendary lawgiver of 9th century BC Sparta) specifically commended the methods of Spartan nurses:

There was much care and art, too, used by the nurses; they had no swaddling bands, the children grew up free and unconstrained in limb and form, not dainty and fanciful about their food; not afraid in the dark, of being left alone; and without peevishness or ill humour, or crying. Upon this account Spartan nurses were often brought up or hired by people of other countries; and it is recorded that she who suckled Alcibiades was a Spartan [37].

Though this nominally describes the practice of the City States of the classical period, it is likely that it also reflected the views of Greco-Roman society in the 1st and 2nd centuries AD, when Plutarch wrote. Rufus of Ephesus, his contemporary and fellow-Greek, had similarly advocated Spartan nurture:

I praise the people called Spartans because they do not give their children enough to satisfy them completely. As a result, they are of good height and their bodies well-proportioned and they suffer no mishap like spasms, melancholy, fear, pain round the heart or anything else. If you want a child to grow tall and straight, with a good complexion, and not turned in on himself, avoid over-feeding him and follow the teaching of the Spartans and the qualities one can observe among them. For when a child is completely satisfied, it sleeps much and becomes lethargic, and its belly is distended and full of wind, and its urine watery [50a].

Although most wet nurses were slaves, some free women worked for wages, and some wet-nursing slaves gained their freedom [39]. Epitaphs of women of the imperial household in the 1st century AD include several wet nurses, and often specify which children they had nursed. For example:

Prima, freedwoman of the Emperor [Tiberius] and Empress [Livia] nurse of Julia [Livilla] daughter of Germanicus [25].

Romans who required a wet nurse could apparently go to the Forum Olitorium where there was a market at which they could be hired, either to care for the child in the home of its parents or to take an infant with them to their own home. Dry nurses or *assae nutrices* could also be hired there [6a]. The 3rd-century writer, Festus, said that for this reason certain columns at the market were called *lactaria* since this was where parents brought infants in need of milk [9]. We have already cited wet-nursing contracts from Roman Egypt (pp.8–9). Another example, from AD 187, is a receipt for payment and may reflect prevailing arrangements, generally, in the Empire of the late 2nd century AD:

Chosion of Sarapion . . . to Tanenteris daughter of Thonis, Greeting. I acknowledge that I have received from you through Heliodorus and his fellow supervisors of the bank at the Serapeum by Oxyrhynchus, for which Epimachus issued the promise of payment, 400 silver drachmas of Imperial coin for nurse's wages, oil, clothing, and all other expenses of the two years for which my slave Sarapias nursed your daughter Helena, styled as daughter of her male parent, whom you have received back after having been weaned and treated with every attention . . . I, Tanenteris daughter of Thonis, with my guardian Demetrius son of Horion, assent, and I have received back my daughter as stated above.

As was the case in Greece, there are numerous grave *steles* and inscriptions to these Roman wet nurses (plate 1.10). As in other societies at this period, the wet nurse and nursing mother were deified as goddesses of maternal love and fertility [39]. Depictions of 'mother goddesses', frequently with a child at the breast, have been found all over the Roman empire [27] (plate 1.11).

The Romans adhered to the widespread belief that the characteristics of the nurse were imbibed by the child through her milk. Therefore, aside from the state of the milk, the ideal wet nurse had to possess particular qualities of age, health, stature, behaviour, and morals (table 1.2). From the wet-nursing contracts of Roman Egypt, and the letter from Italy quoted above, it is clear that the writers of the 1st and 2nd centuries were only quoting from, and elaborating on, well-established

Plate 1.10. Germany, 2nd to 3rd C. AD.
Memorial to a Roman nurse, 'Severina
nutrix'.

Plate 1.11. London, 1st to 2nd C. A D.
Roman mother-goddess suckling one
or two children.

requirements. Table 1.2 lists the qualities of the ideal wet nurse demanded by medical and moral writers. Later medical authors are included for comparison. Soranus also said that she should have had two or three children,

> because women with their first child are as yet unpracticed in the rearing of children [44].

¶ The milk of the nurse was naturally of great importance – a theme which will be reiterated throughout this whole history! It should be white, with a pleasant appearance, taste, and smell; of moderate consistency, and of the correct 'age'. Some writers, such as Pliny, thought that the sex of the wet nurse's own child was important, but Soranus dismissed this:

> At the most she should have had milk for two or three months. For very early milk . . . is thick of particles and is hard to digest, while late milk is not nutritious, and is thin. . . . Some women say that a woman who is going to feed a male must have given birth to a male; if a female . . . to a female. One should pay no heed to these people, for they do not consider that mothers of twins, the one being male and the other female, feed both with one and the same milk. And in general each kind of animal makes use of the same nourishment, male as well as female; and this is no reason at all for the male to become more feminine or for the female to become more masculine [44].

There were several methods for testing the consistency of the milk. The best known was the 'nail test', often credited to Soranus although it was described by Pliny a century earlier [36] and was probably widely used by families employing a wet nurse:

> Moderately thick milk will be recognised by the fact that if a drop is made to fall on the fingernail or a leaf of sweet bay or on something else of similar smoothness, it spreads gently and when rocked it retains . . . the same form. Milk which runs off immediately is watery, whereas milk that stays together like honey and remains motionless is thick [44].

Another widely described test (also mentioned in Indian medical texts) was to mix breast milk with twice its amount of water. Ideally it should stay the same for a short while and then dissolve and remain white in colour:

> For milk which dissolves immediately is watery, and it is worse if it is reduced into fibrous streaks like water in which meat has been washed, for such milk is also raw. But milk which does not disperse for some length of time and settles, so that when the water is poured off it is found as a caseous substance all round the bottom, is thick and hard to digest [44].

Soranus indicated that the nurse's milk should be tested at different times, since it should not change its consistency under different conditions. A further test was to see if the child being nursed by her were in good physical condition. He made an important observation that,

> although it is a sign of suitable milk if the child fed on it is in good physical condition, it does not follow . . . that an ill-developed child . . . is a sign of worthless milk. For it is possible that the milk is suitable but that the child is prevented by some disease from being well-nourished [44].

Once chosen, the wet nurse and the nursing mother had to follow a strict regimen of diet, rest and exercise, to maintain a good milk supply (table 1.3). Various adjustments and medicines were available for women who had insufficient milk. Pliny listed diverse ingredients said to increase milk supply. These included cabbages, colewort and fennel, seeds of the *Agnus castus* tree, anemone, and the boiled stalk of sow thistle [36].

Soranus described a treatment used to dry up the milk:

> If the mother is not going to nurse the newborn herself . . . mix a certain amount of properly ground pyrite, then apply the breast binder which is gradually tightened; for when the vessels collapse the influx is hindered, and thus the milk runs dry; if it does not one must be more liberal in the application of heat and close-fitting bandages.

He clearly understood that lactation was prompted by the stimulus of sucking:

> One should not . . . allow the breasts to be sucked at the first dis-

comfort, as if sucking, due to the secretion of the milk, relieves the tension; for quite on the contrary, more milk streams into the parts in proportion to the sensation of being sucked . . . [44].

It is notable that this period saw the first regular disapproval of the system of wet nursing [15,25,38,49]. Although under Roman law the worth of the newborn infant, especially females, remained low [8], the criticisms of Roman wet nurses and their care may indicate that wet nurses were used more frequently than in former times, or that the women undertaking the role of foster mother were in some way less suitable.

¶ Soranus strongly recommended that infants should be fed only on breastmilk until about six months old, but makes it clear that this was not necessarily general practice:

Those women are too hasty who, after only 40 days, try to give cereal food (as do those for the most part who find nursing a burden) [44].

He thought it equally bad to withhold solid food when the child was old enough to digest it. Galen specified a similar time to introduce other foods: when the infant had cut his first teeth [13]. Both recommended bread as a first solid, but differed in the method of preparation. Soranus advised

crumbs of bread softened with hydromel or milk, sweet wine or honey wine. Later, one should also give soup made from spelt, a very moist porridge, and an egg that can be sipped.

If the infant was thirsty he should not be given milk but,

water or a little watery wine through artificial nipples, for out of these it draws the fluid little by little as from the breasts, without being harmed. Sometimes . . . one should offer a soft piece of bread dipped in diluted wine for the morsels which the wet nurse has formed by munching are harmful because of them being combined with phlegm [44].

Galen disapproved of giving wine, but did not share Soranus' opinion about pre-chewing the child's food:

The infant should be . . . accustomed gradually to more solid food, as women taught by experience do: first bread, and then vegetables and meat and other such things, grinding them before putting them into the babies' mouths [8,13].

Rufus of Ephesus, on the other hand, was an outspoken advocate of wine, even for infants. It is remarkable that the following passage comes from an Arabic translation by ar-Raqīq, of about AD 1000, given the absolute proscription of alcohol in the Muslim world:

The wonderful, special properties of wine are such that it benefits all mankind, of all ages, at all seasons and in all places. One should give infants and children as much as they can tolerate; more than that to adolescents, young men and men in their prime; but for old men there is nothing that will more advance their well-being and bodily health than wine, because they have a great need for what warms them. Children need a thing whose heat is advantageous for them because heat has not yet reached its full measure in them.

The child should be weaned completely from the breast at the age of three, according to Galen; or, in the opinion of Soranus, once he was taking cereal food readily, and had teeth to chew more solid foods 'which in the majority of cases takes place around the third or fourth half-year'. The infant should be weaned gradually by increasing the amount of foods, simultaneously decreasing the quantity of breastmilk. The milk of the wet nurse would slowly dry up due to the lack of the sucking stimulus. Soranus disapproved of abrupt methods of weaning:

> For it is harmful to anoint the nipple with some bitter and evil-smelling things and thus wean the infant suddenly, because a sudden change has an injurious effect and sometimes because the infant becomes ill when the stomach is damaged by the drugs [44].

Because of the climate, spring was recommended as the best season, autumn the worst. It was apparently a practice of some physicians to recommend that females should be weaned six months later than males, because girls were supposedly weaker than boys. Soranus repudiated this idea.

¶ It is plain from Soranus' reference to artificial nipples, and from the discovery of many feeding vessels from this period, that infant feeders existed and were probably widely used during weaning [8,12,20] (plate 1.12). The smaller examples which have been found in infant graves were possibly used in the neonatal period to administer the 'honey and goats' milk' referred to by Soranus. Thus, although no specific mention of artificial feeding has been found, suitable vessels were available in the event of a child needing temporary or more permanent dry nursing. Wet nurses, particularly slaves, seem to have been readily available, but presumably only for the moderately wealthy. Roman feeding vessels from a cemetery in Poitiers were found in the graves of children in the area where the poor were buried [8]. This suggests that such children may have been weaned earlier than was advisable; in a few instances, infants may have been bottle-fed from birth.

The fact that Soranus described the symptoms of rickets [44], and that signs of rickets have been found in the remains of Roman children and adults [11,14,53], suggests that feeding on a milk diet was not prolonged for as long as the physicians advised. Direct suckling by animals was still part of the mythology [45] and is portrayed in statues and wall-paintings, of which the example from Herculaneum is illustrated (plate 1.5).

Plate 1.12. London, 1st to 3rd C. AD.
Roman feeding vessels.

To close this account of infant feeding in Roman times, here is an excerpt from the *Acts of the Christian Martyrs*. It tells of the martyrdom, in Roman Carthage, in AD 203, of a young Christian mother, Perpetua, about 22 years old, and with an infant son at the breast. Perpetua speaks:

A few days later, we were lodged in prison. I was tortured with worry for my baby there . . . Then I got permission for my baby to stay with me in prison. At once I recovered my health. My prison had suddenly become a palace . . . One day, we were suddenly hurried off to trial. 'Are you a Christian?' asked the Governor. And I said, 'yes, I am'. Then the Governor passed sentence on us: we were condemned to the beasts, and we returned to prison in high spirits. But my baby had got used to being nursed at the breast and to staying with me in prison. So I sent to my father to ask for my baby back. But father refused to give him over; and, by the will of God, the baby had no further desire for the breast, nor did I suffer any inflammation; and so I was relieved of any anxiety for my child and of any discomfort in my breasts . . . Now the day of the contest with the beasts was near . . . [25].

Plate 1.13. Byzantine (Armenian)
manuscript illumination of
the Nativity.

Byzantium: the medical literature

Between the 4th and 7th centuries AD, four physicians from Asia Minor
compiled encyclopaedic works which attempted to survey all extant
medical knowledge: Oribasius (AD 325–403), who practised in Rome;
Aetios of Amida, royal physician to the Emperor Justinian I (AD 527–
65); Paul of Aegina (AD 625–90); and Alexander of Tralles (d.605).
The first three summarised the paediatric knowledge of antiquity, including the views of the Greek physicians, Mnesitheus and Diocles, of
the 4th century BC and Rufus of Ephesus (1st century AD) [4]. As we
have seen, much of their information on infant feeding came directly
from Soranus and Galen. Francis Adams' 19th-century translation of
Paul of Aegina [7] is of great value in tracing the origin of medical ideas
about infant nutrition. The sections on the nurse, her milk, neonatal
and mixed feeding and weaning, all have a commentary in which Adams
traced the origin of the statements, and compared the views of Paul
with those of Oribasius and Aetios. He then compares these with the

37

doctrines of the later Arabic school of physicians, in particular Ibn Sīnā (Avicenna, 980–1036), al-Majūsī (Haly Abbas) (d.994) and Alsaharivius. However, subsequent scholarship has revealed the importance of Rufus of Ephesus, as a writer on paediatrics.

Before the 17th century, the three authorities who were most quoted in European paediatric works were Aetios, Paul, and Avicenna. Many of their ideas came from Soranus, but specific attribution is rare; possibly because his text was not readily accessible in Latin translation.

These authors were in basic agreement with Soranus as to the choice of the wet nurse, her diet and regime; but they differed about the best age of the nurse and whether she should recently have had a male child. In addition to the nail test for the consistency and quality of breastmilk, two further methods were described. Oribasius advised:

> You can test it also in this way: pour an eighth part of the milk into a glass vessel; add rennet in proportion, and stir with the fingers, then leave it to set and see whether the curd is less than the whey, for such milk is no good, and the reverse is indigestible: the best is that which contains both in equal proportion [6].

Aetios said that some people tested the quality of milk by using a hair. The hair was moistened with milk and suspended in the air. If all the milk ran off, or only a small drop remained on one part, then this milk must be discarded. If milk clung to the entire hair then this was acknowledged to be the best milk [2].

In a chapter on remedies for inadequacies of milk, Paul of Aegina suggested that, if the woman had insufficient milk, 'the cupping instrument, if applied, will also be of service' [7]. This may mean that the woman should be cupped (i.e. bled) somewhere in the region of the breast; alternatively, it could refer to stimulating lactation by expressing milk into a cup or other container. Paul also suggested remedies for milk which was too thick, too acrid, too thin, or in too great a quantity. The following is similar to the recommendations of Oribasius and Aetios:

> If it be too thick, the phlegm ought to be evacuated by vomits, the most proper of which are those of vinegar and honey . . . also . . . extenuate by labour before meals. Also the following substances are proper . . . wild marjoram, hyssop, savoury, shepherd's needle, thyme, the small radish, and old pickle with vinegar and honey. But if it should be more acrid and thinner than natural, the nurse ought to be relieved from much labour, to be fed upon strong soups, and the flesh of swine, and to be allowed sodden must and sweet wine. If it be in too small quantity, she ought to get soups and a generous diet, with sweet wine for drink: and her breast and nipples should be rubbed . . . That medicines for the formation of milk, are possessed of some efficacy, I am well aware, and yet I do not recommend them in all cases, for they greatly waste the body. They

are the root and fruit of fennel boiled in ptisan, the leaves of the cytisus in dark-coloured wine or ptisan, the sweet gith . . . dill, the root and fruit of the carrot. They are to be first soaked with warm water, and then given. But when the milk is bad, whether it be thick, acrid, or of a strong smell, it is first to be sucked out and then the child is to be applied. For that which is acrid ought on no account to be given to the infant when hungry. But that which has an offensive smell may be corrected by fragrant wine and sweet food [7].

The recommended age of weaning the child from the breast varied from 20 months [2] to two years [6,7]; within the range given by Soranus, but earlier than that advised by Galen.

كتاب القانون في الطّب

لابو علي الشيخ الرّيس

ابن سينا

مع بعض تاليفنه وهو علم المنطق وعلم الطبيعي
وعلم الكلام

R O M AE,
In Typographia Medicea .
M. D. X C III.
Cum licentia Superiorum.

Plate 1.14. Rome, 1593. Avicenna, *Canon of Medicine.*

Islam

What we think of as the Arabian or Islamic school of medicine is essentially the medical system of later Greek antiquity transmitted to the Islamic world in the 9th century AD, and rendered into Arabic. Later in the Middle Ages some of its more important works were translated back into Latin and influenced the works of European physicians at least until the 17th century [4].

The paediatric literature derived mainly from Soranus and the Galenic tradition, via Oribasius and Paul of Aegina [1]. Remarkably, several of the principal Islamic medical writers were not Arabs but Persians: men like ar-Rāzī (Rhazes), al-Majūsī (Haly Abbas) and Ibn-Sīnā (Avicenna). These writers and others, like the Spanish-born Ibn-Rushd (Averroes) and the great Jewish Philosopher Ibn-Maymūn (Maimonides), compiled large works of medical knowledge and disseminated these widely.

Some of their writings include renderings of parts of works by Greek writers, the originals of which have totally perished. Perhaps the most famous work of the Arabic school is the *Canon of Medicine* of Avicenna (AD 980–1036) (plate 1.14). Although it contains relatively little original material, it established itself as the most influential study of paediatrics, and the most widely quoted by later writers on infant care. Avicenna devoted a significant amount of space to infant feeding and associated problems, including a section on neonatal feeding; the qualifications of a good wet nurse and her milk; advice on improving the quality and quantity of the milk, and a regime for the wet nurse or nursing mother. He also described how and when to wean the child (table 1.1) [2,3].

Avicenna, who spent most of his life in Persian courts, advised that an infant should not be suckled by a wet nurse who was mentally deranged; this stricture had the endorsement of the Prophet Muhammad (plate 1.15), because such a woman would adversely affect the child's health and character. In any problem encountered with an infant, according to Avicenna, the remedy was to treat the nurse and, if necessary, to employ another woman as a temporary wet nurse during the treatment. Should the nurse's milk be too thick or have an unpleasant smell, her milk should be drawn and exposed to the air for some time before feeding it to the baby [2]. This suggests that feeding vessels of some kind were available to feed the milk to the child. Although few such containers have been found, some 10th-century Iranian examples survive [6], and it is probable that the sucking horn was commonly employed, since it is occasionally portrayed in manuscripts and carvings from Spain.

Avicenna described a variant of the test for the consistency of breast-milk. When earlier writers suggested adding rennet, he advised

> adding a little myrrh to a small cup of milk and stirred with a finger. If the milk separates into equal quantities of cheese and water it is to be regarded as of good quality [2].

He also appears to have introduced the idea that infants should be breastfed only two or three times a day, particularly in the first few days of infancy [2]. This was repeated by many later writers, who sometimes extended this doctrine to all infants, although it is scarcely feasible that young babies would be satisfied with such restrictive feeding times.

The *Qur'an* laid down the length of time a child should be breast-fed. Islamic physicians observed its recommendations that children be weaned at the age of two years. Since breastfeeding for two years must have resulted in the spacing-out of a family, and ultimately in some measure of population-control which may have been influenced by the available resources of food production, the Qur'anic injunction is today an issue of some moment between Islamic governments anxious to limit population growth, and Muslim fundamentalists. It was not a strict rule, however, since the *Qur'an* does allow the child to be weaned earlier:

> If they desire to wean the child by mutual consent [after] close consultation, it is no sin for them [11].

Whilst the Muslim child was normally suckled by the mother, and the father was responsible for clothing and feeding his wife while she was

Plate 1.15. Tabriz, AD 1306. The birth
of the Prophet Muhammad, from the
World History of Rashid-al-Dīn.

breastfeeding, the *Qur'an* allows that:

> If you wish to give your children out to nurse, it is no sin for you,
> provided that you pay what is due from you in kindness.

If for some reason a divorced mother was unable to breastfeed her child,
the father was expected to provide her with a wet nurse:

> And if they suckle children for you, give them their hire; and
> consult among yourselves, according to what shall be just and
> reasonable. And if you be put to a difficulty herein, and another
> shall suckle the child for him, let him who hath plenty expend
> proportionally in the maintenance of the mother and the nurse out
> of his plenty: and let him whose income is scanty expend in
> proportion [14].

Other writers of the Arabian school touch only briefly on the care of
infants. Rhazes, who died in AD 923, was a celebrated philosopher,
alchemist and doctor. He has been called 'the most creative genius of
medieval medicine' and has been much praised for 'the sureness of his
diagnosis and the cool precision of his case histories'. He wrote two im-

portant paediatric treatises which were frequently quoted by later European physicians: one on smallpox and measles [13], the other on the diseases of children [12]; but neither mention infant feeding, apart from advising that the wet nurse should be treated when a sucking child became ill. Haly Abbas (d.AD 994) similarly advised regulating and treating the nurse; and gave brief instructions on increasing her milk supply and on her diet. Like other physicians, he thought nursing mothers should abstain from pungent, sour and bitter foods, since they would adversely affect their milk [1].

Averroes (1126–98), a Spanish Muslim, referred briefly to infant feeding, but his importance for our purpose was his influence on his pupil Maimonides. Maimonides was born in Cordoba in 1135. He finally settled in Egypt where he served as personal physician to the son of Saladin, and where he died in 1204. He is best remembered for his *Aphorisms,* a collection of 1500 quotations from Galen, divided according to theme into 25 chapters. This has been called the most important body of Jewish writings since the *Talmud* [8,9]. In his *Book of Women,* he gave rules concerning maternal breastfeeding and wet nursing, some of which show the influence of his Muslim teacher [8].

The mother or wet nurse was to suckle for two years, and during this time to abstain from sexual intercourse; even when a wet nurse was employed, or a child weaned early, the mother was nevertheless to abstain for this period of time. If a man married a pregnant or nursing woman he need not be compelled to dismiss her or to consummate the marriage until after the period of nursing, or until the child died [8].

As long as a wife was breastfeeding, the amount of her work should be reduced, and her diet augmented with liquids and other things beneficial for lactation. Should she desire more, or different, foods this was to be allowed, since the suffering of her own body was to take priority over that of the child. A woman who gave birth to twins was not to be compelled to feed both; she should suckle one, and the husband hire a wet nurse for the other. Where a wife was willing to suckle a friend's infant together with her own, the husband was entitled to prevent her from so doing, and allow her to nurse only his child. If she did not wish to suckle her baby, the husband could compel her to nurse it until it was two years old, regardless of whether it was a boy or a girl. If, on the other hand, her husband did not wish her to breastfeed, because it might make her more unattractive, the wife's wish must prevail 'because it is painful for her to be separated from her child' [8].

If the mother were poor, and therefore obliged to nurse her own child, and her husband were affluent enough to free his wife from nursing if she did not wish to breastfeed, then he must hire a wet nurse. A divorced woman could not be compelled to nurse her own baby but, if she were willing, her ex-husband should pay her for doing so. If she

Plate 1.16. 8th C. AD. *Book of Kells*,
Madonna and Child.

were not willing to suckle, she could hand her infant over to him and he must attend to its needs. However, should she have nursed the baby long enough for it to recognise her, she must not be separated from it, and endanger its life; she must be compelled to nurse it for a fee until the age of two years. During this time the father must provide fully for the child's needs, including clothing, food, drink, and ointments [8].

Plate 1.17. England, c.1480. Memorial brass, *Virgo lactans.*

Medieval Europe

Infant-feeding practices in the medieval period in Europe are commonly omitted or barely touched upon by medical historians, yet enough information is available at least to outline the care of infants and children
in the Middle Ages. The opinions of medical writers can be supplemen-
ted by saints' lives of the 12th to the 15th centuries [27,37], poems and
legends [29]; art [13,25] (plate 1.16), particularly the *Virgo lactans* [42]
(plate 1.17) and depictions of birth scenes; from family papers [32] and
from the records of some of the early foundling hospitals [40].

The medical texts principally reflected the views of Soranus and
Galen, modified by Avicenna and Rhazes. In the 11th century, a female
physician, Trotula of Salerno, wrote a book on the diseases of women,
which contained the substance of Soranus, was extant throughout the
medieval period, and was eventually printed in the 16th century [41]. It
offered brief instruction on the diet of infants and the choice of a wet
nurse. Feeding problems were, as usual, attributed to the nurse. On
supplementing the infant's diet, she advised:

> Cylindrical figures of the size and shape of an acorn should be
> given to the infant. He can hold them in his hand and play with

45

them, and sucking from them he will swallow some of it. The meat which is on the breast of hens, pheasants and partridges should be given to him. After he has begun to take foods well and the substance of the mother's breast has begun to change, you should not permit him to suck the breasts in the night. From day to day he should be induced to eat in orderly fashion, taking care that he be not removed from milk in warm weather [41].

Two paediatric manuscripts were in use in several parts of Europe by the 12th century if not before, and influenced subsequent writings on the subject. The *Liber de passionibus puerorum Galeni,* though attributed to Galen, was probably compiled between the 6th and 9th centuries. It is essentially a practical guide to children's ailments, but contains little about infant feeding other than that diseases of infants were the result of the nurse and/or her diet, and treatment should first be directed towards the wet nurse [26]. *[Incipit] practica puerorum passiones puerorum adhuc in cunabulis iacentium (Diseases of children still in the cradle),* of which at least twelve manuscript copies exist in European libraries, was compiled between the 12th and 15th centuries [22]. The late 15th-century writer, Cornelius Roelans, referred to this manuscript repeatedly in his book on children's diseases of 1483 [31], indicating that its existence was known to European physicians.

The *Practica* was a concise guide to the common diseases of infants and contains little about feeding. It gave a modification of the nail test for testing the nurse's milk, and also directed treatment towards the wet nurse and her milk:

The first matter for consideration . . . is the milk on which the child is nourished, whether it be good, and this is determined as follows. For it should be good and of good odour and continuous, and this we learn in the following manner. Let the milk be placed upon a rock or polished sword; if it stands after the manner of a crystal, it is good, but if after the manner of water it is not good . . . If the nurse has no milk, let her eat seed of fennel, lettuce and cumin, ginger and . . . white pepper. Note that everything which increases the milk increases the sperm and vice versa [22].

The medical opinions of the 13th and 14th centuries were contained in encyclopaedic works for the general reader, such as that of Bartholomaeus Anglicus (d. c.1291). In his *De proprietatibus rerum* (c.1230), probably the most widely disseminated medical work in the Middle Ages, he included sections on the infant, the mother, the nurse, the breast, and on milk [4]. Much of this was based on the *Historia animalium* of Aristotle [2]. He stated that the mother is the best nurse because she will have greater love for the child but, if a nurse were necessary, she must take the mother's place, loving and cherishing him as would his own mother [4].

Plate 1.18. Europe. Medieval manuscript
showing woman suckling twins.

The texts of English physicians paid scant attention to infants. Gilbertus Anglicus (13th century) barely referred to children throughout his *Compendium medicinae* (c.1240) [16]. John of Gaddesden's *Rosa Anglica* (c.1314) mentioned children occasionally, but did not devote a chapter to their care and diseases. He recommended a wet nurse, or animal milk direct from the udder, for those suffering from phthisis, a common treatment for this disease until at least the early 19th century. Such a wet nurse needed the traditional qualities:

> The best is the milk of a young brunette with her first child, which should be a boy. The young woman should be well-favoured and should eat and drink in moderation [23].

Bernard of Gordon's *Regimen sanitatis* (14th century) recommended maternal suckling (plate 1.18), although still giving reasons for employing a wet nurse, since 'women nowadays are too delicate or too haughty, or they do not like the inconvenience' [6]; a similar view to that in a 12th-century Bestiary:

> The women of our own race quickly wean even those who they love, and if they are of the richer classes they actually scorn to suckle them [43].

47

Together with other physicians in Europe, notably Aldobrandino of Siena [1], Michele Savonarola [36] and Arnold of Villanova [3], he recommended that boys be weaned from the breast six to twelve months later than girls [6]. This is known to have been the practice in part of France, where girls were weaned at one year, and boys at two years [27]; although reasons varied from Savonarola's 'males live longer than females' [36] to Bernard of Gordon's 'woman is only a guardian of the house, as Galen says, and therefore needs less strength than man' [6]. As to the method of weaning, painting the nipples with mustard or similar substances was mentioned [3]. Treatment of illness in children at the breast was directed towards the wet nurse or nursing mother [6,34].

¶ Non-medical sources make it clear that in most of western Europe, from the early second millennium, many wealthy and noble families employed wet nurses to feed their children, whilst in poorer families the mother nursed her own child [37]. From the 11th century onwards, the use of wet nurses by the wealthy apparently increased, and it has been suggested that this was a reason for the increased fertility among the European aristocracy, which also dates from the 11th century [27]. One wonders if the upper classes were aware of the implications and welcomed, even perhaps encouraged, a proportionate increase in their numbers?

Some wealthy women did nurse their own infants, although this was obviously exceptional enough to draw comment from contemporaries. It is well known that a close bond of love and affection was formed between the child and the woman who nursed him (plate 1.19). For example, the mother of Saint Catherine of Siena had twenty-four children, but the only one she breastfed was Catherine. In later life her mother said that she had a special bond of love for the only child she had suckled [37]. Saint Bernard of Clairvaux, too, was breastfed by his mother. Preachers as well as physicians strongly advocated such maternal breastfeeding. They warned that the child would imbibe the characteristics of the nurse who fed him rather than those of his mother. A sermon by San Bernardino of Siena urged:

> Even if you are prudent and of good customs and habits, and discreet . . . you often give your child to a dirty drab, and from her, perforce, the child acquires certain of the customs of the one who suckles him . . . [35].

From the 11th century on, the wet nurse was taken usually into the child's house where she could be closely supervised by the mother. In some cases both nurse and mother breastfed the baby intermittently so that, should the nurse fall ill, become pregnant, or die, the mother was capable of feeding her child until another nurse could be found [37]. In some areas during the later Middle Ages it was established practice even

Plate 1.19. Pisa, Italy, c.1350. *Madonna del latte,* attributed to Nino Pisano.

for artisans and small shopkeepers to employ wet nurses [37]. This was the accepted custom in Tuscany [20], although possibly it was less common in France. However, wet nursing was obviously thriving in the latter country, since in the *Ordonnances des roys de France,* of 1350, the maximum wages of wet nurses were laid down [9]. Compared with other female servants, the nurses were well paid. A wet nurse taken into the child's home could expect up to fifty shillings a year, plus food and lodging. A wet nurse who accepted the child into her own home could earn up to a hundred shillings per annum; the extra presumably to cover food and other necessities while she was nursing. For comparison, the maximum wage of a chambermaid was set at thirty shillings per annum [9]. The advantage of having the nurse reside at the house was that her diet, exercise, behaviour and sexual relations could be closely supervised although, in comparatively modest homes, it perhaps would have been inconvenient to supply the nurse with room and board.

When wealthy parents did put the child out to nurse, it was generally

49

at no far distance from the child's home, so the parents could keep in contact, in case of illness or other problems. In 15th-century Venice, a wet nurse sent a message to the mother that plague was in her house. The mother promptly arranged for the baby to be brought home, and employed another wet nurse to suckle the child in his own home. There are other examples of mothers going to visit or to fetch their child, immediately they received word from the wet nurse [37]. In Florence, however, in the 14th and 15th centuries, it appears to have been more common to send infants out to nurses in the countryside. Much of the information here comes from J.B.Ross's study of the middle-class child in urban Italy, 14th to 16th centuries [32]. The task of finding suitable wet nurses apparently devolved on an intermediary or an agent. He would then make a contract with the husband of the wet nurse or with his agent. One such intermediary was the self-made merchant, Datini, and letters describing his attempt to find wet nurses for his friends and clients survive. A contract would contain details of the nurse's pay. The diary of a Florentine merchant, Antonio Rustichi, contains details of all the nurses who suckled his 15 children between 1417 and 1436:

> On this day 9th March [1417] I sent out to wet nurse my first child named Lionardo, and I gave him to a *balia* (nurse) of Santa Ambrogio, to Dame Chaterina, wife of Ambrogio, master-mason and farmer, for five lire ten soldi a month, which wages I fixed with Santi di Franchesco . . . and the things I sent with the child are these, and they are all new.

'These' included numerous articles of clothing and swaddling, a coral, a silver ring, and a cradle with coverlet and pillow. In contrast to France, nurses in Florence who were taken into the child's home were much better paid than those taking the child into their own home [37]. This barred all but the very wealthy from employing an in-house wet nurse.

Wet nursing was a desirable profession in 14th- and 15th-century Florence. Groups of eligible country women – especially, it would seem, from the Casentino Valdarno – attended public festivals in the city, and had their own carnival songs in which they displayed their marital state and boasted of their prowess in infant care:

> Here we come, *balie* from the Casentino,
> Each one looking for a baby,
> And here are our husbands
> Who lead us on our way,
> Whoever has a baby, show him to us,
> Male or female, it doesn't matter.
> We shall take good care of him,
> And he will be so well fed,
> That we'll soon have him standing straight
> Like a proud knight.

... We're fine in our way of life,
Prompt and skilful in our trade,
Always when the baby cries
We feel our milk returning
Acting with energy and speed,
We do our duty

... In every matter we know what to do,
So that the baby grows up quickly;
As long as he stays straight and hard
We don't mind getting tired;
And he'll never leave us
Until his nursing is finished:
So you can be quite confident
In sending him to the Casentino [38].

Another song emphasised the basic duties of the wet nurse:

With lots of good fine milk
Our breasts are full.
To avoid all suspicion,
Let the doctor see it,
Because in it is found
The life and being of the creature,
For good milk nourishes
With no trouble and makes the flesh firm ...

We're young married women,
Well experienced in our art,
We can swaddle the baby in a flash
And no-one has to show us
How to use the cloth and bands;
While caring for him we arrange them carefully
Because if he catches cold,
The baby is harmed and the *balia* blamed.

We change three times a day
The wool and linen cloths and white bands
And we never get tired or cross
Being with him so he won't cry ... [38].

Despite these claims, infants rarely stayed with one wet nurse till weaned. It was more usual for the child to move from nurse to nurse, often because these women became pregnant. It is obvious from the frequency of pregnant nurses that the ban on the nurse having sexual intercourse during lactation was honoured more in the breach than in the observance [32].

Diaries of the period suggest that mothers would sometimes feed their child for a few weeks or days before putting it out to nurse, or between nurses. Other children, however, were sent out immediately after baptism, at about three days old. It is recorded of a Sienese notary, to whom twin boys were born in 1385, that one stayed with his mother for five weeks and then went to three successive wet nurses, for six, nine and three months respectively. The other stayed with his mother for two weeks, was sent to a nurse for two months, came back to his mother for eleven days, then to a nurse for six months. Apparently both were weaned at about nineteen months [32]. The majority of infants in the Italian foundling hospitals were wet nursed. Some were kept in the hospital for this purpose, but the majority of nurses took sucklings into their own home [40].

¶ There were no obvious medical reasons why, in the Middle Ages, women should not have fed their own children, so long as they were healthy and had no problems such as cracked or infected nipples or breast abscesses. They did not even have the problem encountered in later centuries, of breastfeeding a child whilst wearing tight corsets and fashionable clothes [11], since, in most instances, women's clothing was loose and enveloping (plate 1.20). Illustrations of breastfeeding women show three examples of suitable clothing. In some cases the upper front of the dress was laced, and could be easily untied, or the top of a low-necked dress was pushed down and the breast brought out when the infant needed feeding. In another example there are vertical slits in the clothing through which the child could suck the breast whenever he wished.

In the Medieval period there is no mention of restricting the child to any type of feeding schedule. Infants were apparently fed on demand [37] (plate 1.21), although in poorer families this was probably restricted, when mothers were working in the fields or within the house. There is some evidence that, in the 14th century, English children of the lower classes were left alone for various periods of time when the mother was working [19].

Problems such as lack of milk, or of the infant being unable to suck properly, are testified in many of the miracles of saints [37]. For poor women such problems must have been serious, since they would have been unable to afford a wet nurse, and animal-nursing was in general frowned upon, because the child might become animal-like [32]. Wet nursing out of charity rather than for wages appears to have been rare. Casual wet nursing of neighbours' children certainly occurred in England, although it could arouse the hostility of husbands. For example, in September 1300 Nicholas le Swon of Bedford murdered his wife because she was spending too much time 'at Robert Asplan's house giving suck to his son' [21].

Plate 1.20. England, c.1512. Memorial
brass to Anne of Wode, who died after
giving birth to twins. Her loose gown
could be unlaced for ease in pregnancy
or in breastfeeding.

There are miraculous tales of elderly women lactating long after they
had ceased childbearing and suckling. In Bologna, a man and his wife
took home an abandoned infant, but were too poor to employ a wet
nurse. No woman could be found to nurse the child out of Christian
charity but, after prayers and a vow to a saint, the wife had milk in her
breasts with which to feed the foundling [37]. Frescoes in the church of
San Giovanni Valdarno in Tuscany depict the miracle of a seventy-five-
year-old woman having milk to feed her grandchild for several months
after the parents had died of the plague [18].

Although nursing by animals was denounced, it must have been used
on occasion. In the 14th century, a Tuscan moralist warned:

Be sure the wet nurse has plenty of milk because if she lacks it she
may give the baby the milk of a goat or sheep or ass or some other

53

Plate 1.21. Germany, 15th C. The water-
nymph Melusine coming secretly at
night to feed her twins.

animal, because the child . . . nourished on animal milk does not
have perfect wits like one fed on women's milk, but always looks
stupid and vacant and not right in the head [32].
Despite this belief, examples of infants fed by animals are indeed recorded. For example, a two-month-old baby was suckled by a goat when
his mother died from plague [32].
Even if the child were not suckled directly by an animal, milk of
various species was certainly utilised in cases of need. There are many
examples from the 9th to 15th centuries of children being fed with a
horn [29] (plate 1.22), and the sucking-horn is also depicted in numerous medieval paintings and carvings [11]. Possibly the earliest source to
mention infant feeding by this method is found in the life of Saint Liud-
gar of Frisia (AD 744–809). Other examples occur in the literature or
mythology of Germany, Iceland, Sweden and France [27, 29]. A French
source refers to the 'cornet' or horn as being as necessary a part of the
nurse's equipment as swaddling clothes and a bib [29]. Several earthenware and wooden feeding vessels have been discovered in France,
Germany and England, dating from between AD 1000 to 1500, but
principally from the 15th century [11].
Food other than breastmilk was fed to infants, although which foods
were used was rarely recorded. The *Lives of the Saints* contains examples
of three-month-old babies drinking fluids other than breastmilk, and of
slightly older children being given solid foods long before weaning [37].
The age of weaning apparently varied between one and two years. Painting the nipples with foul-tasting substances was employed, probably
quite widely, since medical authors condemn the practice [10]. Weaning

Plate 1.22. France, 13th C. Feeding
an infant through a horn.

was sometimes abrupt, due to a nurse's pregnancy or illness, but in
some cases it appeared to be spread over several months [32,37].

As in later centuries, the wet nurse or mother was warned repeatedly
by preachers, physicians, and moralists that she should not sleep in the
same bed as her nurseling, for fear of overlaying and smothering the
child whilst asleep [6,12]. But, since the poor could not afford even a
separate cradle and bedding for the child, and since women disliked
having to get up on cold nights to breastfeed, it remained more common
for the child to share the bed of nurse or mother at least until it was
weaned.

Plate 1.23. Germany, 1491.
Feeding an older infant with pap.

55

Plate 1.24. Augsburg, 1497. Frontispiece
to Metlinger's *Ein regimen der jungen
kinder.*

Infant Feeding: early printed books

The revival of learning in Europe was vastly assisted by the invention of
printing in the mid-fifteenth century. In 1462, following the sack of
Mainz, German printers fled, first to Italy, later to all parts of Europe,
so that printing rapidly became a widespread skill. By the year 1500
many thousands of books had been printed and published, several of
them on medical subjects. Four of these were paediatric texts, published
between 1472 and 1491.

Paulus Bagellardus (?–1492), a physician and, later, a professor of
medicine at Padua, published his *Libellus de egritudinibus (Book of ailments)* in 1472, although it had been written years previously. It was
reprinted several times, and a new edition, published at Lyons in 1538,
had editions by the physician Petrus Toletus. Bagellardus' principal
sources were those of the Islamic school, particularly Avicenna, Rhazes,
and Averroes. Only a small section was devoted to infant feeding, most
of the book being concerned with the diseases of children [1,6]. His
views are given in table 1.5. The second printed paediatric work to

appear was that of a German physician who practised in Augsburg, Bartholomaeus Metlinger (?–1491). His *Ein regimen der jungen kinder (Rules for young children)* was published at Augsburg in 1473, and was also reprinted many times. It was the first important printed work on infant care and paediatrics, the first such work to be written in the vernacular, rather than in Latin (which would have confined its use to the scholarly); and the first to give opinions based upon the author's own experience, rather than being completely reliant upon Greek and Arabic medical texts [4] (plate 1.24).

Metlinger gave detailed instructions on the feeding of infants. These are summarized in table 1.5. Important points were references to the foods to be given to babies, and advice on early weaning, in which he prescribed that water should be boiled; and on the use of a feeding horn. In the first instance he implied that the giving of food other than breastmilk was usual in contemporary infant feeding:

> One should also know about the gruel which is given to it after it has nursed: When the milk of the nurse is good and she has enough the child needs less gruel . . . when the milk is not good or when the wet nurse [or mother] is sick or has little milk or the baby does not thrive on the nursing, one should give more gruel. One should be careful not to burn the child by giving it gruel that is too hot, as it is old wives' opinion that if the gruel will not burn a coarse finger it will not burn the tender child . . . children are to be nourished on gruel and milk until they cut their front teeth [after which other foods could be introduced] [4,6].

On early weaning he stated that:

> If the nursing agrees with the child, it can be allowed to nurse, but if it is not gaining weight or if the wet nurse becomes pregnant, or if one cannot get another wet nurse, it may be necessary to wean the child, but if the child is weaned it should be done in a proper manner, so that each day the nursing is discontinued and water given to drink which has been cooked once and allowed to cool, or sugar water made with an ounce of sugar and a measure of water, and boiled as long as it will take to cook a hard egg. A bread rind may be cooked in it in order that the child may be strengthened. But if the child is young, that is to say under a year, and it must be weaned, one gives it goats' milk to drink out of a cornucopia or a little jug. The milk is boiled with one quart of water and an electuary may be made out of white bread and sugar, as Avicenna tells, rub together one part of fine bread and one-quarter part sugar and mix it as an apothecary would [4,6].

Metlinger refers to the use of animals to draw off the mother's milk during the first fourteen days, since another woman was to breastfeed the child during that time, as, the milk of the mother of the child is not as healthy, and during this time the mother should have her breast sucked by a young wolf [or puppy] or the milk should be sucked off.

This was not always possible, however, as he admitted:

When the mother will nurse the child from the first day when one should put a small amount of honey or rose honey in the mouth so that the milk injures it less [4,6].

The third book was written by the Belgian physician Cornelius Roelans (1450–1525). His *De morbis infantium (On children's diseases)* was published at Louvain in 1483. It was originally only part of a larger medical work which has not survived, and it is extremely rare. Roelans confined his book to the diseases of infants, and it contains little about infant feeding. He said that the first task in curing infants was to regulate the nurse. In several treatments he advised altering her diet, purging her, bleeding her and giving her physick. His book is a compendium of the medical opinions of earlier writers in paediatrics from the Greeks and the Islamic school, especially Avicenna, but also from the more recent medieval and contemporary physicians, such as the Frenchman Jacques Despars (d.1465) [5,6].

The fourth 15th-century work was written not by a physician but by a monk, Heinrich von Louffenburg (d.c.1458). Louffenburg wrote a poem on the care of the body, in which he included instructions about the care of young children. *Versehung des leibs (Care of the body)* was written in 1429 and was published at Augsburg in 1491. His views on infant nutrition were similar to those of Metlinger. His work is notable as being the first printed paedatric text to illustrate the care of infants; in particular the first to depict a feeding bottle of the design still used today [6,7,8].

Plate 1.25. England, c.1200 AD.
From a detail of an enamelled cabinet.

58

Table 1.1. Summary of medical opinions on infant feeding from the Graeco-Roman, Byzantine and Arabian periods.

	Soranus fl.98–117 AD	Galen 130–200 AD	Oribasius 325–403 AD
The first food	Honey or honey and goat's milk	Honey	Honey
Age given first breastfeed	2 days (by nurse) 20 days (by mother)		
Mother or wet nurse	Mother if fit enough; otherwise wet nurse	Mother	Mother
Technique	Express a little before suckling		
Quantity	Frequent small feeds at first; not whenever he cries		
Age at which other foods introduced	6 months (some do at 40 days)	When the first teeth are through	
Foods suggested	Cereal; bread & milk; moist porridge; egg; bread dipped in wine; not to be pre-chewed	Bread; vegetables; meat; milk	
Wine	Water & wine to drink	Forbidden until adult	
Age of weaning	18–24 months providing teeth through and taking other foods well	3 years	2 years
Method of weaning	Gradual; do not anoint breast		
Season of weaning	Spring; not in autumn		
If infant becomes ill	Treat the nurse; back to nurse if newly weaned	Treat the nurse	

Aetios 4th century AD	Paulus Aeginata 625–690 AD	Avicenna 980–1036 AD
	Honey; then milk	Honey
		As soon as possible; wet nurse on 1st day
		Mother
		Express a little before suckling
		2–3 times a day; not too much at first
	When teeth are coming through & seems ready for it	When begins to ask for other foods
Occasional eggs	Milk until 2 years then cereal foods	Pre-chewed bread; bread soaked in wine, honey or milk; bread & sugar cones
Mead or sweet wine diluted with water		Few drops occasionally
20 months	2 years	2 years
		Gradual and slowly; anoint breast if cries for it
Treat the nurse	Treat the nurse	Treat the nurse

Table 1.2. The qualities of the ideal wet nurse according to medical and moralist writers in the Graeco-Roman, Byzantine and Arabian periods.

Qualities	Plutarch 50–120 AD	Soranus fl.98–117 AD	Aulus Gellius 2nd century AD
Temperament and behaviour	Honest; not prostitute or vagabond; manners of a Greek woman	Self-controlled; sympathetic; not bad-tempered or given to lewdness or drunkenness	Honest; chaste; not a drunkard; not a slave or servile
Health		Healthy	Healthy
Age		20–40	
Complexion/colour		Good colour	
Body size/stature		Large frame; fleshy & strong	
Breasts		Medium size; soft & unwrinkled	
Nipples		Medium size; not too porous or compact	
General appearance		Tidy	Not ugly
Nationality	Same country as the child	Greek	Not from foreign or barbarous nation
Her own children: Number State of health Sex		2 or 3	
Last pregnancy		2–3 months	

Oribasius 325–403 AD	Aetios 6th century AD	Paulus Aeginata 625–690 AD	Avicenna 980–1036 AD
	Chaste; cheerful; sober		Cheerful; good moral character; not mentally deranged; not emotional
Not diseased	Healthy; free of illness	Healthy; free of illness	Good health & vigour; no disease
25–35	20–40	25–35	25–35 Healthy complexion
Broad chest; not too fat or thin		Large chest; not too fat or thin	Broad chest; well-developed muscular body; strong neck
Large	Not too small or too large	Large	Moderately large & firm; not soft, flabby or pendulous
Not retracted	Not too small or too large	Not contracted or turned aside	
	Clean		Clean head & eyes
From Thrace or Egypt			
			All full-term
Male		Male	Preferably male
Not long ago		Short time before	1 or 2 months

Table 1.3. The regime to be followed by a wet nurse or nursing mother according to medical writers in the Graeco-Roman, Byzantine and Arabian periods.

Regime	Soranus fl.98–117 AD	Galen 130–200 AD	Oribasius 325–403 AD	Aetios 6th century AD	Paulus Aeginata 625–690 AD	Avicenna 980–1036 AD
Diet	Medium quantity of nourishing, easily digested foods; avoid strongly flavoured foods	Take care in her food & drink	Avoid salty, strongly flavoured & spicy foods; milk allowed	Should include animal food; wine	Avoid salty, bitter & strongly flavoured foods	Wholesome diet; moderate amount of animal food & wine; avoid salty foods
Exercise	Take regular exercise; exercise hands & shoulders; avoid idleness		Do moderate amount of work; exercise arms & shoulders		Exercise arms & shoulders; do some work	Moderate exercise
Breasts	Should not be bound					
Sexual intercourse during lactation	Abstain because it can stimulate menstruation	Abstain because it can stimulate menstruation & bad milk	Abstain		Abstain	Abstain because it causes menstruation & bad milk
Pregnancy		Harms the child; change the nurse				Harms infant & the foetus; change the nurse

Table 1.4. The milk of the ideal wet nurse according to medical writers in the Graeco-Roman, Byzantine and Arabian periods.

Qualities of breastmilk	Soranus fl.98–117 AD	Galen 130–200 AD	Oribasius 325–403 AD	Aetios 6th century AD	Paulus Aeginata 625–690 AD	Avicenna 980–1036 AD
Colour/ appearance	Medium white	White	Even colour			Absolutely white; free of all other colours
Taste	Sweet & pleasant	Sweet	Even taste	Moderate	Moderate	Slightly sweet
Smell	Sweet & pleasant	Sweet	Even smell		Moderate	Pleasant
Consistency/ thickness	Smooth, even, homogeneous; moderately thick	Moderately thick	Even consistency; moderately thick		Moderate	Moderate; not too thick or too thin
Tests for consistency*	Nail test; mixing with water		Nail test; addition of rennet	Nail test; hair test; weigh milk & curd	Nail test; addition of rennet	Nail test; addition of myrrh
When to test	On different occasions; it should remain good under all circumstances					
Age of her milk	2 or 3 months maximum				Fairly recent	1 or 2 months

* see text

Table 1.5. Summary of opinions on infant feeding in the paediatric incunabula.

	Bagellardus 1472	Metlinger 1473	Von Louffenberg 1491
The first food	Sugar or cooked apple & sugar	Honey	Honey, then breast
Age given first breastfeed		3 days; not until its stomach is empty	
Mother or wet nurse	Mother if poor, otherwise wet nurse	Mother but not for first 14 days; meanwhile mother's milk sucked or drawn off	Mother but not at first
Technique		Express milk before feeding; make sure child sucks properly	Express milk before each morning feed
Frequency		According to its needs	2–3 times a day at first, then frequently
Quantity	Not too much	According to its needs; not too much	Small amounts on demand
Age at which other foods introduced	When body is solid	Apparently gruel to supplement breast-milk very early; nothing else until cuts first teeth	When cuts teeth; if expresses desire for other foods
Suggested foods	Solid foods with honey-water, honey wine, milk or sweet wine. Later eggs to suck	Bread & milk; meat soup; pea soup; much later lean, chopped well-cooked meat	Tender, well-boiled meat; boiled pears; pre-chewed pap & bread; bread dipped in wine, honey or pure water
Wine	Diluted wine allowed	Not before 7 years of age	A little well-diluted in water but rarely
Age at weaning	When takes more solid food	2 years	2 years
Method of weaning	Gradually	Gradually; anoint nipples if cries for breast	Gradually; anoint nipples if cries for breast
Artificial feeding		Bread & water; goat's milk from horn; boiled water to drink; milk, water, bread & sugar boiled	
If infant becomes ill	Before weaning, treat the nurse; after weaning, back to the breast	Child must stop sucking; treat the nurse	

Table 1.6. The qualities of the ideal wet nurse described in the paediatric incunabula.

Qualities	Bagellardus 1472	Metlinger 1473	Von Louffenberg 1491
Temperament & behaviour	Good morals; moderate meat-eater; not inclined to drunkenness or anger	Good habits; not given to fright or anxiety; industrious & careful with child	Good character; modest; chaste; clean
Health		Not diseased	Free from illness in eyes and body
Age	23–35	Not too old or too young; not younger than 20; best age 25	Medium age
Complexion	Ruddy	Healthy; tanned	
Stature/body size		Well-built; strong, thick neck	Medium size; shapely
Breasts		Average size; strong & broad; well-formed; not pendulous	
No. own children		2 or 3	
Last pregnancy		More than 6 weeks after full-term delivery	
Her milk:			
Colour		White	
Taste		Sweet	
Smell		Sweet	
Consistency		Average	
Tests for consistency	Nail test; use polished marble or glass	Nail test; addition of rennet or myrrh	

Table 1.7. The regime to be followed by a wet nurse or nursing mother according to the paediatric incunabula.

Regime	Bagellardus 1472	Metlinger 1473	Von Louffenberg 1491
Diet	Abstain from sharp-tasting and salty foods; legumes & fat or salty meat	Avoid strong, salted or spiced foods; meat; fish; milk & wine drunk together. Eat regularly in moderation. Drink beer, fresh water, or water in which herbs boiled	Eat white bread, good meat, rice, lettuce & almonds; peas, beans & gruel boiled in milk; wine to drink; avoid bitter, sour & salty foods
Rest			Plenty of rest & sleep
Exercise	Not too much		Not too much
Sexual intercourse	Abstain		Abstain or only moderately
Pregnancy	Change the nurse	Wean the child, as if nurse was sick	Wean the child
Too much milk		Adjust diet	
Too little milk		Adjust diet; rub breasts; eat udders of lactating goats or sheep	
Too thick milk		Eat less; eat saffron, soups, oatmeal gruel & eggs; avoid pastries, fish, cheese, tender meat & beer. Increase amount of work; if these fail, physick	
Too thin milk		Work less; plenty of sleep; drink milk; eat tender meat, pastries, bread or cereal in milk	

Ancient Near East
REFERENCES
1. Brim, C. J. (1936) *Medicine in the Bible. The Pentateuch. Torah*, New York.
2. Deruisseau, L. G. (1940) Infant hygiene in the older medical literature, *Ciba Symposia 2*, 530-60.
3. Dixon, D. University College, London, personal communication.
4. Diener, L. (1979) Notes on the child in pharaonic Egypt, *Nordisk Medicinhistorisk Årsbok* (English abstract), 45-6.
5. Diener, L. (1983) From contraception to breastfeeding – Increase of family in pharaonic Egypt, *Nordisk Medicinhistorisk Årsbok* (English abstract), 58.
6. Diodorus Siculus (5th century BC).
7. Ebers Papyrus (c.1550 BC) *The Papyrus Ebers. The greatest Egyptian medical document*, trans. Ebell, B., Copenhagen.
8. Flinders Petrie. W. M. (1923) *Social Life in Ancient Egypt*, London.
9. Foote, J. A. (1927) Evidence of rickets prior to 1650, *Amer. J. Dis. Child. 34*, 443-52.
10. Garrison, F. H. (1923) *History of pediatrics*, in Abt, I. A. (ed.), *Pediatrics by various authors*, Philadelphia.
11. Hamada, G. & Rida, A. (1972) Orthopaedics and orthopaedic diseases in ancient and modern Egypt, *Clin. Orth. 89*, 253-68.
12. Hammurabi (22nd century BC) *The code of Hammurabi. King of Babylon 2250 BC*, trans. Harper, R. F., Chicago.
13. Hartemann, J. (1960) Grandeur et décadence de l'allaitement maternel à travers les âges, *Aesculape 43*(12), 3-39.
14. Herodotus (5th century BC) *The famous history of Herodotus*, trans. B. R. (1584), in *The Tudor translations*, 2nd series, *6*, London (1924).
15. *Holy Bible*, Authorised version of King James, London.
16. James, T. G. H. (1983) *An introduction to Ancient Egypt*, London.
17. Jastrow, M. (1911) *Aspects of religious belief and practice in Babylonia and Assyria*, New York. Cited in Garrison, F. H., *History of pediatrics*, in Abt, I. A. (ed.), *Pediatrics by various authors*, Philadelphia (1923).
18. Jonckheere, F. (1955) Un chapitre de pédiatrie Egyptienne l'allaitement, *Aesculape 37*, 203-23.
19. Josephus, Flavius (1st century AD) *The lamentable tragicall historie of the wars and utter ruine of the Jewes*, trans. Lodge, T., London (1602).
20. Kamal, H. (1967) *Dictionary of pharaonic medicine*, Cairo.
21. Klebe, D. & Schadewalt, H. (1955) *Gefasse zur kinderernahrung im wandel der zeit*, Frankfurt am Main.

22. Kottek, S. (1977) Care of children in the Bible and Talmud, *Koroth 7*, 427-36.
23. Leca, A. P. (1971) *La médecine Egyptienne au temps des pharaons*, Paris.
24. Lefkowitz, M. R. & Fant, M. B. (1982) *Women's life in Greece and Rome, A source book in translation*, London.
25. Lindsay, J. (1963) *Daily life in Roman Egypt*, London.
26. Lurker, M. (1980) *The gods and symbols of ancient Egypt. An illustrated dictionary*, London.
27. Margalith, D. (1968) Pediatrics in the Hebrew ancient sources, in *Verhandlungen des XX. internationalen kongresses für geschichte der medizin Berlin 22-27 August 1966*, Hildersheim.
28. Mendelsohn, I. (1948) The family in the ancient Near East, *Biblical Archaeologist 11*, 24-41.
29. Mettler, C. C. (1947) *History of medicine*, Philadelphia.
30. Montet, P. (1958) *Everyday life in Egypt in the days of Rameses the Great*, trans. Maxwell-Hyslop, A. R. & Drower, M. S., London.
31. *Oxyrhynchus papyri part 1* (1898) trans. Grenfell, B. P. & Hunt, A. S. (eds), London: Egyptian Exploration Fund.
32. Peiper, A. (1966) *Chronik der kinderheilkunde*, Leipzig, 4th ed.
33. Posener, G. (1962) *A dictionary of Egyptian civilisation*, London.
34. Preuss, J. (1911) *Biblisch-Talmudische medizin*, Berlin. Cited in Garrison, F. H. (1923) *History of pediatrics*, in Abt, I. A. (ed.), *Pediatrics by various authors*, Philadelphia.
35. Radbill, S. X. (1963) Pediatrics in the Bible, *Clin. Pediat. 2*, 199-212.
36. Radbill, S. X. (1973) Mesopotamian pediatrics, *Episteme 7*, 283-8.
37. Ruffer, M. A. (1921) *Studies in the palaeopathology of Egypt*, Moodie, R. L. (ed.), Chicago.
38. Stevenson Smith, W. (1958) *The art and architecture of Ancient Egypt*, Harmondsworth.
39. *Tebtunis papyri part II* (1907) Grenfell, B. P. & Hunt, A. S. (eds), London.
40. Wallis Budge, E. A. (1925) *Babylonian life and history*, London.
41. Warner, M. (1978) *Alone of all her sex. The myth and cult of the Virgin Mary*, London.
42. Zivanovic, S. (1982) *Ancient diseases. The elements of palaeopathology*, trans. Edwards, L. F., London.

Ancient India
REFERENCES
1. Biswas, D. K. (1971) *Pediatrics at the period of the Caraka Samhita*, Thesis for Doctor of Medicine, University of Dusseldorf.
2. *Caraka Samhita* (c.1st century) trans. Kaviratna, A. C. (1890-1911). Cited in Kutumbiah, P. (1964) Pediatrics in

Ancient India, *Ind. J. Hist. Med. 9*, 22-31.
3. Garrison, F. H. (1923) History of pediatrics, in Abt, I. A. (ed.), *Pediatrics by various authors*, Philadelphia.
4. Kutumbiah, P. (1964) Pediatrics in Ancient India, *Ind. J. Hist. Med. 9*, 22-31.
5. Pal, M. N. (1973) The Ayurvedic tradition of child care. Pediatric wisdom of Ancient India, *Clin. Pediat. 12*, 122-3.
6. Peiper, A. (1966) *Chronik der kinderheilkunde*, Leipzig, 4th ed.
7. *Susruta Samhita* (4th-2nd centuries BC) *An English translation of the Susruta Samhita*, trans. Bishagratna, K. K. L. (1911), Calcutta, Vol.2.

Greece and Rome
REFERENCES
1. Aetios of Amida (6th century AD) *The gynaecology and obstetrics of the VIth century AD*, trans. & annotated Ricci, J. V., Philadelphia.
2. Aristotle (4th century BC) *The works of Aristotle*, vol.4, *Historia animalium*, trans. Wentworth, D., Oxford (1910).
3. Avicenna (10th century AD) in Shah, M. H. (1966) *The general principles of Avicenna's Canon of medicine*, Karachi (1966).
4. Avicenna (10th century AD) in Krueger, H. C. (1963) *Avicenna's Poem on medicine*, Springfield, Illinois.
5. Bartsocas, C. S. (1978) Ancient Greek feeding-bottles, *Trans. Stud. Coll. Phys. Philad. 45*, 297-8.
6. Celsus (1st century AD) *De medicina*, trans. Spencer, W. G., London (1935-8).
6a Deruisseau, L. G. (1940) Infant hygiene in the older medical literature, *Ciba Symposia 2*, 530-60.
7. Drake, T. G. H. (1938) The child in antiquity, *Health*, Spring ed.
8. Etienne, R. (1976) Ancient medical conscience and the life of children, *J. Psychohist. 4*(2), 131-61.
9. Festus (3rd century AD) Quoted in Sussman, G. D. (1982) *Selling mothers' milk. The wet nursing business in France 1715-1914*, Chicago.
10. Foote, J. (1920) An infant hygiene campaign of the second century, *Archs. Pediat. 37*, 173-84.
11. Foote, J. A. (1927) Evidence of rickets prior to 1650, *Am. J. Dis. Child. 34*, 443-52
12. Fildes, V. A. (1981) The early history of the infant feeding bottle, *Nurs. Times 77*, 128-9; 168-70.
13. Galen (2nd century AD) *A translation of Galen's 'Hygiene' (De sanitate tuenda)*, trans. Green, R. M., Springfield, Illinois.
14. Garrison, F. H. (1923) History of pediatrics, in Abt, I. A. (ed.), *Pediatrics by various authors*, Philadelphia.
15. Gellius, Aulus (2nd century AD) *The Attic nights of Aulus Gellius*, trans. Rolfe, J. C., London (1927), vol.2.

16. Gourevitch, D. (1984) *La mal d'être femme; la femme et la médecine dans la Rome antique*, Paris.
17. Herodotus (5th century BC) *The famous history of Herodotus*, trans. B. R. (1584), in *The Tudor Translations*, 2nd series, 6, London (1924).
18. Hippocrates (4th century BC) *Hippocrates*, trans. Jones, W. H. S., London (1923-31).
19. Homer (c.8th century AD) *The Iliad* and *The Odyssey* cited in Rosaria, Sister M. (1917) *The nurse in Greek life*, unpublished PhD dissertation, Catholic University of America, Boston.
20. Hutchings, N. W. 4000 years of infant feeding, *Chemist Drugg. 169*, 714-18.
21. Kaibel, G. (1878) *Epigrammata Graeca ex lapidibus conlecta*, Berlin. Cited & trans. Lefkowitz, M. R. & Fant, M. B. (1982), *Women's life in Greece and Rome. A source book in translation*, London.
22. Kern, J. H. C. (1957) An Attic 'feeding bottle' of the 4th century BC in Leyden, *Mnemosyne 10*, 16-21.
23. Klein, A. E. (1932) *Child life in Greek art*, New York.
24. Lacaille, A. D. (1950) Infant feeding bottles in prehistoric times, *Proc. R. Soc. Med. 43*, 565-8.
25. Lefkowitz, M. R. & Fant, M. B. (1982) *Women's life in Greece and Rome. A source book in translation*, London.
26. Lindsay, J. (1963) *Daily life in Roman Egypt*, London.
27. Liversedge, J. (1976) *Everyday life in the Roman Empire*, London.
28. Lyman, R. B. (1976) Barbarism and religion: late Roman and early medieval childhood, in De Mause, L. (ed.), *The history of childhood*, London, 75-100.
29. McDaniel, W. B. (1948) *Conception, birth and infancy in Ancient Rome and modern Italy*, Florida.
30. McMaster, G. T. (1912) The first woman practitioner of midwifery and the care of infants in Athens, 300 BC, *American Medicine 7*, 202-5.
31. Mettler, C. C. (1947) *History of medicine*, Philadelphia.
32. Oribasius (4th century AD) Cited and partially translated in Still, G. F. (1931) *History of paediatrics*; also cited in *The seven books of Paulus Aeginata. With a commentary*, trans. Adams, F., London (1844-7), vol.1.
33. Osborn, M. L. (1979) Hired mothering through the ages, Howell, J. G. (ed.), *Modern perspectives in the psychiatry of infancy*, New York, 593-616.
34. Paulus Aeginata (7th century AD) *The seven books of Paulus Aeginata. With a commentary*, trans. Adams, F., London (1844-7), vol.1.
35. Plato (4th/5th century BC) *The Republic of Plato*, trans. Cornford, F. M., Oxford (1941).
36. Pliny the Elder (1st century AD) *Historie of the world. Commonly*

called the naturall history of Plinius Secundus, trans. Holland, P., London (1601).

37. Plutarch (1st/2nd century AD) *Life of Lycurgus,* trans. Dryden, J., in Lefkowitz, M. R. & Fant, M. B. (1982), *Women's life in Greece and Rome. A source book in translation,* London.

38. Plutarch (1st/2nd century AD) *The education or bringing up of children,* trans. Elyot, Sir T., London (1533), in Pepper, R. D. (1966), *Four Tudor books on education,* Florida.

39. Pomeroy, S. B. (1975) *Goddesses, whores, wives and slaves. Women in classical antiquity,* New York.

40. Price, T. H. (1978) *Kourothrophos. Cults and representations of the Greek nursing deities,* Leyden.

41. Radbill, S. X. (1976) The role of animals in infant feeding, in Hand, W. D. (ed.), *American folk medicine. A symposium,* Berkeley.

42. Robinson, V. (1938) The nurse of Greece, *Bull. Hist. Med. 6,* 1001-9.

43. Rosaria, Sister M. (1917) *The nurse in Greek life,* unpublished PhD dissertation, Catholic University of America, Boston.

44. Soranus (1st/2nd century AD) *Soranus' Gynecology,* trans. Temkin, O. *et al.,* Baltimore (1956).

45. Stapleton, M. (1978) *A dictionary of Greek and Roman mythology,* London.

46. Still, G. F. (1931) *The history of paediatrics,* London.

47. Stobart, J. C. (1964) *The glory that was Greece,* London, 4th ed.

48. Stobart, J. C. (1964) *The grandeur that was Rome,* London, 4th ed.

49. Tacitus (1st century AD) *Dialogue* 28, cited in Lefkowitz, M. R. & Fant, M. B. (1982), *Women's life in Greece and Rome,* London.

50. Thesleff, H. (ed.) (1965) *The Pythagorean texts of the Hellenistic period,* trans. and cited in Lefkowitz, M. R. & Fant, M. B. (1982), *Women's life in Greece and Rome,* London.

50a Ullmann, M. (1978) *Islamic Medicine,* Edinburgh.

51. Volmer, H. (1959) Infant-mother relations in Ancient Greece, *Pediatrics 23,* 419-20.

52. Webster, T. B. L. (1969) *Everyday life in Classical Athens,* London.

53. Zivanovic, S. (1982) *Ancient diseases. The elements of palaeopathology,* trans. Edwards, L. F., London.

Byzantine
REFERENCES

1. Abrahamse, D. (1979) Images of childhood in early Byzantine hagiography, *J. Psychohist. 6,* 497-517.

2. Aetios of Amida (6th century AD) *The gynaecology and obstetrics of the VIth century AD,* trans. and annotated Ricci, J. V., Philadelphia (1950).

3. Deruisseau, L. G. (1940) Infant hygiene in the older medical literature, *Ciba Symposia 2*, 530-60.
4. Garrison, F. H. (1923) History of Pediatrics, in Abt, I. A. (ed.), *Pediatrics by various authors*, Philadelphia.
5. Lyman, R. B. (1976) Barbarism and religion: late Roman and early medieval childhood, in De Mause, L. (ed.), *The history of childhood*, London, 75-100.
6. Oribasius (4th century AD) cited and partially translated in Still, G. F. (1931) *The history of paediatrics*, London.
7. Paulus Aeginata (7th century AD) *The seven books of Paulus Aeginata. With a commentary*, trans. Adams, F., London (1844-47), vol. 1.
8. Still, G. F. (1931) *The history of paediatrics*, London.

Arabian
REFERENCES
1. Adams, F. (1844) *The seven books of Paulus Aeginata. With a commentary*, London, vol. 1, the commentary to sections II-V.
2. Avicenna (10th century AD) in Shah, M. H. (1966) *The general principles of Avicenna's Canon of medicine*, Karachi.
3. Avicenna (10th century AD) in Krueger, H. C. (1963), *Avicenna's poem on medicine*, Springfield, Illinois.
4. Garrison, F. H. (1923) History of pediatrics, in Abt, I. A. (ed.), *Pediatrics by various authors*, Philadelphia.
5. Kamal, H. (1975) *Encyclopaedia of Islamic medicine*, General Egyptian Book Organisation.
6. Leibowitz, J. O. (1976) Oriental feeding cups (Iranian 10th century) at L. A. Mayer Memorial Institute for Islamic Art, Jerusalem, *Bull. Cleveland Med. Libr. 22*, 64-5.
7. Lemay, H. R. (1978) Arabic influence on medieval attitudes towards infancy, *Clio Med., 13*, 1-12.
8. Maimonides, Moses (12th century AD) *The code of Maimonides Book 4: The book of women*, trans. Klein, I., New Haven & London (1972).
9. Maimonides, Moses (12th century AD) *The medical aphorisms of Moses Maimonides, Vols I & II*, trans. Rosner, F. & Suessman, M. (eds), New York (1970-71).
10. Mettler, C. C. (1947) *History of Medicine*, Philadelphia.
11. Pickthall, M. M. (1948) *The meaning of the glorious Koran*, London.
12. Rhazes (9th century AD) *Practica puerorum*, trans. in Radbill, S. X. (1971) Booklet on the ailments of children and their care which is called *Practica puerorum, Amer. J. Dis. Child. 122*, 372-6.
13. Rhazes (9th century AD) *A treatise on the smallpox and measles by Abú Becr Mohammed Ibn Zacariyá Ar-Rázi (commonly called Rhazes)*, London (1848).

14. Sale, G. (1851) *The Koran, commonly called the Alcoran of Mohammed*, Philadelphia. Cited in Mettler, C. C. (1947) *History of medicine*, Philadelphia.
15. Still, G. F. (1931) *History of paediatrics*, London.
16. White, J. C. (1976) 'Damascan glass nursing bottle' in the Howard Dittrick Museum, *Bull. Cleveland Med. Libr. 22*, 11-17.

Medieval Europe
REFERENCES

1. Aldobrandino of Siena (13th century) *Le régime de corps de Maître Aldebrandin de Sienne, texte française du xiiie siècle*, Landouzy, L. & Pepin, R. (eds), Paris (1911). Cited in Demaitre, L. (1977) The idea of childhood and childcare in medical writings of the middle ages, *J. Psychohist. 4*(4), 461-90.
2. Aristotle (4th century BC) *The works of Aristotle*, vol.4, *Historia animalium*, trans. Wentworth, D., Oxford (1910).
3. Arnold of Villanova (c.1240-1311) *Regimen sanitatis* in his *Opera*, Lyons (1509).
4. Bartholomeus Anglicus (13th century) *On the Properties of things*, trans. Trevisa, J., Oxford (1975).
5. Bayon, H. P. (1940) Trotula and the ladies of Salerno: a contribution to the knowledge of the transition between ancient and mediaeval physick, *Proc. R. Soc. Med. 33*, 471-5.
6. Bernardus Gordonius (1309) *Regimen sanitatis*, Vatican Palatine Latin MS 1174, 14th C. Cited in Demaitre, L. (1977) The idea of childhood and childcare in medical writings of the middle ages, *J. Psychohist. 4*(4), 461-90.
7. Caelius Aurelianus (5th century AD) *Gynaecia; fragments of a Latin version of Soranus' Gynaecia from a thirteenth century manuscript*, Drabkin, M. F. & Drabkin, I. E. (eds), Baltimore (1951).
8. Coulton, G. G. (1918) *Social life in Britain from the conquest to the reformation*, Cambridge.
9. De Laurière, M. (ed.) (1729) *Ordonnances des roys de France*, Paris, vol.2. Cited in Shahar, S. (1983) *J. Psychohist. 10*(3), 281-309.
10. Demaitre, L. (1977) The idea of childhood and childcare in medical writings of the middle ages, *J. Psychohist. 4*(4), 461-90.
11. Fildes, V. A. (1982) *The history of infant feeding 1500–1800*, unpublished PhD thesis, Dept of Human Biology and Health, University of Surrey.
12. Finucane, R. C. (1977) *Miracles and pilgrims. Popular beliefs in medieval England*, London.
13. Forsyth, I. H. (1976) Children in early medieval art: ninth through twelfth centuries, *J. Psychohist. 4*, 29-70.

14. Furnivall, F. J. (ed.) (1868) *Early English meals and manners,* London.
15. Garnier, F. (1973) L'iconographie de l'enfant au moyen âge, *Ann. Demog. Hist.* 135-6.
16. Gilbertus Anglicus (c.1240) *Compendium medicinae.* Cited in Rubin, S. (1974) *Medieval English medicine,* Newton Abbot, Devon.
17. Goodich, M. (1975) Bartholomaeus Anglicus on child-rearing, *Hist. Child. Quart. 3,* 75-84.
18. Grmek, M. D. (1963) Mediaeval frescoes in Serbia and Macedonia, *Ciba Symposium 11*(2), 84-90.
19. Hanawalt, B. A. (1977) Childrearing among the lower classes of late medieval England, *J. Interdisc. Hist. 8*(1), 1-22.
20. Herlihy, D. & Klapisch, C. (1978) *Les Toscans et leur familles,* Paris. Cited in Shahar, S. (1983) *J. Psychohist. 10*(3), 281-309.
21. Hunnisett, R. F. (ed.) (1961) *Bedfordshire coroners' rolls,* Streatley, Beds., vol.41.
22. *Incipit practica puerorum passiones puerorum adhuc in cunabulis iacentium* (12th-15th centuries). Cited and partially trans. in Ruhrah, J. (1925) *Pediatrics from the past,* New York.
23. John of Gaddesden (c.1314) *Rosa Medicinae,* in Cholmeley, H. P. (1912) *John of Gaddesden and the Rosa medicinae,* Oxford.
24. Kroll, J. (1977) The concept of childhood in the middle ages, *J. Hist. Behav. Sci. 13,* 384-93.
25. Lasareff, V. (1938) Studies in the iconography of the virgin, *Art Bulletin 20,* 26-65.
26. *Liber de passionibus puerorum Galeni* (6th-9th centuries) Cited and partially trans. in Ruhrah, J. (1925) *Pediatrics of the past,* New York.
27. McLaughlan, M. M. (1976) Survivors and surrogates: children and parents from the ninth to the thirteenth centuries, in De Mause, L. (ed.), *The history of childhood,* London, 101-81.
28. Myrc, J. (1868) *Instructions for parish priests,* Peacock, E. (ed.), London.
29. Peiper, A. (1966) *Chronik der kinderheilkunde,* Leipzig, 4th ed.
30. Power, E. (1975) *Medieval women,* Postan, M. M. (ed.), Cambridge.
31. Roelans, Cornelius (1483) *De morbis infantium,* Louvain. Cited and partially trans. in Ruhrah, J. (1925) *Pediatrics of the Past,* New York. And in Still, G. F. (1931) *History of paediatrics,* London.
32. Ross, J. B. (1976) The middle-class child in urban Italy, fourteenth to early sixteenth century, in De Mause, L. (ed.), *The history of childhood,* London, 183-228.
33. Rubin, S. (1974) *Medieval English medicine,* Newton Abbot, Devon.
34. Ruhrah, J. (1925) *Pediatrics of the past,* New York.

35. San Bernardino of Siena (1380-1444) *Sermons,* selected Orlandi, D. N. (ed.), trans. Robbins, H. J., Siena (1920). Cited in Ross, J. B. (1976) The middle-class child in urban Italy, in De Mause, L. (ed.), *The history of childhood,* London, 183-228.
36. Savonarola, Michele (d.1462) *Il trattato ginecologico-pediatrico in volgare,* trans. Belloni, L., Milan (1952). Cited in Demaitre, L. (1977) The idea of childhood and child care in medical writings of the middle ages, *J. Psychohist. 4*(4), 461-90.
37. Shahar, S. (1983) Infants, infant care, and attitudes toward infancy in the medieval lives of saints, *J. Psychohist. 10*(3), 281-309.
38. Singleton, C. S. (ed.) (1936) Canzona delle balie, No. XXIX of Trionfi e canzone anonimi and No. XCV in *Canti carnascialeschi del rinascimento,* Bari. Cited in Ross, J. B. (1976) The middle-class child in urban Italy, fourteenth to early sixteenth century, in De Mause, L. (ed.), *The history of childhood,* London, 183-228.
39. Still, G. F. (1931) *The history of paediatrics,* London.
40. Trexler, R. C. (1973) The foundlings of Florence 1395-1455, *Hist. Child. Quart. 1*(2), 259-84.
41. Trotula of Salerno (11th century) *The diseases of women. A translation of Passionibus mulierum curandorum,* Mason-Hoyl, E., New York (1940).
42. Warner, M. (1978) *Alone of all her sex. The myth and cult of the Virgin Mary,* London.
43. White, T. H. (1954) *The book of beasts,* London. Cited in Du Boulay, F. R. H. (1970) *An age of ambition. English society in the late middle ages,* London.
44. Wright, T. (1862) *A history of domestic manners and sentiments in England during the middle ages,* London.

Incunabula

REFERENCES
All four incunabula were described by Ruhrah, who also gave English translations, and Still, who translated excerpts into English.
1. Bagellardus, Paulus (1472) *Libellus de egritudinibus.*
2. Garrison, F. G. (1923) History of pediatrics, in Abt, I. A. (ed.), *Pediatrics by various authors,* Philadelphia.
3. Lehndorff, H. (1951) Bartholomaeus Metlinger, a fifteenth century pediatrician, *Arch. Pediat. 68,* 322-33.
4. Metlinger, Bartholomaeus (1473) *Ein regimen der jungen kinder,* Augsburg.
5. Roelans, Cornelius (1483) *De morbis infantium,* Louvain.
6. Ruhrah, J. (1925) *Pediatrics of the past,* New York.
7. Still, G. F. (1931) *The history of paediatrics,* London.
8. Von Louffenburg, Heinrich (1491) *Versehung des leibs,* Augsburg.

PART TWO

Infant Feeding
1500–1800

Maternal Breastfeeding: Introduction

DURING the 18th century there was a trend among upper- and middle-class mothers, who in previous centuries would have used wet nurses, to reject the latter in favour of breastfeeding their own children. Many factors were involved in this change, particularly changes in medical ideas about the value of colostrum and the increasing social and medical acceptability of artificial feeding, both of which began in the last decades of the 17th century.

Inevitably there is considerable 'overlap' in the discussion of maternal breastfeeding, since the reasons why women did not suckle their own children were inextricably linked with the reasons for the existence and continued employment of wet nurses. Therefore the topic of breastfeeding – who performed it at different periods, and why – permeates all parts of this book. Where they were part of other changes in infant nutrition, major changes in maternal breastfeeding practices are discussed in the context of the former. Chapters 2 to 4 are principally concerned with the age at which infants were put to the breast for the first time; the incidence of maternal breastfeeding in different sections of the population; possible reasons for these class differences; the attitudes of contemporaries towards them; and the techniques and problems of breastfeeding.

CHAPTER TWO

Maternal Breastfeeding:
Neonatal Feeding Practices

"Butter and honey shall he eat." Isaiah, 7, 15

THE IDEA that the mother's first milk or colostrum is a 'bad' substance which should be expressed and discarded before the child is allowed to suck is prevalent in present-day pre-industrial societies in many parts of the world [50,70,73,84]; this chapter will show that it was also a feature of neonatal feeding in pre-industrial Europe.

The 'taboo' against colostrum is probably related to its appearance, which differs in colour and consistency from later breast milk, but this first milk has important protective and nutritive functions. It aids the evacuation of the sticky, black contents (*meconium*) from the neonate's intestine, and contains several antibodies and other proteins which protect the newborn infant from bacterial infections, particularly in the intestine, and also against the fungus which causes the mouth infection known as thrush [33,50].

About the third or fourth day after delivery, colostrum is replaced by more normal-looking breast milk but this retains certain properties until the infant is about two weeks of age. It has large numbers of cells which engulf infective organisms in the gut, and also liberate several protective proteins. In addition, it has concentrated amounts of nutrients, notably zinc, which has been shown to be very important in protecting against neonatal infections; lack of zinc may eventually lead to stunted growth [50].

Clearly, the newborn infant who is breastfed from the first day by its mother, and receives these important substances, will stand a better chance of fighting infections than one who is fed with 'older' breast milk or substitute foods, particularly in a pre-industrial environment. Thus, any change in ideas and/or practice in the feeding of the newborn would significantly affect the health and survival of infants in the first weeks of life.

Between 1550 and the end of the 18th century forty-nine medical writers made recommendations about the first food of neonates, or

81

```
                    A N

          E S S A Y

                  U P O N

          N U R S I N G,

                 A N D  T H E

        Management of CHILDREN,

      From their B I R T H to Three Years of Age.


               By a P H Y S I C I A N,
                    Dr Cadogan of Bristol.

       In a L E T T E R to one of the Governors of
          the F O U N D L I N G  H O S P I T A L.

       Publiſhed by Order of the General Committee
       for tranſacting the Affairs of the ſaid Hoſpital.


               L O N D O N:
        Printed for J. R O B E R T S in Warwick-Lane.
                 M DCC XLVIII.
                          Price 6 d.
```

Plate 2.1. The first edition of William
Cadogan's *Essay* published in 1748.

described the common practice [34] (tables 2.1–2.3). For clarity, these
are given separately for authors writing before and after 1748. This
reflects a natural dividing line in ideas and practice, which apparently
was associated with the publication of William Cadogan's *Essay upon
nursing and the management of children* in 1748 [17] (plate 2.1). The range
of recommendations includes colostrum, breastmilk from another woman, a purge, food, a medicinal substance, and combinations of these
[34].

The purge was not normally a single dose but was repeated at frequent intervals, sometimes for 2 days [47]. The purges recommended
or said to be in common use at different times during the 300-year
period are shown in figure 2.1. The most popular and enduring was
butter/oil of sweet almonds combined with sugar/honey/syrup. This
combination is very ancient; it is mentioned in the Old Testament
(Isaiah, 7, 15) and was recommended by Soranus in the 1st/2nd
century AD [101]. Wine or sugared wine was probably given more
frequently in continental Europe than in Britain [45] (plate 2.2a, b).

Twenty medical authors gave reasons for administering purges or

Figure 2.1. Purges in common use and/or recommended for
the newborn 1500–1800 (named firstly by Paré in 1575 and
lastly by Baudelocque in 1790). Dashed lines indicate purges
discussed by the ancient medical/religious writers.

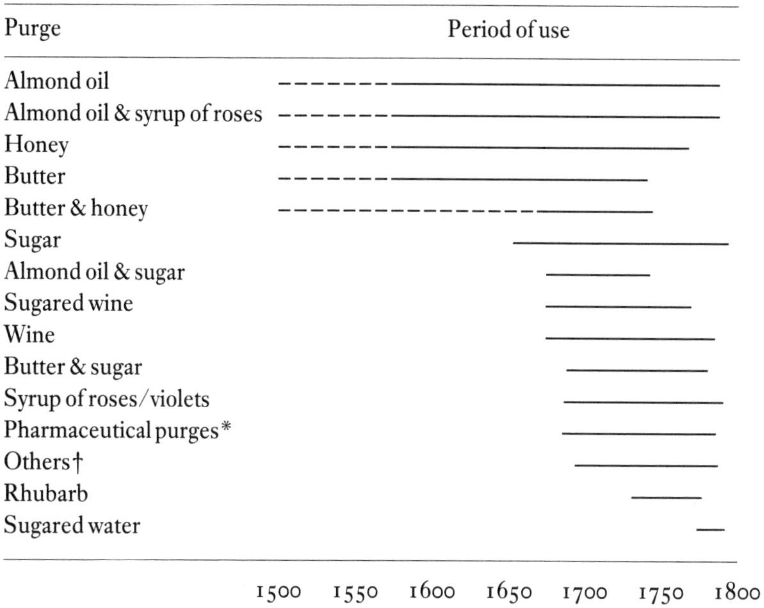

Purge	Period of use
Almond oil	– – – – – – ————————————
Almond oil & syrup of roses	– – – – – – ————————————
Honey	– – – – – – ———————————
Butter	– – – – – – ————————
Butter & honey	– – – – – – – – – – – – – – ————
Sugar	————————————
Almond oil & sugar	—————————
Sugared wine	—————————
Wine	—————————
Butter & sugar	————————
Syrup of roses/violets	—————————
Pharmaceutical purges*	————————
Others†	————————
Rhubarb	—————
Sugared water	—

1500   1550   1600   1650   1700   1750   1800

* Includes mithridate, balsam hystericum, manna, magnesia,
diascordium, cassia, senna, venice treacle, castor oil, cream of
tartar, herb waters: either alone or mixed with the above substances.
† Includes salt water, castile soap in caudle, punch, caudle, gruel.

medicines (see table 2.4) [34]. The purge, medicinal substance and the
first milk or colostrum (if used as a purge) were given to remove the
meconium from the child's stomach and intestines. Less important
functions were the prevention of diseases such as leprosy and falling
sickness, and clearing the mucus from the child's mouth and lungs by
making him cough and vomit [34]. These findings show that there was
a slow change in medical ideas about colostrum (i.e. putting the baby to
the mother's breast within the first few days of birth) dating from the
end of the 17th century. Before this time, mothers were advised not to
breastfeed their child for up to a month after delivery (table 2.5) [34].

There were four main reasons why infants were not to be put to the
mother's breast in the first few days after birth; two affecting the child
and two the mother. Those affecting the child were:

83

Plate 2.2. a) England, 1671. While the
   mother recovers in bed the nurse feeds
   the newly delivered infant with a spoon.
b) *The birth of St John*, after Tintoretto
   (c.1518-94). While the mother recovers
   in bed another woman offers her breast
   to the newborn child.

i) The mother's first milk or 'beestings' was regarded as unpurified
and bad for the child [66,81,78]. Eight writers between 1540 and
1746 said that colostrum was harmful to the child, or was thought
to be so by their contemporaries [34]; ii) The baby would come to

harm if he was given milk whilst still passing meconium (it was believed that the milk and meconium would coagulate in the intestines) [13,52,69,78,88].

Affecting the mother:

i) The mother was not 'rested' or fit enough to feed. She needed to recover from her labour [41,68,69,78,80]; ii) The mother was not cleansed (i.e. she could not feed until the vaginal discharge (lochia) had stopped flowing and she had been 'churched') [41,66]. These findings are tabulated in table 2.6 and show that the major concern of the eleven authors who gave the above reasons was for the health of the newborn child.

Before the child could be safely breastfed the mother had to draw off and discard her first milk. This could be done by other women [41,69,78] with sucking glasses [41,69,78]; by a 'lusty' older child [69,106]; or by a puppy-dog [41]. Meanwhile, once thoroughly purged, the child could be suckled by other women whose milk was 'older' [68,69,81,88].

The change in ideas about the value of colostrum began in the British medical literature in 1672–73 with the publication of the English translation of Mauriceau's midwifery text *The accomplisht midwife* [69]. François Mauriceau (1637–1709), a prominent French surgeon who practised in Paris, was the leading man-midwife and most influential figure in European obstetrics in the 17th century. His textbook, first published in French in 1668, was subsequently translated into at least 7 languages and remained in print for over a century. The change in ideas about colostrum which this book heralded is outlined in figure 2.2.

It is difficult to assess how far this change in medical ideas was reflected in practice. In the 16th and 17th centuries it is unlikely that mothers who had grown up with the familiar age-old taboo against feeding colostrum would have gone against it in any great number, as few mothers would have deliberately wished to harm their newborn child. Certainly the rich, who were most influenced by physicians and also used wet nurses, followed the customary procedure of purging for several days before sending the child to nurse [69]. The wet nurse was not newly-delivered so that infants could not obtain colostrum from the breasts of their foster mother (see chapter 6). Whilst physicians and man-midwives may have been able to influence those women rich enough to pay their fees, it would have taken much longer for the poorer sections of society to have discovered or been informed of new ideas and then persuaded that these could benefit either themselves or their offspring. There were three ways in which these new ideas could have spread among the middle classes and the poor in the 18th century.

First, about 1750 William Hunter (1718–83), in an attempt to reduce the morbidity and mortality from milk fever in the Lying-in Hospital, Brownlow Street, proposed that infants should be put to their

Figure 2.2. Chronology of changes in ideas about colostrum.

Pre-1673   All writers condemned colostrum as harmful and undesirable.
1673   Mauriceau reported that some people believed colostrum had a purgative effect, but did not recommend it.
1694   McMath repeated this belief.
1699   Ettmueller was the first to recommend colostrum in place of the traditional purge.
1719   Dionis was the first to recommend colostrum as more nourishing than any other milk.
1733   Allen recommended colostrum as nourishing for some days.
c.1740   Hoffmann said that experience had shown that people were wrong to advise against the first milk.
1746   Astruc was the last writer to advise against feeding infants with new milk.
1748   Cadogan published his *Essay* and recommended that no child should be given anything whatsoever until he was put to the breast: harm would come to any infant denied colostrum.
1748–   *No* writer considered colostrum was a bad or harmful substance.
1800   The first milk was recommended as good for the child; as an alternative or addition to the traditional purge; and as a preventative against milk fever in the mother [34].
1753   The advantages of early maternal breastfeeding in the prevention of milk fever were first mentioned by Nelson.
1776   Feeding the child with mother's milk from the beginning prevented many infantile disorders was first stated by Rosenstein.

mother's breast within 24 hours of delivery instead of after 3–4 days as had been the custom. This reduced the formerly very high incidence of milk fever to negligible proportions [77]. Milk fever occurred several days after delivery, in women who did not breastfeed. The milk stagnated in the breasts and became a focus for infection and abscesses, which were often exacerbated by vain attempts to 'draw' the breasts by well-meaning helpers. It was characterised by a high fever and significant maternal mortality, and in the 17th and 18th centuries was dreaded as much as puerperal fever [59,77]. Experiments in the lying-in hospitals hastened the understanding that the breastfeeding of infants from the first day protected mothers from contracting milk fever. Since the lying-in hospitals and the Royal Maternity Charity, which delivered women in their own homes, catered for respectable poor women [23], it was the poor rather than the richer women in society who were subjected to this change in medical ideas and thus first benefited from them. It is probable that Hunter's finding would have spread slowly

86

Plate 2.3. *The lying-in room* by Cornelis
Troost (1697-1750). The mother has
her caudle while the baby is spoon-fed
with pap from a porringer.

among the poor by word of mouth (plate 2.3).

Second, the lying-in hospitals and wards were responsible for training physicians and midwives who, on obtaining their licence, went
elsewhere to practise midwifery [23]; young physicians, the man-midwives and particularly the midwives would thus have spread this new
teaching among the poorer classes. It is likely that women would have
been much more ready to adopt a new practice in infant feeding which
was beneficial to their own health and safety during childbearing, than
one which was said (without evidence) to be good for their child, which
might have taken longer to become established practice.

Third, the aristocracy, which was turning from artificial feeding and/
or wet nursing at about the same time [109] (see chapter 11), would also
have been aware of the reduction in maternal morbidity in the lying-in
hospitals [109] as well as forming (together with the gentry and 'middle-
classes') the readership of the new 'advice on babycare' books which
began to appear in the second half of the 18th century [59, 109] and which
advised putting infants to the breast as soon as possible [15, 77, 100].

¶ If the new idea of putting infants to the mother's breast within 24
hours of birth were practised, and did spread gradually through British
society from the end of the 17th century and particularly after 1750,
then this should be reflected in the neonatal mortality rate. Since the
major function of colostrum is protective, lack of it (particularly if

unsuitable substances were given from unclean spoons and dishes in the interim) could be expected to result in a high incidence of neonatal infections, especially of the gastro-intestinal tract. As will be shown throughout this study, the evidence from medical writers in the period 1500 to 1800 is that the most common illness among infants was 'gripes', 'looseness', and 'green stools'. The Liverpool surgeon, William Moss, confirmed that this was the case in the neonatal period. He observed that nearly all newborn infants had gripes and looseness, but this stopped when they were put to the breast after 2–4 days; those who were to be handreared continued to suffer [75].

Colostrum is protective for the first six weeks of life [50] so that the infant mortality rate (0–1 year) would be less sensitive to any change than would mortality in the first month of life. Infant mortality from a mixed sample of parishes [95] shows that, while overall mortality fell slightly from the 1680s onwards, the mortality (0–28 days) fell considerably more sharply from the 1680s until about 1840 (beginning of the Registrar-General's returns) when it levelled off and remained relatively unchanged and independent of changes in the overall infant mortality rate until at least 1875 (see table 2.7 and figure 2.3).

The infant mortality rate (0–1 year) of the British aristocracy fell gradually from 1675, and more significantly from 1750 [44,109,118] (table 2.8). This is rather earlier and more noticeable than the fall in infant mortality in more remote parishes such as Colyton in Devon [118] and the fen villages of Leake and Wrangle [112]. It seems reasonable to suppose that (as in the larger sample shown in table 2.7) a significant part of the fall in these infant mortality figures was also due to a fall in mortality (0–28 days), and that this reflected a more gradual change in neonatal feeding practices among rural parishes than among the rich and fashionable, who would always have had the most up-to-date information and thus have benefited in advance of most of the population.

Some hypotheses for the fall of infant mortality in the 18th century have been proposed (including advances in preventive medicine, improved nutrition and social conditions, increased consumption of cow's milk, and improved maternal care) [12,64,65,109] but none of these satisfactorily explains why the major part of the fall in infant mortality was due to many more infants surviving the first month of life. Nor were improvements in 18th-century midwifery sufficiently dramatic to have contributed significantly [23]. It is suggested therefore that changes in neonatal feeding practices had a major, positive effect on infant mortality (0–28 days). This theory must be viewed with reservation, as there may have been further unknown factors acting simultaneously, but in the absence of any other factor that can be identified as relevant, sufficiently effective, and showing change in the same period, it seems reasonable to attribute the improvement in neonatal survival between

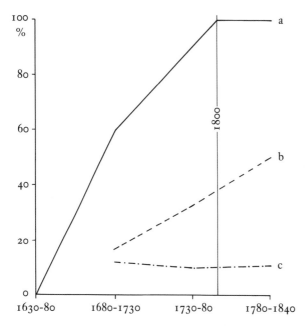

Figure 2.3. a) Percentage of writers recommending early breast-feeding with colostrum; and the percentage fall in b) mortality 0-28 days and c) overall infant mortality, 1630-1840.

the late 17th and early 19th century to changes in ideas and practice of neonatal feeding, particularly early maternal breastfeeding.

The observed decrease in morbidity and mortality from breast diseases and milk fever in the lying-in hospitals should be apparent in maternal mortality figures for the later 18th century. Figures comparable with the periods shown in table 2.7 for infant and neonatal mortality are not available, but the maternal mortality rate has recently been estimated for 13 English parishes of varying size and population between 1600 and 1799 [96,121]. This shows that there was a steadily decreasing mortality from the end of the 16th century until a plateau was reached in the mid-19th century (see table 2.9).

Further study of maternal mortality is necessary before making positive statements about causative factors. There were certainly several occurrences in midwifery practice (most notably the general availability and use of obstetric forceps in the 18th century) which would contribute to a decreasing mortality. It seems likely that early breastfeeding in lying-in women would be just one among several reasons for the steadily improving maternal mortality during the 18th century.

¶ Modern research has shown that there is a critical time after childbirth when *bonding* occurs between the mother and her new child [50,55]. This maternal-infant bond is well known among many mammalian species, and separation of the mother from the newborn at this critical time leads to rejection of the young, and sometimes to destruction by the mother. Preliminary studies have associated lack of bonding in humans with rejection and/or battering of the infant either physically or emotionally [50,55,61]. The critical time for maternal instinct to be established in man is thought to begin in the first minutes after birth and last for about 12 hours; the longer the separation, especially on the first day of life, the greater the chance of emotional rejection of the child by his mother. Early separation has been proposed as a cause of proneness to depression in infants, and emotional coldness or indifference in the mother, whilst the child may grow up unaware of the proper way in which to react to children or how to rear them satisfactorily. Breastfeeding has been shown to be an important mechanism in the maternal-infant bonding process [50,55].

The historical situation may be clarified by relating this modern knowledge to neonatal feeding practices. Newly-delivered mothers who did not see their infants for hours, or sometimes days [47], would have had no opportunity to form any emotional bond so that the child who was fed with physick or food from a spoon, for several days, possibly in a different room [43], would have been a stranger to the mother when finally she was allowed to feed him. First-time mothers in particular experienced problems in learning the technique of breastfeeding [59,111], and, with the additional difficulties which distended breasts presented after several days of non-suckling, they would not have been in an ideal state to enjoy their new child. It is therefore not surprising that some mothers, especially in the 16th and 17th centuries, were apparently indifferent, and content to put their offspring out to nurse. In contrast, women who did breastfeed their infants early on had great love for their children and experienced hopeless grief at their deaths [107,115]. During the 18th century, when gradually more infants were put to the breast within a few hours of birth, the expected result would be greater maternal love and more concern for children than previously; and, as generation succeeded generation of early breastfed children, for the imprinting of maternal instinct and behaviour to be reflected in the childrearing practices of the late 18th and 19th centuries. As noted above, early maternal breastfeeding was beginning to be recommended, and possibly practised, in the last years of the 17th century. Increasing concern for infant and child welfare began two decades later [82] and associated philanthropy was a feature of the 18th century, concurrent with a growing concept of children being different from adults [5,11,87,105,109]. There were undoubtedly other factors at work in this period, but the change in neonatal feeding practices cannot be disregarded as one factor in the change of attitude of British society towards its children which is said to have occurred in the 18th century.

¶ In pre-industrial Britain, feeding neonates with physick and/or food rather than colostrum, and denying the mother and child the physiological and emotional benefits of early breastfeeding, was a cause of i) a high neonatal mortality, mainly from gastro-intestinal complaints; ii) milk fever and breast disorders in the mother; iii) probable failure of maternal-infant bonding in the first few days of life. Change towards early maternal breastfeeding during the 18th century contributed to a notable decline in mortality (0–28 days) and a decrease in maternal morbidity and mortality from milk fever. The change incidentally provided more ideal conditions for the maternal instinct to become established and consequently may have been a factor in the improved emotional attitudes towards infants and their welfare noted during the 18th century.

REFERENCES

1. Aetios of Amida (6th century AD) *The gynaecology and obstetrics of the VIth century AD*, trans. and annotated, Ricci, J. V., Philadelphia.
2. Aitken, J. (1786) *Principles of midwifery*, London, 3rd ed.
3. Allen, J. (1733) *Synopsis medicinae: or A summary view of the whole practice of physick*, London, vol.2.
4. Arbuthnot, J. (1732) *Practical rules of diet in the various constitutions and diseases of human bodies*, London.
5. Ariès, P. (1973) *Centuries of childhood*, Harmondsworth.
6. Armstrong, G. (1771) *An essay on the diseases most fatal to infants*, London, 2nd ed.
7. Astruc, J. (1746) *A general and complete treatise on all the diseases incident to children from their birth to the age of fifteen*, trans. anon., London.
8. Badinter, E. (1981) *The myth of motherhood. An historical view of the maternal instinct*, London.
9. Barrett, R. (1699) *A companion for midwives, childbearing women and nurses. Directing them how to perform their respective offices*, London.
10. Baudelocque, J-L. (1790) *A system of midwifery*, trans. Heath, J., 3 vols, London.
11. Bayne-Powell, R. (1939) *The English child in the eighteenth century*, London.

12. Beaver, M. W. (1973) Population, infant mortality and milk, *Popul. Stud. 27*, 243-54.
13. Bracken, H. (1737) *The midwife's companion, or A treatise of midwifery*, London.
14. Brouzet, N. (1755) *An essay on the medicinal education of children; and the treatment of their diseases*, trans. anon., London.
15. Buchan, W. (1769) *Domestic medicine; or The family physician*, Edinburgh.
16. Burton, J. (1751) *An essay towards a complete new system of midwifery*, London.
17. Cadogan, W. (1748) *An essay upon nursing and the management of children, from their birth to three years of age*, London.
18. Clark, W. (1751) *The province of midwives in the practice of their art*, Bath and London.
19. *Compleat midwife's practice, enlarged, The* (1680), London.
20. Culpeper, N. (1675) *A directory for midwives*, London.
21. Culpeper, N. (1676) *A directory for midwives or, A guide for women in their conception, bearing and suckling their children. Corrected from many gross errors*, London.
22. Dionis, P. (1719) *A general treatise of midwifery*, trans. anon., London.
23. Donnison, J. (1977) *Midwives and medical men. A history of inter-professional rivalries and women's rights*, London.
24. Downman, H. (1788) *Infancy or, The management of children. A didactic poem in six books*, London, 4th ed.
25. Ebrahim, G. J. (1978) *Breastfeeding the biological option*, London.
26. Ebrahim, G. J. (1978) *Mother and child health in developing countries*, London.
27. Ebrahim, G. J. (1979) *Care of the newborn in developing countries*, London.
28. Ebrahim, G. J. (1983) *Nutrition in mother and child health*, London.
29. *English midwife enlarged ... containing two new treatises ... of the diseases of little children, and the conditions necessary to be considered in the choice of nurses and their milk* (1682), London.
30. Ettmueller, M. (1699) *Etmullerus abridg'd: or A compleat system of the theory and practice of physic*, trans. anon., London.
31. Exton, B. (1751) *A new and general system of midwifery*, London.
32. Fildes, V. A. (1979) It's a wonder babies ever survived. The first food of infants 1500-1800, *Nursing Mirror Supplement 149*, viii-xiv; Part 2. Putting mum in the picture. The consequences for maternal and child health, *Nursing Mirror 149*, 22-4.
33. Fildes, V. A. (1980) Neonatal feeding practices and infant mortality during the 18th century, *J. Biosoc. Sci. 12*, 313-24.
34. Fildes, V. A. (1982) *The history of infant feeding 1500-1800*, Unpublished PhD thesis, Dept of Human Biology and Health,

University of Surrey.

35. Fildes, V. A. (1982) Changes in infant feeding practices and ideas from 1600 to 1800 with particular reference to those affecting infant mortality and maternal-infant bonding in Eckart, W. and Geyer-Kordesch, J. (eds), *Heilberufe und kranke im 17. und 18. jahrhundert die quellen- und forschungssituation*, Munster.

36. *Full view of all the diseases incident to children containing a translation of Dr Harris' book upon the acute diseases of infants, and the eminent Dr Boerhaave's treatise upon all their diseases* (1742), London.

37. Foster, E. (1781) *The principles and practice of midwifery*, London.

38. *Gentleman's Magazine* (1765) Unsigned writer *On some of the causes that occasion the mortality of children under two years of age*, London.

39. Glass, D. V. & Eversley, D. E. C. (1974) *Population in history. Essays in historical demography*, London.

40. Gouge, W. (1622) *Of domestical duties. Eight treatises*, London.

41. Guillemeau, J. (1612) *Childbirth or The happie deliverie of women . . . to which is added A treatise of the diseases of infants and young children: with the cure of them*, trans. anon., London.

42. Hamilton, A. (1792) *A treatise on the management of female complaints and of children in early infancy*, Edinburgh.

43. Hedley, O. (1975) *Queen Charlotte*, London.

44. Hollingsworth, T. H. (1957) A demographic study of the British Ducal families in Glass, D. V. & Eversley, D. E. C. *Population in history. Essays in historical demography*, London (1974).

45. Hoffman, F. (*c.*1740) *A system of the practice of medicine vol. 2*, trans. Lewis, W., London (1783).

46. Hunter, W. (1775) *Lectures anatomical and chirurgical by William Hunter*, Library of the Wellcome Institute for the History of Medicine, MS 2966. Also dated 1783.

47. Hunter, W. (1908) An obstetric diary of William Hunter, Stark, J. N. (ed.), *Glasg. Med. J. 70*, 167-77, 241-56, 338-56.

48. Imhof, A. E. (1981) *The amazing simultaneousness of the big differences and the boom in the 19th century – Some facts and hypotheses about infant and maternal mortality in Germany, 18th to 20th century*, International symposium on mortality decline, Lund.

49. James, R. (1746) *The modern practice of physic. As improv'd by . . . H. Boerhaave, and F. Hoffmann . . . Being a translation of the aphorisms of the former with the commentaries of Dr. van Swieten*, 2 vols, London.

50. Jelliffe, D. B. & Jelliffe, E. F. P. (1978) *Human milk in the modern world. Psychosocial, nutritional and economic significance*, Oxford.

51. Johnstone, J. (1657) *The idea of practical physick in twelve books,* trans. Culpeper, N. & W. R., London.
52. Jones, J. (1579) *The arte and science of preserving bodie and soule in healthe, wisedome, and catholick religion: physically, philosophically and divinely devised,* London.
53. Jones, R. E. (1976) Infant mortality in rural North Shropshire, 1561-1810, *Popul. Stud. 30,* 305-17.
54. Jones, R. E. (1980) Further evidence on the decline of infant mortality in pre-industrial England: North Shropshire 1561-1810, *Popul. Stud. 34,* 239-50.
55. Klaus, M. H. & Kennell, J. H. (1982) *Parent-infant bonding,* 2nd Ed., St Louis.
56. *Ladies dispensatory or, Every woman her own physician* (1740), London.
57. Lara, B. (1791) *An essay on the injurious custom of mothers not suckling their own children; with some directions for chusing a nurse, and weaning of children,* etc., London.
58. Leinster, E. (1949) *Emily, Duchess of Leinster, 1731-1814,* Fitzgerald, B., London.
59. Leinster, E. (1949-57) *Correspondence of Emily, Duchess of Leinster (1731-1814),* Fitzgerald, B. (ed.), Dublin.
60. Lowder (Lowther), W. (late 18th century) *Midwifery. Lectures on that subject read by Dr Lowder, Vol.2,* Library of the Wellcome Institute for the History of Medicine, MS 3334.
61. McGurk, H., University of Surrey, personal communication.
62. Mackenzie, C. (1770) *Lectures in midwifery,* Library of the Wellcome Institute for the History of Medicine, MS 3392.
63. Mackenzie, C. (1774) *Mr Mackenzey's Lectures on Midwifery,* ? by D.B., Library of the Royal College of Obstetricians and Gynaecologists, London, Unnumbered MS.
64. McKeown, T. & Brown, R. G. (1955) Medical evidence related to English population change in the eighteenth century, *Popul. Stud. 9,* 119-41.
65. McKeown, T. (1978) Fertility, mortality and causes of death. An examination of issues related to the modern rise of population, *Popul. Stud. 32,* 535-42.
66. McMath, J. (1699) *The expert midwife: a treatise of the diseases of women with child, and in child bed . . . with fit remedies for the various maladies of newborn babes,* Edinburgh.
67. Mantell, T. (1787) *Short directions for the management of infants,* London.
68. Maubray, J. (1730) *The female physician containing all the diseases incident to that sex. . . together with the diet and regimen of both the mother and child,* London.
69. Mauriceau, F. (1673) *The accomplisht midwife, treating of the diseases of women with child, and in childbed . . . with fit remedies for the several indispositions of newborn babes,* trans. Chamberlen, H., London.

70. Mead, M. (1935) *Sex and temperament in three primitive societies*, New York, 3rd ed. (1963).
71. Mears, M. (1797) *The midwife's candid advice to the fair sex; or The pupil of nature*, London.
72. Memis, J. (1765) *The midwife's pocket companion*, London.
73. Mondot-Bernard, J. M. (1977) *Relationships between fertility, child mortality and nutrition in Africa. A tentative analysis*, Paris.
74. Morley, D. (1973) *Paediatric priorities in the developing world*, London.
75. Moss, W. (1781) *An essay on the management and nursing of children in the earlier periods of infancy*, London.
76. Muffet (Moffet), T. (1584) *Health's improvement: or Rules comprising the nature, method, and manner of preparing all sorts of food used in this . Corrected and enlarged by Christopher Bennet*, London (1655).
77. Nelson, J. (1753) *An essay on the government of children*, London.
78. *Nurses guide, the: or The right method of bringing up young children. By an eminent physician* (1729), London.
79. Ojofeitimi, E. O. (1981) Breast-feeding patterns in a Nigerian maternity center, *Clin. Pediat. 20*(6), 412-14.
80. Paré, A. (1575) *The workes of that famous chirurgion Ambrose Parey*, trans. Johnston, T., London, 1634.
81. Pechey, J. (1697) *A general treatise of the diseases of infants and children. Collected from the best practical authors*, London.
82. Pinchbeck, I. & Hewitt, M. (1969) *Children in English society, vol. 1. From Tudor times to the eighteenth century*, London.
83. Platt, B. S. & Gin, S. Y. (1938) Chinese methods of infant feeding and nursing, *Archs Dis. Childh. 13*, 343-54.
84. Ploss, H. H., Bartels, M. & Bartels, P. (1935) *Woman*, Dingwall, E. J. (ed.), London.
85. *Practice of midwifery by a pupil of the late Dr W. Hunter* (1783), London.
86. Richmond, J. B. & Caldwell, B. M. (1963) Child rearing practices and their consequences, in Solnit, A. J. & Provence, S. A. (ed.), *Modern perspectives in child development*, New York.
87. Rodgers, B. (1949) *Cloak of charity. Studies in eighteenth century philanthropy*, London.
88. Roesslin, the Elder, E. (1540) *The byrth of mankynde*, trans. Jonas, R., London, first published 1512.
89. Rosenstein, N. R. von (1776) *The diseases of children and their remedies*, trans. Sparrman, A., London.
90. Rowbottom, M. (undated) *Birth customs among primitive peoples. Notes collected together by M. Rowbottom*, Typescript in Library of the Wellcome Institute for the History of Medicine.
91. Rueff, J. (1550) *The expert midwife*, trans. anon., London (1637).
92. Sainte Marthe, S. de (1584) *Paedotrophiae: or The art of bringing up children*, trans. anon., London (1710).

93. Schaffer, R. (1977) *Mothering*, London.
94. Schofield, R. S. (1970) Perinatal mortality in Hawkshead, Lancashire 1581-1710, *Loc. Popul. Stud. 4*, 11-16.
95. Schofield, R. S. (1979) Infant and child mortality in England in the late Tudor and early Stuart period, in Webster, C. (ed.), *Health, medicine and mortality in the sixteenth century*, Cambridge.
96. Schofield, R. S. (1984) *Maternal mortality in England in the past*, Paper presented at Wellcome Symposium Medicine and Demography.
97. Sharp, Jane (1671) *The midwives book or The whole art of midwifery discovered*, London.
98. Shorter, E. (1977) *The making of the modern family*, Glasgow.
99. Smellie, W. (1752) *A treatise on the theory and practice of midwifery*, London, vols 1 and 3.
100. Smith, H. (1774) *Letters to married women on nursing and the management of children. The third edition, revised and considerably enlarged*, London.
101. Soranus of Ephesus (1st/2nd century A D) *Soranus' Gynecology*, trans. Temkin, O. et al., Baltimore (1956).
102. Spence, D. (1784) *A system of midwifery*, Edinburgh.
103. Stern, D. (1977) *The first relationship: infant and mother*, London.
104. Still, G. F. (1931) *The history of paediatrics*, London.
105. Stone, L. (1977) *The family, sex and marriage in England 1500-1800*, London.
106. Thomson, J. (c.1772-85) *An analysis of midwifery with the diseases incident to pregnancy and those which commonly happen in the month, to child-bed women*, Library of the Wellcome Institute for the History of Medicine, MS 4779.
107. Thornton, A. (1875) *The autobiography of Mrs. Alice Thornton of East Newton, Co. York*, Jackson, C. (ed.), Durham.
108. *Trace elements in human nutrition* (1973) WHO Technical report series, no.532, Geneva.
109. Trumbach, R. (1978) *The rise of the egalitarian family*, New York.
110. Ulrich, L. T. (1982) *Good wives. Image and reality in the lives of women in Northern New England 1650-1750*, New York.
111. Underwood, M. (1784) *A treatise on the diseases of children*, London.
112. West, F. (1974) Infant mortality in the east fen parishes of Leake and Wrangle, *Loc. Popul. Stud. 13*, 41-4.
113. Whiting, J. W. M. & Child, I. L. (1964) *Child training and personality: a cross-cultural study*, New Haven and London.
114. Willmott Dobbie, B. M. (1982) An attempt to estimate the true rate of maternal mortality, sixteenth to eighteenth centuries, *Med. Hist. 26*(1), 79-90.

115. Willoughby, E. (1844) *So much of the diary of Lady Willoughby as relates to her domestic history and to the eventful period of the reign of Charles the first Vol. 1 1635-48*, London.
116. Willughby, P. (1630-69) *Observations in midwifery. As also the country midwife's opusculum or vade mecum*, Blenkinsop, H. (ed.), Warwick (1863).
117. Wood, C. B. S. & Walker-Smith, J. A. (1981) *MacKeith's Infant feeding and feeding difficulties*, Edinburgh and London.
118. Wrigley, E. A. (1968) Mortality in pre-industrial England: the example of Colyton, Devon, over three centuries, *Daedalus 97*, 546-80.
119. Wrigley, E. A. (1977) Births and baptisms: the use of Anglican baptism registers as a source of information about the number of births in England before the beginning of civil registration, *Popul. Stud. 31*, 281-312.
120. Wrigley, E. A. & Schofield, R. S. (1981) *Population history of England 1541-1871*.
121. Wrigley, E. A. & Schofield, R. S. (1983) English population history from family reconstitution: summary results 1600-1799, *Popul. Stud. 37*, 157-84.
122. Young, T. (1761) *De lacte*, Inaugural dissertation, University of Edinburgh, cited in Still, G. F. (1931) *History of paediatrics*, London.
123. Young, T. (late 18th century) *Young's midwifery*, Library of the Wellcome Institute for the History of Medicine, MSS 5106 & 5107.

CHAPTER THREE

Maternal Breastfeeding:
The Incidence and Practice of
Maternal Breastfeeding

"A mother to be nurse, that's great and faire,
Is now held base: true mothers they be rare."
Richard Brathwaite, *The English Gentlewoman*, 1631

FOR THOUSANDS of years there has been controversy over who
should suckle young babies: the mother or a hired wet nurse. Wet nursing, as we have seen, was well established in most ancient societies
[49,116,186,234], particularly in Greek and Roman civilisation, where the
availability of slave women reduced problems of supply [83,182,190,211].
The practice spread throughout the Greek colonies and the Roman
Empire, and it is possible that wet nursing was introduced into Britain
during the Roman occupation. By the medieval period it was well-established for European women of the upper classes to employ wet nurses.
Not only royal and aristocratic infants, but also the children of wealthy
merchants and those women who ran businesses, were so reared, to free
the mother from the chores of child-rearing [183]. In this chapter, unless
otherwise stated, the discussion is confined to the upper strata of British society. The impression gained over years of study is that the great
majority of British infants were breastfed at home by their mothers.

Philosophers, physicians, and some theologians repeatedly condemned mothers who did not breastfeed their own children, but this had
little discernible effect on the behaviour of the wealthy [82,83,181,211].
Because of the continuing concern of physicians, moralists and theologians, the subject of 'maternal breastfeeding versus wet nursing'
received more attention in all types of literature than did other aspects
of infant nutrition: as, for instance, the sermons and written works of
Puritans during the late 16th and 17th centuries testify.

During most of the 16th century, condemnation of women who did
not suckle was minimal. It seems to have begun on a small scale after the
Reformation and, by the early 17th century, puritan theologians in particular were devoting sermons and large tracts of popular conduct books
to the evils of non-breastfeeding mothers [13,87,91,178,209]. Writers
gave the impression (either directly or by implication) that women were

Plate 3.1. Holland, mid-17th C. Engraving
by C. de Visscher. For paupers, a good
supply of breastmilk was essential for
the survival of their children, and the
poor were often said to have more,
and better, milk than the rich.

not breastfeeding mainly to suit their own social life and had little love
either for their children or for God. The only recorded aristocratic
mother to condemn wet nursing in print came from a family holding
puritan beliefs [36]. She was Elizabeth, Countess of Lincoln, mother
to the Arbella who married Isaac Johnson, one of the 'Winthrop fleet'
which carried puritan members of the Massachusetts Bay Company
to Salem in the 1630s [32]. During the late 16th and 17th centuries the
women of the stricter protestant sects were apparently more likely to
breastfeed their own children than those of similar station who did not
subscribe to such religious views [33,154,165,196,224]. A similar fact has
been noted for Germany in the same period, where Pietists, a strict protestant sect, also saw breastfeeding as a religious duty [85].

There is no doubt that some mothers, possibly a substantial number,
in pre-industrial England did not breastfeed their own children. Evidence shows that wives of the aristocracy, gentry, wealthy merchants,
wealthy farmers, scholars, lawyers, physicians, and some clergymen
regularly used wet nurses throughout the period 1500 to 1800 [70].
Their use apparently increased during the 17th century, and by the

Plate 3.2. England, 1636. From a
memorial brass to Benjamin and
Elizabeth Brand.

early 18th century women whose husbands had a relatively modest income (such as shopkeepers) were not feeding their own children [138,]. Although there was increasing concern, from the early 17th century on, that this custom of the wealthy was spreading to women of lower station [36,165], no evidence has been found to suggest that wet nursing flourished in all classes of society on the same great scale as it did in France and parts of Central Europe [72,201,222] (plate 3.1).

Wet nursing was an ancient, deeply-ingrained and widely-accepted social custom, and wealthy mothers who decided to nurse their own babies were sufficiently exceptional to attract comment (often adverse) both from close friends and relatives and from the wider social circle. In the late 16th and 17th centuries breastfeeding mothers often excited the disapproval of friends, particularly males [165,168,197]; referred to this fact, with pride, in letters [168]; had the fact engraved upon their tombstones (plate 3.2); and left extra money in their wills to those children who were breastfed by their mother, at the expense of those put out to nurse. For example, in the mid-17th century, John Greene, an Essex lawyer, left £1000 to each of his daughters, except Margaret, who was to have £100 more 'because her mother nursed her' [89]. It was well established that a much closer relationship existed between mothers and the children they suckled than between mothers and children put to nurse [37,81,105,224] (plate 3.3).

¶ The reasons why women did not breastfeed were manifold. Authors of all types enumerated the common excuses or objections which were raised against maternal suckling (table 3.1 [70]). The most frequently repeated statements were that women did not breastfeed because it would have adverse effects on health, figure and beauty; believing that suckling would make them look old before their time. It also involved

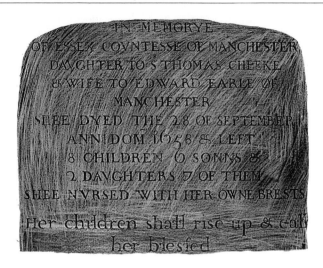

IN MEMORYE
OF ESSEX COVNTESSE OF MANCHESTER
DAVGHTER TO S THOMAS CHEEKE
& WIFE TO EDWARD EARLE OF
MANCHESTER
SHEE DYED THE 28 OF SEPTEMBER
ANN DOM 1658 & LEFT
8 CHILDREN 6 SONNS &
2 DAVGHTERS 7 OF THEM
SHEE NVRSED WITH HER OWNE BRESTS
Her children shall rise up & call
her blesced

Plate 3.3. England, c.1658. Monument to
Lady Essex, Countess of Manchester.

restraints in dress; breastfeeding mothers could not dress fashionably,
and what clothes they did wear they believed would quickly become
soiled. Perhaps most were concerned to retain good-shaped breasts
[70].

Fears about sagging and scarred breasts were a reality for all women
during this period as evidenced by the many pages which midwifery
writers devoted to diseases of breasts and nipples and to their remedies.
It was apparently not unusual for women who breastfed to lose their
nipples completely, either because of repeated cuts which became infected and left disfiguring scar tissue, or because hungry older children
(equipped with teeth) chewed them off [146,152,198]. Some mothers
were said to pretend they had no (i.e. inverted) nipples, no milk, or
related problems which rendered them unable to suckle [25,87,91], but
religious authors complained that only the rich were afflicted with
insufficient breastmilk [87,165,178]. The Puritan, Henry Smith (1597),
agreed that women could not suckle if they had no milk:

> But whose breasts have this perpetual drought? Forsoothe it is like
> the goute, no beggars may have it, but citizens or Gentlewomen. In
> the ninth chapter of *Hosea*, drie breasts are named for a curse: what
> lamentable happe have Gentlewomen to light upon this curse
> more than other? Sure if their breasts be drie, as they say, they
> should fast and pray together that this curse may bee removed from
> them [209].

It is possible that women in this period were indeed more prone to inverted nipples than is the case today. Fashionable clothes were underpinned by corsets made of leather, metal, or bone, most of which flattened the breasts (plate 3.4) [27,42,88]. Young girls were put into these corsets or stays from the age of 2½ or 3 years, and were thereafter tightly laced throughout their waking lives (so tightly laced that some fatalities were recorded in very young girls as a result of fractured ribs being forced into their lungs) [43,65,216]. Any woman whose nipples had a tendency to be inverted or otherwise misshapened would be further handicapped, in regard to breastfeeding, by this clothing.

By the late 17th century some medical writers had begun to connect this problem with women's clothing [12,61]. For example, the Lancashire physician Edward Baynard (1706) complained about women who wanted to be fashionable, whose nipples and breasts were 'squashed and flattened' and 'sometimes worse accidents attend these hard lacings, as cancers, scirrhous, and hard tumours in the breast' [12]. Charles White of Manchester stated in 1773 that,

> the small flat nipple which lies buried in the breast is generally occasioned by the tight dress, which has for some centuries been so constantly worn in this island, by the female sex of all ages, and of almost all ranks, the most laborious and necessitous alone being excepted. This dress by constantly pressing upon the breast and nipple reduces it to a flat form, instead of that conical one, with the nipple in its apex, which it ought to preserve; and the nipple is buried in the breast. By being constantly kept in this position, it contracts adhesions; it is prevented from coming out; the whole breast is deprived both of its beauty and use . . . The tightness of the stays is alone sufficient to do much harm, but they are also often made hard and unpliable by pack thread and whalebone, which must greatly increase the mischief . . . Hence it will appear evident why women of rank, and those in the middle stations of life meet with difficulty in giving suck to children . . . [and] why hard working, labouring women, who are obliged to go very loose about their breasts generally make good nurses, and that too with very little trouble [236].

It was probably the case that many women used wet nurses simply because it was the custom or fashion, without thinking very deeply about it – in the same, often unthinking, way that some women today employ bottle-feeding [169,184]. But a significant reason why wet nurses flourished was the attitude of men; many husbands forbade their wives to breastfeed [70]. A few authors complained that some women used this only as an excuse; that they persuaded their husbands to send the child to nurse, so that they could avoid the chores of breastfeeding [92,214, 193]. The following examples, however, demonstrate that men did have

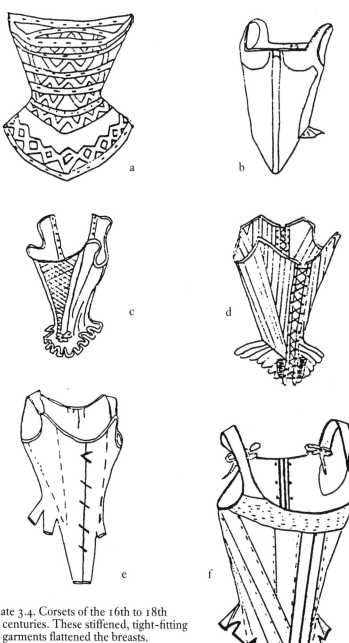

Plate 3.4. Corsets of the 16th to 18th centuries. These stiffened, tight-fitting garments flattened the breasts.
a) c.1530; b) early 17th C.; c) 1650;
d) 1660; e) early 18th C.; f) c.1775.

strong views about who was to fed their children:

i) When Anne Newdigate (neé Fitton), sister to a lady-in-waiting to Elizabeth I, decided to nurse her own child in 1598, her father wrote 'I am sorry that yourself will needs nurse her'. And the godfather, Sir Godfrey Knollys, wrote 'I should like nothing that you play the nurse if you were my wife' [168].

ii) In *The Winter's Tale* (c.1611) Leontes says to his wife:
'Give me the boy. I am glad you did not nurse him' [197].

iii) The Puritan, William Gouge, said in 1622:
Husbands for the most part are the cause that their wives nurse not their owne children. If husbands were willing that their wives should performe this dutie, and would perswade and encourage them thereto, and afford them what helpes they could, where one mother now nurseth her child twenty would do so' [87].

iv) Elizabeth Clinton, the Countess of Lincoln, said in 1622 that she had not fed her own children because:
partly I was over-ruled by another's authority, partly deceived by some ill-counsel and partly I had not so well considered of my duty in this motherly office [36].

v) In 1695 the non-conformist minister Henry Newcome said:
Very oft the father is unwilling that his wife should undertake this office . . . I have known some fathers at first averse to their wives nursing, who after some experience of those pleasing diversions that are to be found in the constant company of a little babe, would not on any terms lose the repetition of that pleasure, by turning the next abroad to a strange nurse [165].

This last comment was probably a reference to himself. After putting his first child out to a wet nurse he felt sufficiently guilty about it to write a book-length persuasive to mothers to breastfeed their own children [166].

vi) The London apothecary James Nelson said in 1753:
A man cannot be conversant with life and not see that many a sensible woman, many a tender mother, has her heart yearning to suckle her child, and is prevented by the misplac'd authority of a husband [164].

vii) In 1792, Mary Wollstonecraft, in *Vindication of the rights of woman*, still believed the father's desire for sexual relations was the reason for the survival of wet nursing:
There are many husbands so devoid of sense and parental affection that during the first effervescence of voluptuous fondness, they refuse to let their wives suckle their children [245].

Modern writers have ascribed the antipathy of husbands towards their wives breastfeeding to a 'taboo' against sexual intercourse during the period of lactation [72,110], said to have originated from Galen [216].

Although, in the 2nd century A D, Galen wrote, 'I order all women who are nursing babies to abstain completely from sex relations' [82], by the 16th and 17th centuries this injunction appears to have been applied only to wet nurses employed in the child's home. No evidence has been found during this study to indicate that the Galenic injunction was at all regarded either by British parents or by medical and theological authors writing in English. In some circumstances, wet nurses were forbidden the company of their husbands for fear they would become pregnant, as a result of which it was thought that their milk would deteriorate or dry up, and the child suffer [61,93,117,170,198]. There was not any general agreement about this point even for employed wet nurses, and some authors pointed out that poor women slept with their husbands without harm to the child [50,61,152]. Hunt (1972) believes the taboo (if it existed) was not observed in 17th-century France [110], and Lockwood (1978) found it was not observed in early 18th-century New England [136]; the evidence from this study tends to show a similar non-observance in Britain.

An interesting point is that, for several hundred years before the 18th century, Roman Catholic doctrine in response to the taboo on sexual intercourse during lactation was to put the child out to nurse, 'to provide for the frailty of her husband by paying the conjugal due'. Catholic theologians did not condemn the practice of wet nursing, but indeed recommended it as the solution for the incompatibility of breastfeeding and conjugal functions [72]. As has been seen, this teaching was in direct contrast to the doctrine of the strict protestant sects from the late 16th century onwards, in England and Germany. This difference in religious teaching provides a possible explanation for the very widespread practice of wet nursing in catholic France and some other parts of Europe, compared to the relatively low incidence in protestant England.

Mothers were influenced also by other members of their family and by midwives [36,71,165,226], as described by the anonymous author of the *Ladies physical directory* in 1739:

> The first thing that many midwives and nurses, who are recommended to persons of quality, endeavour to find out, is how their women's inclinations for managing their children stand; if they find out they are the least inclin'd either to a wet nurse, or to the bringing them up by hand, they immediately encourage it, and give several instances of very fine children who have been brought up in that way, without in the least mentioning the many, many more who were that way lost. . . . For one lady who is really too sickly and weakly to undertake this good and pleasant office [of breastfeeding] for her infant, there are five who are impos'd upon by those about them in that respect, and are persuaded they are not able to suck their own children, when they are [125].

By the 1770s it was becoming more acceptable for upper-class women to breastfeed, although young mothers had still to overcome opposition from older women who had been brought up in the tradition of wet nursing [130,226]. In 1776, Lady Louise Conolly described the problem which faced the young Duchess of Leinster when she was expecting her first baby:

> I will let you into the secret that she intends nursing her child. William [her husband] at first was afraid she was too delicate; but upon my opinion that barring accidents it will do her good instead of harm, he comes into it; but I have advised her not to say a word about it, for fear of a combination against her. Lady Kildare [her husband's grandmother] I am sure will toss up her nose and say 'Lord, Ma'am, what a fancy! How should she know how to nurse a child?' Nancy Burgh and twenty more, I dare say, will make an outcry about it, so that she does not mean to tell anybody of it, but do it; if she is well . . . I encourage them both as much as possible in it. Dear Lady Kildare is what I most fear about it, but I hope she won't make a point of her not doing it [130].

This shows that by the late 18th century the climate of opinion was much more in favour of maternal suckling than had been the case just two or three generations earlier, when great strength of purpose was needed by upper-class women who were determined to go against the cultural norm, as the following tract of 1695 suggests:

> I have observed that those ladies, who contrary to this prevailing custom [wet nursing] have undertaken the nursing of their own babes, have oft met with unhandsome reflections and bitter taunts from others of the contrary practice . . . A lady that will condescend to be a nurse, though to her own child, is become as unfashionable and ungenteel as a gentleman that will not drink, swear and be profane . . . and if ever you saw the modesty of such an one assaulted by the railery and scorn of a company of debauchees, when he happens to fall among them; you may imagine the need those few ladies have of courage and resolution, who by nursing their own children, expose themselves to the taunts and derision of the many, who decline that office [165].

But the fashion in the later 18th century towards more women feeding their own children was not necessarily a happy circumstance for some mothers, who (like some who had used wet nurses) suckled against their will. Stone (1977) quotes the following reminiscences of the 1770s and 1780s, from the novel *Belinda*:

> It was the fashion in that time for fine mothers to suckle their own children; so much the worse for the fine brats. Fine nurses never made fine children. There was a prodigious point made about the matter; a vast deal of sentiment and sympathy, and compliments

Plate 3.5. England, 1796. In this Gillray
cartoon the fashionable mother offers
a brief breastfeed before departing for
her evening's entertainment.

and enquiries. But after the novelty was over, I became heartily sick
of the business; and at the end of three months my poor child was
sick too – I don't much like to think of it – it died. If I had put it out
to nurse I should have been thought by my friends an unnatural
mother; but I should have saved its life [216] (plate 3.5).

¶ It is now well-established that women who breastfeed their infants
regularly and frequently, and give no supplementary foods, have a
period of lactation amenorrhoea, during which ovulation is suppressed
[79,102,115,199,200]. This period of infertility is of varying lengths in
different women and in different societies, and is affected by the dietary
state of the mother, the frequency of lactation, and the strength with
which the child sucks [79,115]. Ovulation tends to return when additional foods are given, and if the child is fed at statutory, infrequent,
times (as in most modern western cultures) rather than 'on demand'
[104,115]. Lactation has been recognised as an important natural form of
contraception in traditional societies, Short (1976) stating that:

throughout the world as a whole, more births are prevented by lactation than all other forms of contraception put together [199].

It has commonly been assumed that women in pre-industrial Britain were unaware of the contraceptive advantages of breastfeeding, although the evidence that women in one Buckinghamshire parish completed their families and *then* continued breastfeeding for up to 11 years by wet nursing other women's children appears to negate this assumption [143]. Preliminary studies in other wet-nursing communities are producing similar findings [34,70a]. It is very unlikely that women in general, and midwives in particular, were unaware that, if they breastfed, the return of menstruation would be delayed. It is the kind of information which mothers would pass on to their daughters, and for this reason would not necessarily appear in written records. References to the relationship between breastfeeding and temporary infertility are infrequent, but sufficient have been found in the medical and religious literature to make it clear that the significance of lactation amenorrhoea was known, not only to women but also to men [70].

The comments relating to this subject between 1500 and 1800 were of three types: i) that the wish to have more children quickly was a valid reason for a woman not to breastfeed [10]; ii) that women who breastfed had fewer pregnancies [24,50,51,165,179,228]; iii) that women should breastfeed in order to avoid pregnancy [50,51,210].

Some remarks of Newcome (1695) suggest that the effect of breastfeeding was well known rather than confined to the medically educated:

> So vain is that popular pretense that nursing is an impediment to fruitfulness, and to be declin'd by great persons for the better securing of succession, by a numerous posterity: for if those bear faster who dry up their breasts, they that nurse their children commonly bear longer, and bring more up to maturity [165].

Other comments were patently based upon personal observation. The surgeon-midwife, Pierre Dionis (1719), speaking of France, where maternal breastfeeding was rarer than in Britain (and incidentally the average family size was greater) [201,203], noted that married women usually had a child every year, but those that suckled had only two or three at most. He advised women who wished to avoid pregnancy to breastfeed, since pregnant women often died whereas death was rare in nursing mothers [50]. Also referring to France, Brouzet (1755) suggested ending the practice of all wet nurses and suckling mothers, by handfeeding infants instead, so that the whole of women's fertile years would be used, and the population increase, since, for two-thirds of the time of suckling, women were barren [24].

A London physician, Hugh Smith (1774), thought that breastfeeding would prevent miscarriages by delaying conception:

> When it is confined all together to the breast ... the mother, under

these circumstances, would not again conceive so quickly, and miscarriages would thereby be in great measure prevented [210]. This view is supported by modern research [163]. Similarly, the Devon physician Hugh Downman (1788) promoted suckling as a means of protecting mothers from the exhausting effects of repeated child-bearing as 'the nursing time was meant by wisest Nature, as a stay' [51]. In 1783 Lord John Cavendish visited his great-niece, Georgiana, whom the Duchess of Devonshire was suckling herself. The Duchess later said,

> Lord John teased me with saying . . . that a dairymaid was a better nurse than a fine lady [but her husband had explained to her that what made his uncle] abuse suckling is their impatience for my having a son and their fancying I shan't so soon if I suckle [226].

Only one reference has been found to a woman referring directly to the prevention of conception by breastfeeding. Fox (1966) quoted the 18th-century American example of one Elizabeth Drinker who, while her elder daughter, Sally, was in labour with her 6th child, reminded her that she was so close to the menopause that suckling might well make this her last pregnancy:

> She was now in her 39th year, and that this might possibly be the last trial of this sort, if she could suckle her baby for two years to come, as she had several times done heretofore [76].

The way in which male authors promoted the contraceptive advantages of breastfeeding, and yet tried to reconcile them with the wishes of the upper classes to obtain numerous offspring, suggests that the knowledge of temporary barrenness during lactation was known to all classes in society and was one reason why the practice of wet nursing was perpetuated [10,24,51,165]. Despite the part which *may* have been played by taboo on sexual intercourse during the nursing period, this was clearly not the only reason why wealthy women were persuaded by husbands and by custom to employ wet nurses. When the wishes of the rich for many children were matched by the wishes of their social inferiors for family limitation, then the ideal situation existed for the practice and perpetuation of wet nursing [201,203].

¶ Despite condemnation of the objections to maternal breastfeeding raised by women, it was accepted that there *were* valid reasons why certain women from all classes were genuinely unable to breastfeed their own children. Though some may have feigned ill-health or problems with nipples, genuine incidents were undoubtedly much more common, and far more serious, than they are today, when adequate ante- and post-natal care and a wide range of effective treatments are avilable [202].

Thirty-four, mainly medical, writers discussed the circumstances in which it was better for a woman to employ a wet nurse than to breastfeed (table 3.2) [70]. These we will classify as a) affecting the mother; b) relating to breasts, nipples, or milk; c) affecting the child; d) other considerations.

The major factors affecting the mother were:
i) sickness and ill health [93,95,125,189,198,228];
ii) weakness or delicacy [28,93,117,198,208];
iii) proneness to nervous disorders, low spirits, etc. [26,164,191];
iv) suffering from consumption (at that time believed to be hereditary) or some other hereditary disease (which could affect her milk and thus be transmitted to the child [51,95,191];
v) if she was not in her right mind [36].

Factors affecting the breasts, nipples or milk were:
i) lack of good nipples [5,12,191];
ii) sore nipples [87,191];
iii) sore or infected breasts [31,146,189,198];
iv) corrupted milk [146,189];
v) insufficient, or lack of, milk [12,117,161,209,223].

Only Ste Marthe (1584) thought that sickness in the child was an acceptable reason.

Today, sickness or ill-health of the mother is rarely accepted as a reason for not breastfeeding (it is contra-indicated only in a few very serious conditions, such as congestive cardiac failure, eclampsia, typhoid, and puerperal mania) [115]. But it must be remembered that severe illnesses in women were very much more common before the 20th century [202,187], and many of those associated with childbirth, such as puerperal fever and milk fever, were accompanied by hyperpyrexia (very high temperature) and delirium. Also, many women probably had insufficient iron, calcium, and vitamins A and D in their diet to support several pregnancies [2,55], so that conditions such as iron-deficiency anaemia would have been relatively common [55], particularly in upper-class women who endured many more pregnancies than the rest of the female population [129,142].

Thus the frequent references to weakness and delicacy in wealthier women, as compared to the poorer classes in England, may have been accurate reporting. The diet of most of the population was quite different from, and in many ways better balanced and healthier than, that of the wealthy [2,55,242]. If the average number of children born was four or five per family [129,142,143], then the drain on the mineral and vitamin stores of the average mother would have been considerably less than on a woman from the wealthier classes, for whom families of ten or twelve were common, and instances of up to thirty pregnancies per woman were not unknown [100,142,224]. In these circumstances breastfeeding may well have been medically inadvisable.

Similarly, conditions affecting the nipples and breast are treatable today and (except in the case of breast abscesses caused by antibiotic-resistant bacteria) are not medical indications for ceasing to breastfeed [115]. But when mechanical breast-pumps, antiseptic conditions and antibiotics were not available to treat these conditions, then the wisest council was indeed to rest the nipple or breast and thus prevent the child from ingesting infected milk.

Prolonged breastfeeding is still contra-indicated in the event of a new pregnancy, and poor health of the child may make suckling difficult or impossible [115], for example, in conditions such as jaundice, prematurity, cerebral birth-injury and cleft palate. As will be seen later, before 1800 hand-feeding was often employed for these children [93,207,240].

¶ Over the whole three centuries of this survey, there was near unanimity (table 3.3) among medical and religious writers that, in principle, the mother was the best nurse; but 10% of those who expressed such views qualified them by noting circumstances in which this might not be so. The only writer who was explicitly against mothers feeding their own children was Robert Burton, on the grounds that mothers had their faults as well as nurses, and that there was a greater choice of the latter. In his famous *Anatomy of Melancholy* (1621), he observed that the nurse could correct the child's 'ill-disposed temperature which he had from his parents' [30].

Of twenty-nine medical and religious writers who recommended alternatives to maternal breastfeeding, twelve wrote in the 16th and 17th centuries, and gave a unanimous verdict in favour of wet nursing. But of the seventeen writers of the 18th century, only ten gave exclusive preference to wet nursing, the others being in favour, in certain circumstances, of hand-feeding (table 3.4) [70]. This suggests the change in possible feeding methods which occurred in the 18th century. Before then, it was recognised that there was really no safe alternative to the wet nurse, but the increasing incidence of hand-feeding in the 18th century (see chapter 11) made possible the demise of the wet nurse without involving the mother in breastfeeding.

To reinforce and support their recommendations for maternal suckling, authors of all types cited examples from Nature, the mythology and literature of the ancient world, the Bible, and from specific peoples and races who breastfed their own children (table 3.5) [70].

Popular examples quoted were:

i) the Spartans' choice of the youngest son to be King because he was the only one suckled by his own mother [44,165,170,198];

ii) Spanish-born Blanche of Castile who was the mother of St Louis of France (1215–70) and refused to allow anyone but herself breastfeed her son [24,30,93];

iii) The Virgin Mary [13,36,178,209,223]; iv) Old Testament women, particularly Eve, Sarah, Rachel, Rebecca, the wife of Samuel, the mother of David [13,50,87,91, 162].

The example of other animals suckling their young was repeated throughout this period as the natural method of feeding; women being reproached as the only mothers in Nature who did not feed their own offspring. The following statements are representative of this view: i) mothers were not *true* mothers if they refused to suckle their own children [13,51,62,170,172]; ii) it was *unnatural* and inhumane to send a child away to another woman to be fed [12,61,124,209,210]; iii) there was no difference between a woman who refused to suckle and one that killed her child in the womb [93,124].

Some writers presented maternal suckling as a God-given duty [13,87, 124,225]. Others presented it at length as the duty or job of mothers, although not necessarily prescribed by God [9,26,31,93,223].

Forty-two writers gave specific reasons for recommending maternal breastfeeding (table 3.6) [70]. Mother's milk was generally thought to be better than milk from any other source. During the 16th and 17th centuries the qualities of different milks were frequently discussed. Two important beliefs were associated with milk: i) That the characteristics of the woman or animal were transmitted through their milk into the child [6,20,87,170,191,217]; ii) That breast milk was the blood which had fed the child in the womb and was converted into white blood in the breasts once the child was born. Thus the mother's milk was the same blood which had nourished the child in the womb, with which it was familiar, and which obviously suited it; therefore it was best for the child to continue to be nourished by the same blood [63,93,170,189,223].

Suckling was said to benefit the mother in several ways:
i) by ensuring her health and recovery after childbirth [31,95,210,228];
ii) by preventing women's diseases [5,124,156,191];
iii) by making mothers happier [164];
iv) by giving them pleasure and satisfaction [31,170,210];
v) by carrying less likelihood of her dying [161].

In addition to preserving general good health, the child breastfed by his mother was less likely to develop rickets [86]; have less trouble when he began teething [112]; would avoid numerous ailments and stunted growth [6]; and was less likely to die [87,125,210].

The mother/child relationship would be strengthened by breastfeeding since suckling was: i) a means of the mother expressing natural love for the child [10,146,152]; ii) laying down bonds of affection, love, respect and attachment between mother and child [51,87,170,210]. The quality of the mother's care for her own child was said to be greater than that of a hired nurse [45,61,62,172].

The above findings are reinforced by looking at what were said to be

Your callousness, Eglé, now bears its fruit!
Responding more than you to Nature's cries,
To serve her laws, and give back hurt for hurt,
From You he flies.

Unforced, untempted, he prefers his Nurse!
If long acquaintance should his fear remove,
Will you not shame to earn by artifice
What's hers by Love?

Plate 3.6. France, c.1780. The nurse-
child bond is seen to be stronger than
that between mother and child.

the benefits for mother and child when maternal breastfeeding *was*
undertaken (table 3.7) [70]. The main benefits for the mother were said
to be: pleasure and enjoyment; beauty; good health and fewer children.
The mother-child relationship would be closer, and last into adult life;
and the child would benefit by resisting disease and death.

The effects on the mother, the child and the mother-child relationship were also discussed in the context of women who did not breastfeed
their own children; the adverse consequences of maternal non-breastfeeding being discussed by twenty-five authors (see table 3.8) [70].

Adverse consequences for the maternal-child relationship were said to be: i) loss of ties of affection, respect, love and obedience, especially in early life [61,91,127,209,210,232]; ii) happiness and relationships within the family suffered as a result of brothers and sisters being fed by different women [6,50,165]. Related to this was the fact that children fed by wet nurses normally preferred their nurse to their biological mother, especially when they were older [50,92,93,124,165]. This is admirably illustrated (plate 3.6) in a French engraving of 1780 and in the accompanying verses.

Consequences for mothers who did not suckle were said to be:
i) poor health or disease [31,62,87,165,171];
ii) an early death [62,210];
iii) loss of beauty [210];
iv) repeated childbirth [51];
v) she missed all the pleasures of seeing her child grow and develop [36,195]; the child not fed by his mother was thought to be more likely to die in infancy [13,62,125].

The main reasons for recommending maternal breastfeeding, therefore, were the qualities of the mother's milk, the health of the mother and the child, with less attention paid to the maternal-child relationship and the superior quality of a mother's care. The main benefits were to the mother's health and, to a much lesser extent, the mother-child relationship. The major consequence of mothers not feeding their children was the non-formation or breakdown of the maternal-child bond, during infancy and in later life, with the other main effect being on the health and well-being of the mother. The relative concern about each of these factors appears to have changed during the 300-year period under consideration, particularly in the 18th century, so we will summarise each in turn.

i) *16th century* writers and preachers wanted the mother to breastfeed because her milk was more suited to the child and she was likely to look after her own baby much better than a hired nurse. Both of these factors were concerned with the welfare of the *infant,* the health of the mother not being considered at all, although the main benefits of breastfeeding were to the mother's health, and a good maternal-child relationship. The principal consequence of non-suckling was thought to be the lack of the mother-child bond and, to a lesser extent, the mother's health and happiness.

ii) *The 17th century* was not markedly different except that more emphasis was laid upon the maternal-infant bond when trying to persuade mothers to breastfeed. The emphasis was still upon the child rather than the mother, although the latter was still seen as the principal beneficiary in terms of health. The major adverse consequence of non-suckling was still thought to be a poor mother-child relationship.

iii) *The 18th century* showed a quite different emphasis. Although the quality of the mother's milk was still judged important, a major reason for recommending maternal suckling was the preservation of the *mother*'s health; only to a lesser extent, the health of the child. The superior quality of a mother's care was no longer emphasised. The health of the mother and (much less) the health of the child benefited from maternal breastfeeding, the adverse effects of not breastfeeding being on the mother-child relationship and the mother's health.

Thus the 18th-century writers were much more concerned with the health of the mother than was the case in the 16th and 17th centuries, and (apparently) with the health of the child. The latter is balanced by the belief in the 1500s and 1600s in the superior care which was said to be given to infants by their own mothers, since this also may be taken as concern for the infant's well-being. (For example, consider such statements as 'Children nursed by their mothers are for the most part more cleanly, and neatly brought up, freer from diseases; not so many die' [87].)

The emergence of the mother as a major consideration in the discussions, arguments and persuasions of the 'mother versus wet nurse' debate, is a feature of the second half of the 18th century. To confirm this, and to clarify the relative importance given to the three major arguments (i.e. the mother; the child; the maternal-child relationship), all the statements and discussion given in the preceding pages have been summarised (first by century in table 3.9; and then in the two periods 1500–1747 and 1748–1800, table 3.10). 1748 has been taken as a natural dividing line, indicating the changes which occurred at about this date, particularly associated with the publication of Cadogan's *Essay* [31]. They are based upon the writings of forty-six medical and religious authors [70].

The analysis confirms the definite change in emphasis in the discussion of maternal breastfeeding during the 18th century, and particularly after 1748. The health and well-being of the baby received much the same amount of attention throughout the period 1500 to 1800, but clearly there was a marked increase in concern for the health and happiness of the mother, accompanied by a considerable decline of interest in the quality of the relationship between a breastfeeding mother and her child. This change could be related to the fact that all the works after 1748 were medical texts, whilst the period 1500–1747 included 11 non-medical works whose authors may have been more interested in promoting ties between mother and child. It seems unlikely that this greatly influenced the results, since the medical authors were in a majority throughout, and writers of all types of work in each period have been shown to have had similar views on maternal breastfeeding. What effect such medical opinions may have had on common practice and attitudes is, of course, a different question.

It is likely that medical writers realised that the most persuasive argument to a mother was the preservation of her own health and life, particularly after experiments at the lying-in hospitals had demonstrated this to be true [164]. During the mid- to late 18th century these same authors were advising handfeeding as the preferred alternative to breastfeeding (table 3.4 and chapter 11), and there was a general climate of opinion against wet nurses [70,226], so that emphasis of the maternal-infant relationship may not have carried so much weight with women as formerly. The problem of close nurse-child relationships, at the expense of maternal-infant affection which had characterised the 16th and 17th centuries, need not be a consideration in a period when it was possible for mothers to supervise the handfeeding of their children at home. The change of emphasis may thus have reflected current practice in both periods. Concern with the problems of close nurse-child relationships and lack of affection towards parents in later life was widely apparent at least until the early years of the 18th century, and thus received most attention; but by the second half of this century, it was established that women could avoid breast problems and diseases such as milk fever if they breastfed [164], so that it was politic for authors to accentuate this advantage to the detriment of others.

A further point in favour of a real change in attitudes is the evidence for a changing readership in the 18th century. After 1750, writers of popular medical books addressed themselves directly to mothers, whereas before 1750 they had addressed themselves largely to midwives, nurses, or to no-one in particular. If books were to be read by mothers, then primarily the advantages to mothers needed to be emphasised. There is some evidence [71,226] that, by the mid-18th century, women themselves were deciding by which method their babies should be fed, where previously it had been fathers who made this decision, or had exercised the power of veto [226]. Fathers may have been more concerned by the degree of respect and affection accorded to them by their children, and thus more open to arguments which emphasised the value of maternal breastfeeding in forming these ties. This again suggests that the form of persuasion written and preached at different periods may well have related to popular practice, and related to changes in social attitudes. Stone (1977) and Trumbach (1978) have postulated a change of attitude towards wives in the 18th century, with the latter becoming the close and sometimes loving companions of their husbands, in contrast to rather distant marital relations before this period [216,226] (plate 3.7). If this view is correct, then it clarifies the new accent upon the mother's health and happiness observable in written persuasives for maternal breastfeeding.

These findings do not support the views of modern writers, who perceive a marked change for the better in attitudes towards infants and

Plate 3.7. Rowlandson's engraving (1787)
of a sailor's return to his family senti-
mentalises the loving family bond.

children in the 18th century [3,201,216,226]. The degree of concern for
the health and well-being of the baby (at least in discussions about
breastfeeding) increased only slightly between the 16th and 18th centuries; and, in works written before 1700, the infant was paid considerably more attention than the mother, and notably less in the later 18th
century. Quite clearly any increased attention the new baby received
among the upper and middle classes in regard to maternal breastfeeding
was secondary to that paid to the mother, and related to the close
bonding which would be afforded by a certain period of maternal
breastfeeding.

¶ Comparatively few writers showed any interest in the *technique* of
breastfeeding, presumably because it was considered to be the province
of women and midwives. The care and preparation of the breasts and
nipples for breastfeeding was mentioned only by a few authors, most of
whom were practitioners in midwifery [70]. Three instructed women to

117

wash the nipples before and after feeding, and when preparing other food or after working [45,195,198,195]. The main worry was to prevent problems arising in the nipples and breasts, by frequent washing with alum solutions or hardening with spirits [9,18,25], or with the protective use of nipple shields or special cloths [63,152,198].

The method of breastfeeding, exactly how it was to be accomplished and in which position the child should be held, attracted only modest interest [70]. When the child was first put to the breast, women were advised to spurt some milk into its mouth to encourage it to suck [93,146], and to offer the breast frequently to encourage the supply of milk [170,210], although the baby was to be restrained from taking too much [93,99]. Both breasts were to be given at each feeding [191,198], otherwise the child would become accustomed to using only one hand [175] or would 'grow crooked' [191]. As to posture, James Nelson (1753) thought that the mother should suckle in whichever position she preferred, although when in bed the child was to take the breast lying down so that the mother would not have to sit up in bed and become fatigued [164]. This was contrary to the view of Dionis (1719) who insisted that women should sit up at night when breastfeeding for fear they would fall asleep and overlay the child [50]. Cadogan (1748) also thought that the child should not lie down whilst being fed [31]. Nelson (1753) complained that, during feeding,

> the child should yield to the mother, not the mother to the child.
> That distorted posture so commonly seen in suckling gives great
> pain to the back, and cramps all the limbs [164].

But only Brown (1777) gave detailed (and accurate) instruction on position:

> When you give an infant the breast, put its arm under yours, and
> hold the child quite close to you, and let the feet come close to your
> side; then they can take fast hold at once [25].

Slightly more interest was shown in the frequency of breastfeeding; twenty-seven authors discussed the times at which infants should be given the breast [70]. The time of feeding was to be decided either by the child (demand feeding) or by the mother (scheduled feeding). A striking observation was the complete change of medical opinion about this point in the mid-18th century (table 3.11). Whereas the child had generally been fed on demand by the wet nurse, and most physicians had agreed with this practice, when more mothers began to suckle their own children those same mothers began to be advised to strictly control both the number of feeds and the time at which their infants were fed. Demand feeding was endorsed by seventeen writers, whilst six recommended fixed times for offering the breast [70]. Whichever type of feeding was employed, seven authors were very averse to feeding babies during the night, mainly because this disturbed the mother's sleep.

It is doubtful whether scheduled feeding was ever widely practised, although a certain number of women did employ it: Moss (1781) said: 'it is the custom in some places to try and confine the child to regular feeding times' although he thought this was not always possible [161]. Brouzet (1755) recorded that:

women ... are afraid of being slaves to their children ... but some of them are such slaves to their pleasures, that they won't suffer the wench to bring them the squalling brat, on any account whatsoever, to receive the breast, if it is not his hour [24].

In her popular advice book of 1767, Sarah Pennington showed that scheduled feeding may have been the only way in which wealthier women could reconcile their social responsibilities with breastfeeding, whatever their personal wishes:

Whatever may be your own inclinations, such is your situation in life, and such the customs of the world you must live in, that it will not be in your power to have your children always with you; should you suckle them, they will be brought to you only at stated times, and left at others to the care of a servant [176].

The fashion for scheduled feeding may have been fleeting since, after 1748, those who opposed it and favoured demand feeding were all writing in the period 1787–92, and the Scottish physician and midwife, Alexander Hamilton, stated emphatically in 1792 that he was against feeding 'only at stated periods ... those children are most healthy and thriving who are least restricted and permitted to take the breast at pleasure' [95]. Almost certainly the change in medical views was associated with the trend of upper-class women feeding their own children and (as first-generation mothers) needing advice on how to do this (plate 3.8). It is significant that four out of the six writers who proposed scheduled feeding addressed themselves to a lay rather than a medical readership [31,161,164,210].

If the advice to breastfeed according to schedule was carried out, then this could have been frustrating for the baby since being fed on demand is said to fulfil a primary psychological need in the child [162a]. It also could have affected the fertility of mothers. Although more upper-class women began to breastfeed, the fact that they may have employed infrequent scheduled feeding would reduce the contraceptive effect of lactation [115,122]. This, plus the earlier age of weaning which was also a feature of the second half of the 18th century (see chapter 15), would have reduced any contraceptive advantage which these women might have gained by suckling their own children.

Some physicians discussed the number of feeds to be given each day. The ancient medical writers, such as Paul of Aegina (7th century AD) and Avicenna (10th century AD), had recommended suckling only two or three times a day, and these frequencies were referred to by Roesslin

Plate 3.8. Edinburgh 1796. John Kay's
satire on fashionable Scottish mothers
shows how dresses could be adapted
to allow them to breastfeed with
convenience!

(1540), Jones (1579) and Guillemeau (1612). The German, Friedrich
Hoffman (c.1740), described the usual practice in the late 17th/early
18th centuries:

> For the most part the breast is given in the first months every two
> hours; after three or four months, six or seven times a day; and at
> length only twice or thrice a day, till the year be completed [99].

Dionis (1719) thought that once every two hours and once or twice at
night was sufficient in the early months, whilst Mantell (1787) believed
it did not matter how many times a day the child was put to the breast so
long as too much milk was not given each time [50,147].

The above writers all advocated demand feeding. Those who proposed a strict timetable for suckling suggested 4 to 6 times during 24
hours [24,31,210]. For example, Hugh Smith (1774) suggested the
following schedule for giving breastfeeds: i) 6–7am; ii) 1 hour after the
mother has breakfasted (about 9–10am in this period); iii) just before
the mother's dinner 'if she pleases' (about 2–3pm); iv) 5–6pm 'being
2 or 3 hours after dinner'; v) 10–11pm just before mother goes to bed.

This timetable of approximately 4-hourly feeds is therefore very similar to that employed today for young babies in institutions of the western world [115].

The few writers who discussed the size of feed left the quantity of milk to the desires and growing needs of the child [50,146,152,195], or to the good judgement of the mother or nurse [117]. Some warned about overfeeding infants with breast milk [117,189,175] since this could result in problems such as vomiting [146,147,152,195], wind [63,152], obesity [146], and excessive crying [147]. The consensus was to give moderate amounts fairly frequently, and giving too much was preferable to giving too little. In contrast, it is interesting that William Cadogan (1748), the first advocate for scheduled feeding, advised 'letting it have as much as it will take out of both breasts at each time' in 24 hours [31]. Thus within reason the demand-fed child could have as much milk as he required, as frequently as he requested it, and this fact is confirmed by the warnings about overfeeding. Therefore, the 16th- and 17th-century infant largely had control of his food supply and consequently his mother or nurse. The post-1748 child ideally had his food supply controlled completely by his mother or nurse. He could have as much as he wanted at each feed, but only when the woman decided to make it available. This additionally illustrates that from the mid-18th century the mother, rather than the infant, was the main object of consideration.

¶ Until the late 18th century it was a social norm for upper- and middle-class mothers to employ wet nurses rather than feed their own children. Although this custom was greatly criticised by protestant theologians after the Reformation, the criticism had little effect in practice, except upon puritan women for whom breastfeeding was regarded as a religious duty. Reasons for women not breastfeeding included regard for their health, figure and dress; the influence of husbands; general custom; and the busy social life of the mother. In many cases these reasons were probably real, due to the physical restraints and effects of tight corsetting; the prevalence of breast and nipple injury and disease; the tradition of husbands deciding upon feeding methods; the influence of the women's family; and of current fashion. The so-called 'taboo' on sexual intercourse during lactation was probably not observed in Britain and hence was not a real consideration in the decision whether or not to breastfeed. The contraceptive effect of breastfeeding was certainly known to educated men, and probably by word of mouth was known to women. Knowledge of this may have played a part in the continued practice of wet nursing. Acceptable reasons for women not breastfeeding included sickness, weakness, and sore or infected nipples, all of which were fairly common, particularly among wealthy women who had had many pregnancies.

Medical and religious writers consistently believed that the mother made the best nurse for her child and gave many arguments to support this opinion, but failing this ideal most regarded a wet nurse as the best substitute. In the 18th century a small number preferred the substitute of hand feeding. Reasons for preferring the mother to breastfeed included the superior quality of her milk, the benefits of the health of mother and child, and concern for the maternal-child relationship. Maternal breastfeeding was said to benefit the mother much more than the mother-child relationship or the child. If mothers did not breastfeed this was chiefly seen to have an adverse effect on the mother-child relationship, and to a lesser extent the mother's health and beauty; it also resulted in later problems with close nurse-child relationships.

The mid-18th century saw a change in emphasis in the discussions and persuasives about breastfeeding with the major advantages stated to be the good health of the mother, whereas in the 16th and 17th centuries the main concern was for a good mother-child relationship. This may have been due to medical writers realising that preservation of her own health (backed up by evidence from the lying-in hospitals) was more likely to affect a mother's decision; the increasingly popular alternative of handfeeding; the emergence of books written to and for mothers after 1750; and the increasing part played by mothers in the decision about the method of feeding babies. The degree of concern for the health of the child, in relation to breastfeeding, increased only slightly between 1500 and 1800; the infant was paid considerably more attention than the mother before 1700, and much less after that date. Any increased attention paid to the child in the 18th century was secondary to that paid to the mother.

Demand feeding was the most usual method of breastfeeding until c.1748, when strictly scheduled suckling 4–6 times a day was first introduced, although it was probably never widely practised except by wealthy society women. By the end of the 18th century medical writers were again advocating demand feeding. Before c.1748 the quantity and timing of breastfeeds was in the hands of the child whereas after 1748 these were ideally under the control of the mother.

REFERENCES

1. Aitken, J. (1786) *Principles of midwifery,* London, 3rd ed.
2. Appleby, A. B. (1979) Diet in sixteenth century England: sources, problems, possibilities, in Webster, C. (ed.), *Health, medicine and mortality in the sixteenth century,* Cambridge, 97-116.
3. Ariès, P. (1973) *Centuries of childhood,* Harmondsworth.
4. Aristotle (4th century BC) *The works of Aristotle. Vol. 4 Historia*

animalium, trans. Wentworth, D., Oxford, 1910.

5. Armstrong, G. (1771) *An essay on the diseases most fatal to infants*, London, 2nd ed.
6. Astruc, J. (1746) *A general and complete treatise on all the diseases incident to children from their birth to the age of fifteen*, trans. anon., London.
7. Avicenna (10th century AD) in Shah, M. H., *The general principles of Avicenna's Canon of medicine*, Karachi, 1966.
8. Badinter, E. (1981) *The myth of motherhood. An historical view of the maternal instinct*, London.
9. Barrett, R. (1699) *A companion for midwives, childbearing women and nurses. Directing them how to perform their respective offices*, London.
10. Batty, B. (1581) *The christian man's closet*, trans. Louth, W., London.
11. Baudelocque, J-L. (1790) *A system of midwifery*, trans. Heath, J., 3 vols, London.
12. Baynard, E. (1706) *The history of cold bathing: both ancient and modern. Part II*, London, 2nd ed.
13. Becon, T. (c.1550) *The catechism of Thomas Becon with other pieces written by him in the reign of King Edward the Sixth*, Ayre, J. (ed.), Cambridge, 1844.
14. Birch, T. (1744) *The life of the Honourable Robert Boyle*, London.
15. Blasco, L. T. (1913) *La Virgen de la leche en el arte*, Barcelona.
16. Boaistuau, P. (1566) *The theatre or Rule of the world*, trans. Alday, J., London.
17. Bracher, M. D. (1982) Breastfeeding in Central Java, *Population Studies 36*, 413-29.
18. Bracken, H. (1737) *The midwife's companion or, A treatise of midwifery*, London.
19. Bramston, J. (1845) *The autobiography of Sir John Bramstone, K.B. of Skreens in the County of Chelmsford*, London.
20. Brathwaite, R. (1631) *The English gentlewoman*, London.
21. *Breastfeeding* (1978) DHSS Report on medical aspects of food policy; panel on child nutrition, London.
22. Brim, C. J. (1936) *Medicine in the Bible. The Pentateuch. Torah*, New York.
23. Brooke, H. (1766) *The fool of quality or, The history of Henry, Earl of Moreland*, London.
24. Brouzet, N. (1755) *An essay on the medicinal education of children; and the treatment of their diseases*, trans. anon., London.
25. Brown, S. (1777) *A letter to a lady on the best means of obtaining the milk in order to the suckling of the infant*, London.
26. Buchan, W. (1769) *Domestic medicine; or The family physician*, Edinburgh.
27. Buck, A. (1979) *Dress in eighteenth century England*, London.
28. Bullinger, H. (1541) *The christen state of matrimonye*, trans. Coverdale, M., London.

29. Burton, J. (1751) *An essay towards a complete new system of midwifery*, London.
30. Burton, R. (1621) *The anatomy of melancholy*, Oxford.
31. Cadogan, W. (1748) *An essay upon nursing and the management of children, from their birth to three years of age*, London.
32. Caulfield, E. (1932) The Countesse of Lincolne's nurserie, *Am. J. Dis. Child. 43*, 151-62.
33. Caulfield, E. (1952) Infant feeding in Colonial America, *J. Pediat. 41*, 673-87.
34. Cavallo, S. (1983) Strategie politiche familiari intorno al baliatico. Il monopolio dei bambini abbandonati nel Canavese tra sei e setticento, in *Quaderni Storici* 53/a XVIII (2) 391-420; 735-8.
35. Cholmley, H. (1787) *The memoirs of Sir Hugh Cholmley*, London.
36. Clinton, E. (1622) *The Countesse of Lincolne's nurserie*, Oxford.
37. Coke, M. (1889) *The letters and journals of Lady Mary Coke*, Home, J. A. (ed.), Edinburgh.
38. Cone, T. E. (1975) Benjamin Franklin on breastfeeding and why women of Paris cannot nurse their babies, *Pediatrics 55*, 467.
39. Cone, T. E. (1976) *200 years of feeding infants in America*, Columbus, Ohio.
40. Cone, T. E. (1979) *History of American pediatrics*, Boston.
41. Conway, A. (1930) *Conway letters. The correspondence of Anne, Viscountess Conway, Henry More, and their friends, 1642-1684*, Nicolson, M. (ed.), London.
42. Cunnington, C. W. & Cunnington, P. (1966) *Handbook of English costume in the seventeenth century*, London.
43. Cunnington, P. & Buck, A. (1978) *Children's costume in England 1300-1900*, London.
44. Culpeper, N. (1675) *A directory for midwives*, London.
45. Culpeper, N. (1676) *A directory for midwives; or, A guide for women in their conception, bearing and suckling their children. Corrected from many gross errors*, London.
46. Dee, J. (1842) *The private diary of Dr John Dee*, Halliwell, J. O. (ed.), London.
47. Defoe, D. (1728-29), *The compleat English gentleman*, Bulbring, K. D. (ed.), London, 1890.
48. De Mause, L. (ed.) (1976) *History of childhood*, London.
49. Deruisseau, L. G. (1940) Infant hygiene in the older medical literature, *Ciba symposia 2*, 530-60.
50. Dionis, P. (1719) *A general treatise of midwifery*, trans. anon., London.
51. Downman, H. (1788) *Infancy or, The management of children. A didactic poem in six books*, London, 4th ed.
52. Drake, T. G. H. (1935) Infant welfare laws in France in the 18th century, *Ann. Med. Hist. 7* (N.S.), 49-61.

53. Drake, T. G. H. (1937) Infant nutrition in Paris in the year 1780, *Can. Med. Ass. J. 37*, 595-7.
54. Drake, T. G. H. (1940) The wet nurse in France in the eighteenth century, *Bull. Hist. Med. 8*, 934-8.
55. Drummond, J. C. & Wilbraham, A. (1957) *The Englishman's food. A history of five centuries of British diet*, London.
56. Ebrahim, G. J. (1978) *Breast feeding: the biological option*, London.
57. Ebrahim, G. J. (1978) *Mother and child health in developing countries*, London.
58. Ebrahim, G. J. (1979) *Care of the newborn in developing countries*, London.
59. Ebrahim, G. J. (1983) *Nutrition in mother and child health*, London.
60. Emmison, F. G. (1964) *Tudor food and pastimes. Life at Ingatestone Hall*, London.
61. *English midwife enlarged . . . containing two new treatises . . . of the diseases of little children, and the conditions necessary to be considered in the choice of their nurses and milk*, London, 1682.
62. Erasmus, D. (1526) *The whole familiar colloquies of Erasmus of Rotterdam*, trans. Bailey, N., Glasgow, 1877.
62a Espine, A. D. (1908) Rousseau et l'allaitement maternel, *Revue medicale de la Suisse Romande 28* (9), 1-11.
63. Ettmueller, M. (1699) *Etmullerus abridg'd: or A compleat system of the theory and practice of physic*, trans. anon., London.
64. Evelyn, J. (1908) *The diary of John Evelyn (1620 to 1706) with an introduction and notes by Austin Dobson*, London.
65. Ewing, E. (1977) *History of children's costume*, London.
66. Exton, B. (1751) *A new and general system of midwifery*, London.
67. Feldman, W. M. (1927) *The principles of ante- and post-natal child hygiene*, London, ch.2: History of child hygiene.
68. Felgate, T. M. (1978) *Suffolk heraldic brasses*, Ipswich.
69. Ferrier, S. (1898) *Memoir and correspondence of Susan Ferrier 1782-1854*, Doyle, J. A. (ed.), London.
70. Fildes, V. A. (1982) *The history of infant feeding 1500-1800*, unpublished Ph D thesis, University of Surrey, Department of Human Biology and Health.
70a Fildes, V. A. (1984) The English wet nurse and her role in infant care 1538-1800. In press. *Med. Hist.*, 1986.
71. Fitzgerald, B. (1949) *Emily, Duchess of Leinster, 1731-1814*, London.
72. Flandrin, J-L. (1979) *Families in former times. Kinship. Household. and sexuality*, trans. Southern, R., Cambridge.
73. Folley, S. J. (1970) The milk-ejection reflex: a neuro-endocrine theme in biology, myth and art, *Perspect. Biol. Med. 13*, 476-90.
74. Forsyth, D. (1911) The history of infant feeding from Elizabethan times, *Proc. Soc. Med. 4*, 110-41.

75. Foster, E. (1781) *The principles and practice of midwifery*, London.
76. Fox, C. E. (1966) *Pregnancy, childbirth and early infancy in Anglo-American culture 1675-1830*, Dissertation for PhD, University of Pennsylvania, University microfilms, 67/7838.
77. Freke, E. (1913) *Mrs Elizabeth Freke. Her diary 1671 to 1714*, Carbery, M. (ed.), Cork.
78. Fretwell, J. (1877) A family history, in *Yorkshire diaries and autobiographies in the seventeenth and eighteenth centuries*, Durham.
79. Frisch, R. (1978) Population, food intake, and fertility, *Science* 199, 22-30.
80. *Full view of all the diseases incident to children*, London, 1742.
81. Gailhard, J. (1678) *The compleat gentleman: directions for the education of youth*, London.
82. Galen (2nd century AD) *A translation of Galen's 'Hygiene' (De sanitate tuenda)*, trans. Green, R. M., Springfield, Illinois.
83. Gellius, A. (2nd century AD) *The Attic nights of Aulus Gellius*, trans. Rolfe, J. C., London, vol.2, 1927.
84. *Gentleman's Magazine* (1765) Unsigned writer *On some of the causes that occasion the mortality of children under two years of age*, London, December 1765.
85. Geyer-Kordesch, J., personal communication.
86. Glisson, F. (1651) *A treatise of the Rickets, being a disease common to children*, trans. Armin, P., London.
87. Gouge, W. (1622) *Of domestical duties. Eight treatises*, London.
88. Green, R. & Cassin-Scott, J. (1975) *Costume and fashion in colour 1550-1760*, Poole, Dorset.
89. Greene, J. (1928-29) The diary of John Greene (1635-57), *Eng. Hist. Rev. 43*, 385-94, 598-604; *44*, 106-17.
90. Greenwood, R. & Norris, M. (1976) *The brasses of Norfolk churches*, Norfolk churches Trust Ltd.
91. Griffith, M. (1633) *Bethel: or A forme for families*, London.
92. Guazzo, M. S. (1581 and 1586) *The civile conversation*, trans. Pettie, G. & Young, B. in *The Tudor translations*, 2nd series *8*, Webley, C. (ed.), London.
93. Guillemeau, J. (1612) *Childbirth or The happie deliverie of women... To which is added a treatise of the diseases of infants and young children: with the cure of them*, trans. anon., London
94. Gunther, M (1945) Sore nipples. Causes and prevention, *Lancet 2*, 590-3.
95. Hamilton, A. (1792) *A treatise on the management of female complaints and of children in early infancy*, Edinburgh.
96. Handelsman, A. (1979) Modern nursing. An etching by John Kay, 1796, *J. Hist. Med. 34*, 223 and facing.
97. Hartemann, J. (1960) Grandeur et décadence de l'allaitement maternel à travers les âges, *Aesculape 43* (12), 3-39.
98. Hedley, O. (1975) *Queen Charlotte*, London.

99. Hoffmann, F. (c.1740) *A system of the practice of medicine*, vol.2, trans. Lewis, W., London, 1783.
100. Hollingsworth, T. H. (1957) A demographic study of the British ducal families, in Glass, D. V. & Eversley, D. E. C. (eds), *Population in history. Essays in historical demography*, London.
101. *Holy Bible.* Authorised version of King James, London.
102. Houston, M. J. *et al.* (1980) The contraceptive effects of lactation, *Nursing Times*, 10 July, unpaginated.
103. Houston, M. J. (1981) Breast feeding: success or failure, *J. Adv. Nurs. 6*, 447-54.
104. Howie, P. *et al.* (1981) Effect of supplementary food on suckling patterns and ovarian activity during lactation, *Brit. Med. J. 283*, 757-63.
105a Howie, P. *et al.* (1981) How long should a breastfeed last? *Early Human Development 5*, 71-7.
106. Huard, P. & Laplane, R. (1979) *Histoire illustré de la puériculture, aspects diététiques, socio-culturels et ethnologiques*, Paris.
107. Hufton, O. H. (1974) *The poor of eighteenth century France, 1750-1789*, Oxford.
108. Hufton, O. H. (1979) Women, work and the family in eighteenth century France, *Bull. Soc. Soc. Hist. Med. 25*, 7-9.
109. Hughes, H. S. (1940) *The gentle Hertford. Her life and letters*, New York.
110. Hunt, D. (1972) *Parents and children in history: the psychology of family life in early modern France*, New York and London.
111. Hunter, W. (1775) *Lectures anatomical and chirurgical by William Hunter*, 1775, Library of the Wellcome Institute for the History of Medicine, MS 2966. Also dated 1783.
112. Hurlock, J. (1742) *A practical treatise on dentition*, London.
113. Imhof, A. E. (1981) *The amazing simultaneousness of the big differences and the boom in the 19th century. Some facts and hypotheses about infant and maternal mortality in Germany 18th and to 20th century.* Paper given at International symposium on mortality decline, 22-26 June, Lund, Sweden.
114. James, R. (1746) *The modern practice of physic As improv'd by ... H. Boerhaave, and F. Hoffmann ... Being a translation of the aphorisms of the former with the commentaries of Dr van Swieten*, 2 vols, London.
115. Jelliffe, D. B. & Jelliffe, E. F. P. (1978) *Human milk in the modern world. Psychosocial, nutritional and economic significance*, Oxford.
116. Jonckheere, F. (1955) Un chapitre de pédiatrie Egyptienne l'allaitement, *Aesculape 37*, 203-23.
117. Jones, J. (1579) *The arte and science of preserving bodie and soule in healthe, wisedom, and catholick religion: physically, philosophically and divinely devised*, London.

118. Josselin, R. (1976) *The diary of Ralph Josselin 1616-1683*, Macfarlane, A. (ed.), Oxford.
119. Klaus, M. H. & Kennell, J. H. (1982) *Parent-infant bonding*, St Louis, 2nd ed.
120. Klein, H. S. & Engerman, S. L. (1978) Fertility differentials between slaves in the United States and the British West Indies: a note on lactation practices and their possible implications, *William & Mary Quarterly 35*, 357-74.
121. Knodel, J. & Van der Walle, E. (1967) Breastfeeding, fertility and infant mortality: an analysis of some early German data, *Popul. Stud. 21*, 109-31.
122. Knodel, J. (1977) Breastfeeding and population growth, *Science 198*, 1111-15.
123. Lactatio (1797) in *Encyclopaedia Britannica 9*, 506.
124. *Ladies dispensatory or, Every woman her own physician*, London, 1740.
125. *Ladies Physical Directory: by a physician. 7th edition with large additions, alterations and amendments*, London, 1739.
126. Lane, M. (1975) *Samuel Johnson and his world*, London.
127. Lara, B. (1791) *An essay on the injurious custom of mothers not suckling their own children; with some directions for chusing a nurse, and weaning of children, etc.*, London.
128. Lasareff, V. (1938) Studies in the iconography of the virgin, *Art Bulletin 20*, 26-65.
129. Laslett, P. (1971) *The world we have lost*, London, 2nd ed.
130. Leinster, E. (1949-57) *Correspondence of Emily, Duchess of Leinster (1731-1814)*, Fitzgerald, B. (ed.), Dublin, 3 vols.
131. Levin, S. (1980) The great bottle, *Adler Mus. Bull. 6*, 7-11.
132. Levinson, A. (1917-22) The pediatric section of a medical cyclopedia of the seventeenth century, *Bull. Soc. Med. Hist. Chicago 2*, 110-18.
133. Levy, D. M. (1934) Experiments on the sucking reflex and social behaviour of dogs, *Am. J. Orthopsych. 4*, 203-24.
134. Lithell, U-B. (1981) Breastfeeding habits and their relation to infant mortality and marital fertility, *J. Fam. Hist. 6*, 182-94.
135. Lithell, U-B. (1981) *Breastfeeding and reproduction: studies in marital fertility and infant mortality in 19th century Finland and Sweden*, Doctoral dissertation, University of Uppsala, Sweden.
136. Lockwood, R. (1978) Birth, illness and death in 18th century New England, *J. Soc. Hist. 12* (1), 111-28.
137. McCann, M. F. *et al.* (1981) *Breastfeeding, fertility and family planning*, Population Reports. Series J. 24, vol.9, no.5.
138. McHenry, L. C. & MacKeith, R. (1966) Samuel Johnson's childhood illnesses and the King's Evil, *Med. Hist. 10*, 386-99.
139. Mackenzie, C. (1770) *Lectures in midwifery*, Library of the Wellcome Institute for the History of Medicine, MS 3392.
140. Mackenzie, C. (1774) *Mr Mackenzey's Lectures on midwifery*, ? by D. B., London, Library of the Royal College of

Obstetricians and Gynaecologists, Unnumbered MS.

141. Macklin, H. W. (1931) *Monumental brasses*, London.
142. McLaren, D. (1978) Fertility, infant mortality and breast-feeding in the seventeenth century, *Med. Hist. 22*, 378-96.
143. McLaren, D. (1979) Nature's contraceptive. Wet nursing and prolonged lactation: the case of Chesham, Buckinghamshire 1578-1601, *Med. Hist. 23*, 426-41.
144. McLaren, D. (1979) The individualism of good mothering, *Soc. Soc. Hist. Med. Bull. 24*, 36-8.
145. McLaren, D. (1979) Emmenologia: a curse or a blessing? *Soc. Soc. Hist. Med. Bull. 25*, 65-7.
146. McMath, J. (1694) *The expert midwife*, Edinburgh.
147. Mantell, T. (1787) *Short directions for the management of infants*, London.
148. Marcy, P. T. (1981) Factors affecting the fecundity and fertility of historical populations. A review, *J. Fam. Hist. 6* (3), 309-26.
149. Marshall, D. (1926) *The English poor in the eighteenth century. A study in social and administrative history*, New York. Reprinted 1969.
150. Marshall, R. K. (1983) *Virgins and viragos. A history of women in Scotland from 1080-1980*, London.
151. Masnick, G. S. (1979) The demographic impact of breast-feeding: a critical review, *Human Biology 51* (2), 109-25.
152. Mauriceau, F. (1673) *The accomplisht midwife, treating of the diseases of women with child, and in child bed . . . with fit remedies for the several indispositions of newborn babes*, trans. Chamberlen, H., London.
153. Mead, M. (1935) *Sex and temperament in three primitive societies*, New York, 3rd ed., 1963.
154. Meade, S., Letter to her mother, Margaret Fox (née Fell) 7 April 1686, *Abraham MSS No. 30*, Friends House Library, London.
155. Mears, M. (1797) *The midwife's candid advice to the fair sex; or The pupil of nature*, London.
156. Memis, J. (1765) *The midwife's pocket companion*, London.
157. Middlemore, M. P. (1941) *The nursing couple*, London.
158. Mondot-Bernard, J. M. (1977) *Relationships between fertility, child mortality and nutrition in Africa. A tentative analysis*, Paris.
159. More, Sir T. (1516) *Utopia*, trans. Robinson, R., London, 1624.
160. Morris, C. (1934) *The diary of a west country physician AD 1684-1726*, Hobhouse, E. (ed.), London.
161. Moss, W. (1781) *An essay on the management and nursing of children in the earlier periods of infancy*, London.
162. Muffet (Moffet), T. (1584) *Health's improvements: or Rules comprising the nature, method, and manner of preparing all sorts of food used in this nation. Corrected and enlarged by Christopher Bennet*, London, 1655.

162a Musson, P. H., *The psychological development of the child,* New Jersey.

163. Myles, M. F. (1975) *Textbook for midwives with modern concepts of obstetrics and neonatal care,* Edinburgh and London.

164. Nelson, J. (1753) *An essay on the government of children,* London.

165. Newcome, H. (1695) *The compleat mother or, An earnest persuasive to all mothers (especially those of rank and quality) to nurse their own children,* London.

166. Newcome, H. (1852) *The autobiography of Henry Newcome MA,* Parkinson, R. (ed.), Manchester.

167. Newdigate-Newdegate, Lady (ed.) (1898), *The Cheverals of Cheveral Manor,* London.

168. Newdigate, A. (1898) *Gossip from a muniment room. Being passages in the lives of Anne and Mary Fitton 1574-1618,* Newdigate-Newdegate, Lady (ed.), London. 2nd Ed.

169. Newson, J. & Newson, E. (1974) *Patterns of infant care in an urban community,* Harmondsworth.

170. *Nurses guide: or The right method of bringing up young children. By an eminent physician,* 1729, London.

171. Osborne, W. & Denman, T. (1776) *Sketches of the practice of midwifery. From the lectures of Drs Osborne and Denman,* Library of the Wellcome Institute for the History of Medicine, MS 2098.

172. Paré, A. (1575) *The workes of that famous chirurgion Ambrose Parey,* trans. Johnson, T., London, 1634.

173. Paulus Aeginata (7th century AD) *The seven books of Paulus Aeginata. With a commentary,* trans. Adams, F., London, 1844-47, vol.1.

174. Pearson, L. E. (1957) *Elizabethans at home,* California.

175. Pechey (Peachey), J. (1697) *A general treatise of the diseases of infants and children. Collected from the best practical authors,* London.

176. Pennington, S. (1767) *Letters on different subjects,* London, vols 3 & 4.

177. Percy, H. (1595-96) *Instructions to his son by Henry Percy, 9th Earl of Northumberland,* Harrison, G. B. (ed.), 1930.

178. Perkins, W. (1612-18) *The complete works,* Cambridge, vols 1 & 3.

179. Petty, Sir W. (1927) *The Petty papers,* Marquis of Lansdowne (ed.), London, vol.1.

180. Ploss, H. H., Bartels, M. & Bartels, P. (1935), *Woman,* Dingwall, E. J. (ed.), London, vol.3.

181. Plutarch (1st century AD) *The education and bringing up of children,* trans. Elyot, Sir T., London, 1533, in Pepper, R. D., 1966, *Four Tudor books on education,* Florida.

182. Pomeroy, S. B. (1975) *Goddesses, whores, wives, and slaves. Women in classical antiquity,* New York.

183. Power, E. (1975) *Medieval women*, Postan, M. M. (ed.), Cambridge.

184. *Present day practice in infant feeding* (1974) DHSS Report on health and social subjects No. 9, London.

185. Quillet, C. (1655) *Callipaedia or, An art how to have handsome children*, trans. anon., London, 1710.

186. Radbill, S. X. (1973) Mesopotamian pediatrics, *Episteme 7*, 283-8.

187. Ramazzini, B. (1713) *De morbis artificum of Bernardino Ramazzini (diseases of workers). Revised with translations and notes by Wilner Cave Wright*, Chicago, 1940, 506-9.

188. Richmond, J. B. & Caldwell, B. M. (1963) Child rearing practices and their consequences in Solnit, A. J. & Provence, S. A. (ed.), *Modern perspectives in child development*, New York, 627-54.

189. Roesslin the Elder, E. (1540) *The byrth of mankynde*, trans. Jonas, R., London, first published 1512.

190. Rosario, Sister M. (1917) *The nurse in Greek life*, Unpublished PhD dissertation, Boston.

191. Rosenstein, Nicholas Rosén von (1776) *The diseases of children and their remedies*, trans. Sparraman, A., London.

192. Rous, M., Letter to her mother, Margaret Fox (née Fell) (28 April 1672), *Abraham MSS no.16*, Friends' House Library, London.

193. Rousseau, J-J. (1762) *Émile*, trans. Foxley, B., London, 1911.

194. Rutter, M. (1981) *Maternal deprivation reassessed*, Harmondsworth, 2nd ed.

195. Sainte Marthe, S. de (1584) *Paedotrophiae: or The art of bringing up children*, trans. anon., London, 1710.

196. Schnucker, R. V. (1974) The English puritans and pregnancy, delivery and breast feeding, *Hist. Childh. Quart. 1*, 637-58.

197. Shakespeare, W. (c.1611) *The winter's tale*, Act 2 Scene 1, in Alexander, P. (ed.), *The complete works of William Shakespeare*, London and Glasgow, 1960.

198. Sharp, J. (1671) *The midwives book or The whole art of midwifery discovered*, London.

199. Short, R. V. (1976) The evolution of human reproduction, *Proc. R. Soc., Series B 195*, 3-24.

200. Short, R. V. (1982) *The biological basis for the contraceptive effects of breastfeeding*, Background document for WHO Workshop on breastfeeding and fertility regulation, Geneva, February 1982.

201. Shorter, E. (1977) *The making of the modern family*, Glasgow.

202. Shorter, E. (1977) *Women's diseases before 1900*, Unpublished seminar paper.

203. Shorter, E. (1978) *The great transformation of mother-infant relations, eighteenth to twentieth centuries*, Unpublished paper.

204. Shorter, E. (1983) *A history of women's bodies*, London.

205. Sibbald, R. (1932) *The memoirs of Sir Robert Sibbald (1641-1722),* Hett, F. P. (ed.), London.
206. Sibbald, S. (1926) *The memoirs of Susan Sibbald (1783-1812),* Hett, F. P. (ed.), London.
207. Sloane, H. (1748) *Letter to John Milner, vice-president of the Hospital for the maintenance and education of exposed and deserted young children,* 28 October 1748, quoted in full in Brownlow, J., 1847, *Memoranda; or Chronicles of the Foundling Hospital,* London.
208. Smellie, W. (1752) *A treatise on the theory and practice of midwifery,* London, vols 1 and 3.
209. Smith, H. (1597) *The sermons of Maister Henrie Smith gathered into one volume,* London.
210. Smith, H. (1774) *Letters to married women on nursing and the management of children. The 3rd edition, revised and considerably enlarged,* London.
211. Soranus of Ephesus (1st/2nd century AD) *Soranus' Gynecology,* trans. Temkin, O. *et al.,* Baltimore, 1956.
212. Spence, D. (1784) *A system of midwifery,* Edinburgh.
213. Spencer, H. R. (1927) *The history of British midwifery from 1650 to 1800,* London.
214. Steele, R. (1711) On abuses in nursing children, *The Spectator,* no.246, Wednesday, 12 December.
215. Stone, L. (1965) *The crisis of the aristocracy 1558-1641,* Oxford.
216. Stone, L. (1977) *The family, sex and marriage in England 1500-1800,* London.
217. Strong, L. C. (1953) Mother's milk and the offspring, *J. Hist. Med. 8,* 210-14.
218. Sussman, G. D. (1974) The wet-nursing business in Paris 1769-1876, in Newman, E. D. (ed.), *Proceedings of the first annual meeting of the Western society for French history,* March 14-15, New Mexico State University Press, cols 179-94.
219. Sussman, G. D. (1975) The wet nursing business in nineteenth century France, *French Hist. Stud. 9,* 304-28.
220. Sussman, G. D. (1977) Parisian infants and Norman wet nurses in the early nineteenth century: a statistical study, *J. Interdisciplinary Hist. 7,* 637-53.
221. Sussman, G. D. (1977) The end of the wet-nursing business in France 1874-1914, *J. Fam. Hist. 2,* 237-58.
222. Sussman, G. D. (1982) *Selling mothers' milk. The wet-nursing business in France 1715-1914,* Chicago and London.
223. Tansillo, L. (1566) *The nurse. A poem,* trans. Roscoe, W., Liverpool and London, 1800, 2nd ed.
224. Thornton, A. (1875) *The autobiography of Mrs Alice Thornton of East Newton, Co, York* Jackson, C. (ed.), Durham.
225. Tillotson, J. (1728) *The works of the most Reverend Dr John Tillotson,* London, 9th ed., vol.1, first published 1683.

226. Trumbach, R. (1978) *The rise of the egalitarian family*, New York.
227. Tucker, M. J. (1976) The child as beginning and end: fifteenth and sixteenth century English childhood, in De Mause, L. (ed.), *History of childhood*, London, 229-57.
228. Underwood, M. (1784) *A treatise on the diseases of children*, London.
229. Ulrich, L. T. (1982) *Good wives. Image and reality in the lives of women in Northern New England 1650-1750*, New York.
230. Vaughan, V. C. *et al.* (1975) Nutritional requirements and disorders and Ordinary care of the newborn infant, in *Nelson textbook of pediatrics*, Philadelphia, 10th ed., 147-206; 333-6; 393-403.
231. Verney, M. M. (1930) *Verney letters of the eighteenth century*, London.
232. Vives, Johannes Ludovicis (1540) *Instructions for a christian woman*, trans. Byrd, R., London.
233. Wake, J. (1953) *The Brudenells of Deene*, London.
234. Wallis Budge, E. A. (1925) *Babylonian life and history*, London, 2nd ed.
235. Warner, M. (1978) *Alone of all her sex. The myth and cult of the Virgin Mary*, London.
236. White, C. (1773) *A treatise on the management of pregnant and lying-in women*, London.
237. Whiting, J. W. M. & Child, I. L. (1964) *Child training and personality: a cross-cultural study*, New Haven and London.
238. Wieschoff, H. A. (1940) Artificial stimulation of lactation in primitive cultures, *Bull. Hist. Med. 8*, 1403-15.
239. Willoughby, E. (1844) *So much of the diary of Lady Willoughby as relates to her domestic history and to the eventful period of the reign of Charles the first, vol. 1 1635-48*, London.
240. Willughby, P. (1630-69) *Observations in midwifery. As also the country midwife's opusculum or vade mecum*, Blenkinsop, H. (ed.), Warwick, 1863.
241. Wickes, I. G. (1953) A history of infant feeding, *Archs. Dis. Childh. 28*, 151-8; 232-40; 332-40; 416-22; 495-502.
242. Wilson, C. A. (1976) *Food and drink in Britain. From the stone age to recent times*, Harmondsworth.
243. Winchester, B. (1955) *Tudor family portrait*, London.
244. Witowski, G-J. (1903) *Les seins dans l'histoire*, Paris.
245. Wollstonecraft, M. (1792) *Vindication of the rights of woman*, Harmondsworth, 1982.
246. Wood, C. B. S. & Walker-Smith, J. A. (1981) *MacKeith's infant feeding and feeding difficulties*, Edinburgh and London, 6th ed.
247. Zglinicki, F. von (1979) *Die wiege: volkskundlich-kutur-geschichtlich-kunstwissenschaftlich-medizin-historisch*, Regensberg.

CHAPTER FOUR

Maternal Breastfeeding:
Problems of Lactation and Instruments
associated with Breastfeeding

"[she] began to have sore brests so that the childe did not
sucke for three days to gether that wee ware faine to put it
forth to norse into the country for wife was in such paine
with her brests." Nehemiah Wallington, 1598–1658

WHEN AN ample supply of good-quality breast milk was the only
reliable means of feeding a young baby, it was essential to maintain
enough to nourish the child while avoiding extremes of breast discomfort in the mother (plate 4.1). This is emphasised by the space that
midwifery writers gave to problems of breast-milk supply and the health
of the breasts and nipples during lactation. Sixteenth- and 17th-century
physicians and midwives apparently paid more attention to this subject
than did those of the 18th century, which may reflect the fact that the
alternative of handfeeding was by then available, but may also relate to
the increasing specialisation of textbooks on medical subjects. From the
1730s, books on paediatrics and infant management began to be published separately from texts on midwifery, and therefore problems of
lactation may have been confined more to the latter.

It was common for many pages of recipes and remedies to be given
for conditions of the breast. What follows is more concerned with the
general principles of care and treatment than with pharmacology, and
so will be about the type of treatment advised or used; and, where
relevant, the main ingredients of suggested remedies. Problems of
lactation were not confined to wealthy women, although most writers
clearly had the latter in mind, when dealing with problems of the drying
up of the milk when they did not want to breastfeed. But most of the
following applies to all women who breastfed their own, or someone
else's, children.

Reasons for a declining supply of breast milk (and methods for
increasing it) were discussed by 19 authors between 1534 and 1790,
and no less than a dozen explanations were current. They were:
  i) too much fasting, hunger, and thirst [11,14,29,50,54];
  ii) extraordinary evacuations (of stool, urine, sweat) [11,14,20,29,54];

Plate 4.1. A thank-offering for
a good supply of breastmilk.

iii) sickness in the mother [11,20,29,50], especially high fevers [14,54];
iv) the inability of breasts to make milk [11,14,29,54];
v) strong emotions (fear, anger, grief, worry, etc.) [14,20,54];
vi) great weakness of the child so that it does not suck the breasts
properly or sufficiently hard [14,20,54];
vii) too much hard labour, resulting in excessive sweating [14,54];
viii) too little blood (i.e. anaemia) [14,54];
ix) disease in the breast [50];
x) compression of the breasts [20];
xi) drinking 'acid liquors' or 'austere wine' [20];
xii) women not knowing how to manage themselves (i.e. maintain a
milk supply [8].

Four types of treatment were used to increase the milk supply, and
those prescribed by nineteen writers (table 4.1) included internal remedies, local applications, drawing the breasts, and other treatments. A
massive number of internal remedies were prescribed, and they included more than 65 different ingredients, but certain substances re-
curred as particularly superior lactogogues: i) the seed or root of
fennel, either alone or with other herbs or liquids; ii) anis or *aniseed*;
iii) powdered *crystal*; iv) parts of the body, or the products, of *cows* (e.g.
powdered dugs, udders or hoofs; broth of the tongue; milk, butter and

cheese); v) powdered *earthworms*; vi) *dill*; vii) *parsnip*; viii) *lettuce*; ix) *rocket*.

Different substances were preferred in different periods. Those favoured in the 16th century were aniseed, fennel, lettuce and powdered crystal [6,18,47,50]; in the 17th century, fennel, powdered crystal and powdered earthworms, with aniseed, dill and rocket relatively favoured [11,13,14,29]; fennel was still approved in the 18th century [25,44,51], together with products of cows (table 4.2) [1,2,51]. Local applications consisted of plaisters or fomentations to be applied to the breast, again consisting of many different 'simples' [14,20,47,50,54], but the most popular ingredients to be given internally (fennel and aniseed) were considered equally effective when applied locally. Sucking the breasts, either by another person, a young animal (usually whelps) or with an instrument was advised to encourage milk secretion [8,9,50]. Other remedies included rubbing the breasts with the hand [50] and cold sea bathing [41]. The *Ladies Dispensatory* (1740) opined that mothers with a weak constitution who could not tolerate a 'high diet' might do better to wean the child or put it to another nurse. Rosenstein (1776) said that it was no use trying to increase the milk supply if the woman were pregnant.

Today when the physiological mechanism of lactation has been elucidated, it is known that the principal reasons for a failing milk supply are: i) poor sucking in the infant, due to such factors as weakness, prematurity, low birth weight, and neonatal conditions such as jaundice; ii) emotional interference with the 'let down' reflex in the mother, which is related particularly to lack of knowledge and confidence, socio-cultural uncertainties and environmental psycho-social stress; iii) problems with technique, which may be related to circumstances in ii) [17,28]. Hunger and thirst, and loss of body fluids, unless prolonged (as in famine conditions), probably have only a temporary effect on the supply of breast milk.

Thus, without the benefits of modern physiological knowledge, 17th-century midwives were well aware of the main causes of lactation failure; particularly the English writers Jane Sharp (1671) and Nicholas Culpeper (1676), and the German, Michael Ettmueller (1699). But they do not appear to have related remedies to causes. The most important factor in improving the milk supply is to increase the frequency and intensity of the sucking stimulus on the nipple, which stimulates the secretion of prolactin in the anterior pituitary gland. Without this stimulus other methods are ineffective [17,28].

If the major problem, however, lay in psycho-social factors affecting the mother, then it is possible that such visible efforts on her behalf as internal and local remedies would have helped her relax sufficiently to enable her to breastfeed successfully. The effectiveness of such remedies would, however, have depended greatly upon the degree of reassurance administered at the same time [26,28]. If those upper-class mothers who breastfed knew that they were going against the cultural norm then, unless they were particularly self-confident and determined, they might well have had to deal with considerable emotional strain. It has been established that 'cultural confusion inhibits lactation' [28], so that problems of a failing milk supply could have been a greater problem among wealthy woman going against the fashion of wet nursing before the early 1700s; and (later in the 18th century) among those who attempted against their inclinations to follow the new fashion of maternal breastfeeding. The latter may have had the additional problem of relatively infrequent scheduled feeding which offers less frequent, and often less intense, stimulus from the sucking infant [28,32].

Folk beliefs and sympathetic lore go far to explain why certain substances were thought to increase milk production. Some were related to moistness in plants, and so believed to increase moisture (i.e. milk) in the body 'by sympathy' [54]. Others, such as the strong belief in the efficacy of fennel as a lactogogue (which survived until the 20th century) was a folk-belief in many parts of the world [22]. In many areas of the world various white substances such as milkthistle and milk stones are thought to aid lactation [54,36], through association of their properties (whiteness, moistness, nourishment) with the production of breast milk. The ingestion of different parts of the cow was undoubtedly related to its reputation as a prolific milk-producer. This is confirmed by Jane Sharp's (1671) comment:

> Some prescribe the hoofs of a cow's forefeet dried and powdered, and a dram taken every morning in ale: I think it should be the hoofs of the hinderfeet, for they stand nearest the udder, where milk is bred.

¶ Oversecretion of milk was attributed to women having too much blood or a 'strong lactificall faculty' [14,29], and to the child sucking too much [14,54]. Some 17th-century writers gave methods for reducing the amount of milk secreted, but presumably this problem was much less urgent than a lack of milk; and very few midwives gave remedies. Specific herbs were said to be good for repelling milk. These included mints, calamints, smallage, *Agnus castus,* and coriander [14,29,54]. Other remedies were: i) local applications such as poultices and cataplasms [14,19,29,38,39]; ii) venesection, cupping or bleeding [14,29]; iii) eating very little [14,38]; sucking the breast using a glass or puppy [14] (plate 4.2); v) keeping the belly open [19]. Jane Sharp had the best solution:

> Some women . . . are so well tempered to increase milk that they can suckle a child of their own, and another for a friend; and it will not hurt their own child.

Plate 4.2. Painting (signed A. Utrillo) of
a young mother using whelps to relieve
oversecretion of milk.

Engorgement of the breasts is one of the commonest problems in
breastfeeding and is normally associated with inadequate emptying,
particularly in the neonatal period when babies suck relatively small
amounts [28]. As Baudelocque (1790) noted, this would have been a
problem to wet nurses who had been lactating for several weeks or
months and suddenly changed from feeding a hungry older child to a
newborn baby. The remedy is to empty the breasts by expression, or by
utilising a breast pump, as was recognised by Sharp (1671) and Culpeper (1676). Although the various 'reducing' remedies suggested
probably had little effect, local applications, especially when warmed,
can provide comfort and are still used by midwives and mothers today
[42,59].

Related to the problem of dealing with excessive breast milk was that
of the drying-up of the milk, either soon after giving birth (because the
woman was not going to breastfeed) or because the child had to be
weaned suddenly. Sixteenth- and 17th-century writers were again more
concerned with this topic than were those of the 18th century; twelve
gave methods for drying-up breast milk (table 4.3). They included local

applications, purging, dieting, bleeding, drawing the breasts and internal remedies. In addition, Mauriceau in 1673 advised:

> I know some women who hold it for a very great secret, and most certain and fit to drive the milk effectually back; and that is to put on her husband's shift yet warm immediately after he hath taken it off and wear it until the milk be gone: but in case the milk doth in the meantime vanish, 'tis superstitious to believe that this shirt is the cause of it.

Again he wrote:

> I have sometimes seen women apply to their breasts, with no small success, the linnen-covers of salt-butter pots; it is a drying-remedy, and fit to soak up the moisture of these parts and may be used; provided the remedies before mentioned have discursed the milk.

In more recent times various methods have been used to dry up women's milk including firm bandaging, administration of oestrogens, and reduction of fluids, but the most usual treatment at present is to give Bromocryptin, or to do nothing. Without the stimulus of sucking, the milk supply ceases without any interference, although some discomfort may ensue for a few days [28]. Drawing the breast would stimulate production of more breast milk, as was recognised by Mauriceau (1673) and the *English Midwife Enlarged* (1682), but the principal remedies offered would again have provided localised comfort, which is important, particularly during the puerperium.

Other remedies were related to 'reducing' the body fluids, and although by themselves these would not have dried up the milk, they would not have affected the natural decrease in milk production which occurs in the absence of the sucking stimulus on the nipple [17,28].

¶ Problems with the breasts and nipples attracted much attention, particularly from surgeons and midwives, who were likely to be consulted when such problems arose (table 4.4). At all periods (including the present) [24,28] the major problem for breastfeeding women has been sore or infected nipples, usually the result of small cracks becoming infected. Many difficulties with the breasts apparently caused less worry in the 18th century than in the preceding 200 years; probably as a result of the general knowledge that these could be largely prevented if suckling was commenced within a few hours of birth. Whereas the incidence of sore, cracked and infected nipples would be unaffected by such a change, a reduction would be expected in the incidence of swollen, engorged, lumpy and inflamed breasts. This is confirmed by the findings of the lying-in hospitals [43]. The types of problems which affected the nipples were: i) soreness (especially in first-time mothers); ii) cracks, clefts and fissures; iii) ulcers and loss of the nipples;

iv) nipples obstructed or deformed by scar tissue from suckling a previous child.

Various reasons were given for the apparent high incidence of sore nipples, the main one being that hungry children, frustrated by getting insufficient milk, or were not getting it easily, were liable to bite and 'mump' the nipple. Whether or not the child had teeth, this led to sores which eventually could develop into ulcers and consequent loss of the nipple [7,9,15,19,38,39]. Infants who suffered from conditions such as thrush, aphthae, and the pox (syphilis) were said to cause sore nipples in their nurses [9,19,38,39], and damage resulting from the pox was said to be very difficult to heal. Other writers blamed prolonged sucking [40], not suckling for several days, and allowing attendants to draw the nipples [56], and small or scarred nipples which frustrated the child [38,54].

Remedies for sore nipples were given by 17th- and some 18th-century writers. Minor cracks and fissures were treated with local applications, particularly ointments. But the most important treatment was to stop the child sucking at the affected breast to give it a chance to heal (even though this might involve weaning the child early).

Instructions were given on how to reconstruct a new nipple if a woman wanted to nurse again after the resulting ulcer had healed:

When the nipples are quite lost it is very difficult to give a child longer suck; because it can take no hold to suck the milk, and also the small holes of the nipple are closed up by the ulcers. But if . . . she shall desire to give suck, another woman must by degrees make her new nipples, after the ulcer shall be perfectly healed, whose sucking with her mouth will draw them out, and by this means unstop the root of the old nipples; or using a fit instrument of glass . . . with which the woman herself may also suck them five or six times a day; and to shape them and so preserve them, being thus drawn out, from sinking into the breast again, let her put upon them a small cap of wood, or other matter . . . and doing so by degrees after the nipples are quite form'd and unstopp'd, she may again give her child suck [39].

Similar instructions were given by the *English Midwife Enlarged* (1682) and MacMath (1694). That such instructions were given demonstrates that such severe problems as loss of a nipple as a result of breastfeeding were not infrequent in the 17th century, and there was probably a high incidence of infections of all degrees of severity until very recent times.

Not allowing the child to suck at the affected breast was also the principal treatment recommended for various other breast problems, although excess milk was to be drawn by other means, to prevent milk accumulating in the breasts and causing further difficulties. Local applications such as plaisters and poultices were widely used and these would have had the important function of providing obvious attention and comfort to the woman. Today, conditions of the breast are rarely a reason for women to stop breastfeeding. But, before antiseptics and antibiotics were available, the child would have been adversely affected by ingesting milk from an infected breast, so that the safest remedy was that suggested: to draw off excess milk mechanically and to put the child only to the unaffected breast, to another nurse, or to wean it, provided it was not too young.

¶ Specially designed instruments to facilitate breastfeeding are known from the mid-16th century but, although the earliest mention or illustration found dates from 1545, such instruments, or improvisations of them, must have been in use much earlier, since the problems for which they were employed had existed since mothers first put children to the breast. Very few examples survive, since items such as breast pumps were made of easily breakable glass; nipple shields made of metals such as tin, lead and pewter could be melted down and re-used. There is the additional point that they were used only by women and (unlike feeding bottles) were not particularly attractive or 'collectable'. The evidence given here is derived from descriptions and illustrations in medical texts and from surviving artefacts.

Two types of instrument were employed: i) sucking glasses; ii) nipple shields. Sucking glasses were used to relieve engorgement or to express milk when the breasts were inflamed or infected, or when the nipples were cracked. All descriptions refer to glasses and no evidence has been found to show that they were made from any other material. No surviving examples have been identified from the 16th to the 18th century although some museums have 19th-century pumps which are of similar design (plate 4.3). Sucking glasses were mentioned and/or illustrated by sixteen medical authors between 1545 and 1800 (plate 4.4) and, whatever the country of origin, all the illustrations show the same basic design, although only that by Ferrarius (1577) shows a sucking glass in use (plate 4.4a). Comparison of Ferrarius' illustration and the description 150 years later in the *Nurses Guide* (1729) shows that there was no change in basic design:

> This instrument of glass . . . has two openings, one of which is wide and flat, to be apply'd to the breasts; and the other like a neck or gullet, long and narrow at the end, that it may be put into the mouth [44].

Medical writers thought their main advantage was that women could suck their own breasts rather than having to resort to children, puppies or attendants to draw off excess milk [19, 38, 39]:

> They may let children or little whelpes sucke their breasts, whereby they may draw out the milke that is fixed fast in their dugges,

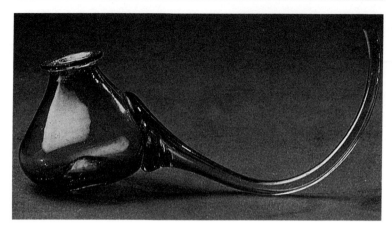

Plate 4.3. A rare example of an unbroken
sucking glass from Altare, Savona, Italy.

> instead whereof we have invented this instrument of glasse, where-
> with, when the broader orifice is fastened or placed on the breast or
> dugge, and the pipe turned upwards towards her mouth, she may
> suck her own breasts herself [45].

If she did not possess such a sophisticated sucking glass, a woman could
use a small glass or glass vial which had been warmed in hot water; this
was applied to the breast until it was filled with milk and the process was
repeated as often as necessary [15,45].

Glasses could also be used by women with inverted nipples who
wanted to breastfeed, as Johannes Scultetus (1655) described (plate
4.5):

> The nipples of those that give suck are oftentimes so hid within the
> breast, that the child newborn can neither take hold of them with
> its mouth, nor suck any milk out of them. In such a case let either
> the child's nurse set the bottom of the glass to the nipple that lies
> hid, and lay hold of the mouth of the pipe with her mouth, and draw
> forth the nipple by sucking; or one that is of years shall set the long
> glass [k] to the nipple, and with a band shall bind it fast to the
> breast; and when this is done, let her take the narrower end of the
> glass between her lips, and drawing as before, let her suck forth the
> nipple that lieth hid. Amatus Lusitanus filleth a glass with a narrow
> mouth [l] with scalding water, which he poureth forth again when
> the glass is made very hot with it, and he presently claps the mouth
> of the glass to the nipple; for this presently sticks fast to the nipple,
> and draws it out so forcibly, that the child may lay hold of it with
> the mouth. Moreover these instruments not only draw out the

Plate 4.4. a) Breast pump in use. From Ferrarius, *De arte medica infantium* (1577).

b) Sucking glass described by Scultetus, *The chyrurgeon's storehouse* (1674).

nipples, but milk also. But if there be no need to draw forth milk with the nipple, a thumb-stall made of ivy wood is most safely set on to draw the nipple [53].

Small numbers of nipple shields have survived (plate 4.6). They were made of lead, pewter, tin, horn, bone, ivory, wood, silver or glass and had three main functions: i) to raise inverted or retracted nipples or to help in the formation of new nipples after ulceration had occurred. In these cases they were used in conjunction with sucking glasses; ii) to prevent sore or ulcerated nipples; iii) in the treatment of sore, cracked, or infected nipples. They also prevented soiling of the clothes by excess breast milk, and by the 19th century were used as a base for attaching an artificial nipple or cow's teat [16].

There is very little difference in basic design between 16th-century nipple shields and those in use today, and there is no reason to believe that they were any less effective than those of the 20th century [28], although their greater weight may well have made them less comfortable to wear. Improvised nipple shields were made from hollowed nutmegs [20, 49, 60] and mention was also made of 'little wax caps, or leaden ones . . . which must have several small holes in them' [39]. Wax caps were

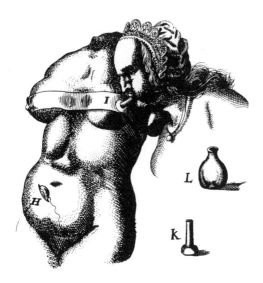

Plate 4.5. From Scultetus, *The chyrurgeon's
storehouse* (description in text).

referred to by other midwifery writers and were probably devices which
could easily be made at home with candle wax [14,19,38,54].

To prevent sore nipples, and in their treatment, the nipple shield was
applied to the breast before the child was allowed to suck [14,37,45,54] ;
it also functioned by keeping dressings in place whilst allowing milk to
escape through the holes [19,31]. To correct lost, inverted or retracted
nipples it was to be worn all the time to keep the nipple out, and only
removed to feed the baby [7,15,38,39].

Instruments were probably referred to by Gouge (1622) when he
complained that some women:

> are themselves the cause of wanting milk because they will not let
> it be drawne downe; or because they will not use meanes (for
> meanes there are) to get and increase milke. There are meanes
> also to raise nipples where the breasts are very flat [23].

Ralph Josselin in 1642 recorded:

> it pleased God my wives breasts were sore which was a grievance
> and a sore cutt to her but with use of meanes in some distance of
> time they healed up [30].

Sarah, sister of the Duchess of Leinster, suffered from retracted nipples, and instruments were used for some time after her delivery in an
effort to raise them. Six days after the birth of Sarah's child in December
1768 her sister wrote:

Plate 4.6. Nipple shields, 1545–1830.
a) from Reiff *Schwangerer Frawen Rosengarten* 1545.

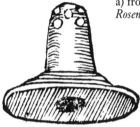

b) Lead shield, from A. Paré *The workes* 1634.

c) 'Silver cap' or nipple shield, from Scultetus *The chyrurgeon's storehouse* 1674.

d) Silver nipple protector, hallmarked 1751.

e) Wooden nipple shield, c.1830.

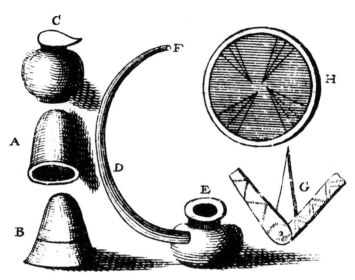

Plate 4.7. A,B Nipple caps, C cupping
glass, D,E,F sucking glass, G lancet,
H 'plaister', from Dionis, *A general
treatise of midwifery* (1719).

her milk is come and her breast frequently drawn, but as yet the
child has not strength to suck, her milk not coming free enough.
Four days later:
> This is her tenth day, but alas the nursing scheme fails, and what
> is worse, the child neither feeds kindly nor can they get it to suck
> now; ... It has all along been provoking, for Sal has abundance of
> milk but the nipple would never come out, till now by drawing it
> various ways she has brought it about, and the child won't take it.
Nine days later:
> The nursing scheme would not do; she had quantities of milk ...
> but her nipple could not be drawn out without the greatest diffi-
> culty, and the child not being strong would not do it [34].

This aptly illustrates the failure to breastfeed in an obviously determined, upper-class, first-time mother, due to the joint factors of inverted nipples and the weak sucking of the baby. At a time when doctors
were complaining about the prevalence of inverted nipples among
upper- and middle-class women, the nipple shield and sucking glass
were indispensable items of equipment for such women who wished to
attempt breastfeeding their own babies (plates 4.7 and 4.8).

146

Plate 4.8. Glass container for wearing over
the nipples under the woman's clothes
to catch any excess breastmilk.

¶ Problems associated with lactation were very common, the most
serious being insufficient breast milk. The principal causes of lactation
failure were understood in the 17th century but suggested remedies
may have had only limited effect. An added cause may have been the
emotional strain upon upper-class mothers who tried to go against the
current fashion, of wet nursing in the 16th and 17th centuries, and
maternal breastfeeding in the late 18th century.

Various conditions of the breasts and nipples resulting from suckling
were a great problem, the most frequent being sore or infected nipples,
for which the suggested abstention from feeding would have been an
effective treatment.

Instruments used to facilitate breastfeeding included glass breast
pumps, for expressing excess milk, and nipple shields, made usually of
metal, both of which were used throughout this period. The design of
nipple shields has not varied since at least 1575 and they were used in
the treatment of inverted, cracked or infected nipples; in the prevention
of sore nipples; and for the formation of 'new nipples'.

REFERENCES
1. Arbuthnot, J. (1732) *Practical rules of diet in the various
constitutions and diseases of human bodies*, London.
2. Baudelocque, J-L. (1790) *A system of midwifery*, trans.
Heath, J., 3 vols., London.
3. Baynard, E. (1706) *The history of cold bathing: both ancient and
modern. Part II*, London, 2nd ed.
4. Bennion, E. (1979) *Antique medical instruments*, London.
5. Bidault, P. & Lepart, J. (1972) *Étains medicaux et pharmaceutiques*, Paris.

6. Boorde, A. (1547) *The breviary of helthe for all manner of sicknesses and diseases the which may be in man or woman,* London.

7. Bracken, H. (1737) *The midwife's companion or, A treatise of midwifery,* London.

8. Brown, S. (1777) *A letter to a lady on the best means of obtaining the milk in order to the suckling of the infant,* London.

9. Burton, J. (1751) *An essay towards a complete new system of midwifery,* London

10. Chamberlain, M. (1981) *Old wives' tales. Their history, remedies and spells,* London.

11. *Compleat midwife's practice enlarged, The* (1680), London.

12. *Cow and Gate collection of feeding vessels catalogue,* undated, Trowbridge, Wiltshire.

13. Culpeper, N. (1653) *The English physitian. Enlarged,* London.

14. Culpeper, N. (1676) *A directory for midwives; or a guide for women, in their conception, bearing and suckling their children,* London.

15. Dionis, P. (1719) *A general treatise of midwifery,* trans. anon, London.

16. Drake, T. G. H. (1946) Antiques of medical interest: nipple shields, *J. Hist. Med. 1,* 316-17.

17. Ebrahim, G. J. (1978) *Breastfeeding the biological option,* London.

18. Elyot, Sir T. (1534) *The castel of helth,* London.

19. *English midwife enlarged, The* (1682), London.

20. Ettmueller, M. (1699) *Etmullerus abridg'd: or a compleat system of the theory and practice of physic,* trans. anon., London.

21. Ferrarius, O. (1577) *De arte medica infantium,* Brescia.

22. *Funk and Wagnall's Standard dictionary of folklore, mythology and legend,* Leach, M. (ed.), London, 1972.

23. Gouge, W. (1622) *Of domestical duties,* London.

24. Gunther, M. (1945) Sore nipples. Causes and prevention, *Lancet II,* 590.

25. Hoffmann, F. (c.1740) *A system of the practice of medicine vol.2,* trans. Lewis, W., London, 1783.

26. Houston, M. J. (1981) Breastfeeding: success or failure, *J. Adv. Nurs. 6* 447-54.

27. Howie, P. *et al.* (1981) Effect of supplementary food on suckling patterns and ovarian activity during lactation, *Brit. Med. J. 283,* 1-7.

28. Jelliffe, D. B. & Jelliffe, E. F. P. (1978) *Human milk in the modern world,* Oxford.

29. Johnstone, J. (1657) *The idea of practical physick in twelve books,* trans. Culpeper, N. & W. R., London.

30. Josselin, R. (1976) *The diary of Ralph Josselin 1616-1683,* Macfarlane, A. (ed.), Oxford.

31. *Ladies dispensatory or, Every woman her own physician*

(1740), London.
32. *Ladies physical directory: by a physician. 7th edition with large additions, alterations, and amendments* (1739), London.
33. Leach, P. (1974) *Babyhood. Infant development from birth to two years*, Harmondsworth.
34. Leinster, E. (1949-57) *Correspondence of Emily, Duchess of Leinster (1731-1814)* Fitzgerald, B. (ed.), Dublin.
35. Levin, S. (1968) Nipple shields. *S. Afr. Med. J. 42*, 1289-90.
36. McDaniel, W. B. (1948) *Conception, birth and infancy in ancient Rome and modern Italy*, Florida.
37. Mackenzie, C. (1774) *Mr Mackenzey's lectures on midwifery*, ? by D. B., London, Library of Royal College of Obstetricians and Gynaecologists, Unnumbered MS.
38. McMath, J. (1694) *The expert midwife*, Edinburgh.
39. Mauriceau, F. (1673) *The accomplisht midwife*, trans. Chamberlen, H., London.
40. Memis, J. (1765) *The midwifes's pocket companion*, London.
41. Moss, W. (1781) *An essay on the management and nursing of children in the earlier periods of infancy*, London.
42. Myles, M. F. (1975) *Textbook for midwives with modern concepts of obstetrics and neonatal care*, Edinburgh and London.
43. Nelson, J. (1753) *An essay on the government of children*, London.
44. *Nurses guide, The: or the right method of bringing up young children. By an eminent physician* (1729), London.
45. Paré, A. (1575) *The workes of that famous chirurgion Ambrose Parey*, trans. Johnson, T., London, 1634.
46. Petrus, H. (Pope John 21st) (1550) *The treasuri of helth*, trans. anon., London. Written in 13th century.
47. Phaire, T. (1545) *The boke of chyldren*, London. Reprinted 1955, Edinburgh.
48. Pollock, L. A. (1983) *Forgotten children: parent-child relations from 1500 to 1900*, Cambridge.
49. Reiff, W. H. (1545) *Schwangerer frawen rosengarten*, Frankfurt.
50. Roesslin the Elder, E. (1540) *The byrth of mankynde*, trans. Jonas, R., London, first published 1512.
51. Rosenstein, N. R. von (1776) *The diseases of children and their remedies*, trans. Sparrman, A., London, 1765.
52. Schadewalt, H. von (1957) Historisches zur naturlichen sauglingsernahrung, *Deutsche medizinische wochenschrift 82 (37)*, 1-14.
53. Scultetus, J. (1655) *Armamentarium chirurgicum*, Ulm. Also *The chyrurgeon's storehouse*, trans. E. B., London, 1674.
54. Sharp, J. (1671) *The midwives book or The whole art of midwifery discovered*, London.
55. Short, R. V. (1982) *The biological basis for the contraceptive effects of breastfeeding*, Background document for WHO Workshop on Breast feeding and fertility regulation, Geneva, February 1982.

56. Smith, H. (1774) *Letters to married women on nursing and the management of children*, London, 3rd ed.
57. Sowerby, L. (1652) *The ladies dispensatory containing the natures, vertues, and qualities of all herbs and simples useful in physick*, London.
58. Spence, D. (1784) *A system of midwifery*, Edinburgh.
59. Spock, B. (1973) *Baby and childcare, revised English edition*, London.
60. Thomson, J. (c.1772-85) *An analysis of midwifery with the diseases incident to pregnancy and those which commonly happen in the month to child-bed women*, Library of the Wellcome Institute for the History of Medicine, MS 4779.
61. *Wellcome collection at the Science Museum, London*, Excerpts from the unpublished and uncompleted catalogue.
62. White, C. (1773) *A treatise on the management of pregnant and lying-in women*, London.
63. Wolveridge, J. (1671) *Speculum matricis; or The expert midwives handmaid*, London.
64. Young, T. (late 18th century) *Young's midwifery*, Library of the Wellcome Institute for the History of Medicine, MSS 5106 and 5107.

Wet Nursing

CHAPTER FIVE

Wet Nursing:
Wet Nursing as a Social Institution

"Nothing is so common as the rent breasts for
children to suck." William Cobbet, *Rural Rides*

MUCH has been written on the subject of wet nursing in Europe, particularly in France, where it was a highly organised industry (plate 5.1),
controlled by the state from the 13th century [11,,20,23,42,72,79]. In
contrast, the study of the British wet nurse has suffered virtually total
neglect; the two historians who have investigated aspects of this phenomenon in the late 16th and 17th centuries [30,51] came across evidence
almost by accident whilst examining other, wider issues. Due in part to
this neglect, and because wet nursing was such a widespread social
institution throughout Europe, historians have tended to assume that
wet nursing was more or less the same wherever it occurred, so that in
consequence Britain has been lumped together with the rest of Europe
in any discussion of the qualities, terms of employment and conditions
of the wet nurse, and particularly the abuses of which she was supposedly guilty [17,72].

Here, discussion will concentrate on wet nursing in the British Isles.
The reasons for their employment and the parts of society they served
have been mentioned in preceding chapters; here the aim is to describe
the women employed, their terms of employment, their desirable qualities, and the problems which arose from the practice of wet nursing in
Britain. This chapter is confined to the wet nurse employed by women
from the middle and upper strata of society, whose reluctance or
inability to breastfeed has been discussed in chapter 3. The wet nurses
employed to nurse the infant poor, who were the responsibility of the
English parish, are discussed in chapter 11. (The failure to distinguish
between the privately employed wet nurse and those engaged by the
parish may well have led to the generalised inclusion of British wet
nurses in discussion of European wet nursing.) After 1740, a third type
of wet nurse was employed in England. She worked for the newly-estab-
lished *London Foundling Hospital,* and her selection and employment
was regulated by the Hospital Governors. The foundling hospital

Plate 5.1. *Bureau des nourrices,* Paris, c.1800.

nurses (as far as they are the concern of this book) are principally discussed in chapter 11 although their terms of employment are occasionally used here for the purpose of comparison.

¶ The women who were privately employed as wet nurses in Britain were usually from the lower, but not the poorest, classes of rural society. An investigation of one Buckinghamshire parish between 1578 and 1601 (McLaren 1979 [51]) showed that Chesham women, who took in nurse children from London (approximately 27 miles) and Oxford (approximately 28 miles), were frequently the wives of artisans. The occupations of their husbands included wood-turners (a prominent local trade), weavers, tailors, tilers, a glover and a miller. Several men whose occupations were not stated employed 'servants'. The occupation of one wet nurse before her marriage was described as 'servant'. McLaren's findings are supported in a study of 61 parishes which accepted nurse children from London between 1538 and 1800 [29]. Parishes which accepted (and buried) nurse children tended to line the main highways out of London, especially the routes known as Watling Street, the Great North Road, and the main roads leading to Dover and the south coast (see figure 5.1). Although influenced by local trades and conditions, the occupation or mode of address accorded to the nurse's husband and/or the woman herself, as seen in table 5.1, indicates a family of the artisan or middling sort rather than the very poor. This

153

Figure 5.1. Parishes known to accept nurse children from London, 1538-1800. (◉ = parishes burying large numbers of nurse children.)

Table 5.1. The occupation, or mode of address, of husbands of
wet nurses in 17 parishes around London between the 1560s and
the 1740s (tabulated from information given in Fildes 1984;
with additional material from Newall, personal communication,
and Allison 1963). The parishes are: Compton-cum-Shefford
and Dunstable, Beds; Chesham, Bucks; Cheshunt, Elstree,
Much Hadham, King's Langley, St Peter's and Totteridge,
Herts; Lewisham, Kent; Kensington, Middlesex; Morden,
Putney, Wimbledon and Wandsworth, Surrey; plus Aldenham,
Herts, and Ealing, Middlesex.

Decade	Occupation or mode of address
1560s	A man keeping many servants
1570s	Glover, weaver, sexton of the church
1580s	Carpenter, cobbler, joiner, miller, tailor, tiler, weaver
1590s	Husbandman (8), labourer, locksmith, miller (2), Mr, shovel-maker (2), tailor, turner (3), a man keeping many servants, nurse herself formerly a servant
1600s	Churchwarden, labourer, turner, a man keeping many servants
1610s	Trencher-maker, turner
1620s	Brickmaker, mealman, turner/shovelmaker
1630s	Coachman, labourer (3), tailor
1640s	Brewer, cooper, labourer (2), tailor, waterman
1650s	Blacksmith, bricklayer (2), gardener, labourer, servant, thatcher, waterman, weaver
1660s	Blacksmith, bricklayer, innkeeper, Mr (2), shoemaker, waterman
1670s	Carpenter, cowleech, Dr, farrier, labourer (2), miller (2), Mr (3), musician, tailor (2), waterman
1680s	Shoemaker
1690s	Carpenter, clerk of the parish, churchwarden, farmer, gardener, Mr, saddler, yeoman (2), nurse addressed as Nurse, nurse herself a midwife
1700s	Blacksmith, butcher, clerk, cordwainer, farmer, servant, tailor, nurse addressed as Nurse
1710s	Labourer (4), Mr, parish constable, waterman
1720s	Blacksmith, churchwarden & constable of the parish, Mr (3), parish overseer of the poor (2), physician, weaver, nurse addressed as Mrs
1730s	Day labourer, nurse addressed as Mrs
1740s	Labourer, nurse addressed as Nurse

reinforces McLaren's point that, because of their occupation, the husbands of Chesham wet nurses would have had regular and economic trade links with London and other large towns, and could have acted as intermediaries in the availability and 'placing' of nurse children.

In the period covered by McLaren's study of Chesham Dr John Dee, the mathematician and recondite philosopher of Mortlake in Surrey, whose son Arthur was also an alchemist, employed wet nurses from the neighbouring parishes of Barnes, Barne Elms and Petersham (which took in nurse children from London ten miles away [80], as did nearby Putney and Richmond [30]). In his diary [14] Dee gave most of these women the prefix 'nurse' as if this was their usual occupation. When he had to find temporary replacements to suckle his children in 1581 and 1591 he referred to them as 'Goodwife' rather than 'nurse' and appears to have paid them slightly more. This indicates that the temporary nurses were not normally wet nurses (in the occupational sense) but were either helping him out while another regular wet nurse was found, or were prepared to suckle another child occasionally – at a price. In 1622 the Puritan William Gouge said those commonly chosen to be nurses were 'poore countrie women which have much work to doe and little help' and maintained their home by 'nursing other folks children'. A century later Daniel Defoe (1728) referred to women such as dairymaids, woolcombers and cookmaids being employed by the gentry, or often 'a farmer's wife, or a plowman's wife, for such we are fond of ... because they are what they call wholesome and sound.' However, he also referred to wet nurses being the meanest of the labouring poor. According to Richard Steele in *The Spectator* (1711), women said they wanted to be nurses because of 'having an ill husband, and that she must make a shift to live'; and later medical authors referred to nurses being 'common people' [57] and as being 'generally poor' [46].

The discrepancy between the findings for the late Tudor and Stuart periods and the statements of theological and medical writers may be due to the latter exaggerating the poorness and meanness of wet nurses in order to reinforce their arguments in favour of maternal suckling, especially since, during the same period, John Evelyn's nurse in 1620 was the wife of a tenant farmer [26]; Henry Newcome's child in 1649 was nursed at the home of a tanner [60]; the wet nurse acquired in an emergency for the Prince of Wales in 1688 was the wife of a brickmaker [40]; as was the nurse of Samuel Johnson in 1709 [45]. In a popular novel of 1766 a wet nurse was described as the 'robust wife of a neighbouring farmer' [7].

If the incidence of wet nursing did increase throughout the 17th and the first half of the 18th centuries, as has been suggested [30, 54, 89], parents may have had to resort to employing, as nurses, women from poorer classes than those of artisans and tenant farmers. But there may be some confusion here with parish nurses, who were often themselves receiving parish relief [53], or with the specific problem of finding good wet nurses inside large towns, especially London. Several references were made by medical writers to the latter difficulty [2,56,90] although James McMath of Edinburgh said: 'Nor are good nurses hard to be got, and with all the laudable properties' [52].

In the second half of the 18th century wet nurses could be obtained in an emergency from the lying-in hospitals [32,89]. For example, in 1760 when Lady George had not hired a wet nurse in preparation for the birth of her daughter

> one was to be got from the Lying-in hospital yesterday. They must, you know, in that case take what they can get, and a nurse got in such a hurry and in London, I'm afraid the chance [of the child doing well] is much against [47].

Despite the misgivings of the above writer, Lady Caroline Fox, the lying-in hospitals in this period only delivered respectable poor women who had obtained in advance a written character reference [18], so that again they were not the lowest stratum in society. Samuel Johnson's great friend, Mrs Thrale, breastfed her first child in 1764, but became so thin in the process that a goat had to be purchased so that she could restore her own health by drinking its milk. For her subsequent 11 children (born between 1765 and 1783) her physicians procured wet nurses from the lying-in hospital [43].

A paediatrician (Forsyth 1911) has written that it became fashionable in the 18th century for families to choose wet nurses who had borne illegitimate children, especially first-time mothers. Unfortunately, he does not state where he obtained this information, so it remains an unconfirmed view; although, as he suggests, it could be one explanation for increased concern at this time for the wet nurse's own child. Some physicians (particularly Dr Thomas Denman, and Dr Richard Croft, the royal accoucheur) tried to establish an institution specially for the children of wet nurses. This suggests that industrialisation was accompanied by a change in the wet nursing industry.

The system of sending children to nurses many miles outside large towns was clearly a highly developed and important social institution in the 16th and 17th centuries [29,30,51] and there must have been regular links between cities (especially London) and the surrounding villages, with some degree of organisation either by individuals in the parish [80] or within the town itself.

The wives of men with a reason to travel, and thus the means to establish contacts, were therefore in a good position to be wet nurses, not least because of the technical difficulties which might arise over regular payments. In the 18th century, with increased movement from the countryside into towns; some improvement of roads and means of transport; and the growth of newspapers, which were used as a means of advertising both by and for wet nurses [82,84], these links became less important or were eroded. An institution for the children of wet nurses would have been unnecessary in regard to family circumstances (as we understand them) in the 16th and 17th centuries. Nearly all the wet nurses found in this period were married women, living with their husbands, and had children of their own [12,14,26,27,36,45]. Nurses who were employed within the child's home may have been either widows or unmarried, but this was not always the case [78].

¶ It was rare for nurses to be employed in the child's own home except in the case of royalty and the higher aristocracy. The royal wet nurses were normally themselves members of the aristocracy or higher gentry and were therefore unrepresentative of wet nurses in general [39,61,62]. Some parents employed a nurse in the house for some of their children while putting others out to nurse. It may therefore have depended upon the family commitments of the available wet nurse as much as the wishes of the parents [60,81]. The most usual method was for parents living in towns to send their children out to the surrounding villages [30,80,91], and for families in the country to use women from nearby villages [14,24,27,33,36] (plate 5.2).

A lawyer, Hugh Cholmeley, was living in London when his first son was born in 1624, and he was sent out to a wet nurse in Wateringbury, Kent (approximately 28 miles). When his son, Hugh, was born in 1632 he was living in Yorkshire, and the child was sent out to a local woman [12]. Because of the distances and the state of the roads, it is highly unlikely that town parents visited their children regularly, if at all. It should not be assumed that children nursed within a short distance of their own home were visited any more frequently. The cases of Samuel Johnson and Jane Austen, who were visited by their mothers every day, are well-documented [45,77], but these appear to have been exceptional. The children of John Dee were apparently visited by one of their parents only once every 1–2 months in the late 16th century [14], whilst others went several months or even a year or more without seeing their parents [12,33], although friends or relatives sometimes visited in the interim. Contemporary accounts indicate that a message was sent to parents if the child was sick or dying, although parents often arrived too late [4]. Children who died at nurse were not usually taken home for burial and parents did not always attend their funeral, leaving arrangements for this with a relative or the nurse herself. For example, the wealthy goldsmith, Sir William Herrick, lost two of his children in this way:

My son Thomas (born 3rd May 1602) was nursed at Petersham
. . . lived not long and was buried in the church there [and Eliza-

Plate 5.2. *La belle nourrice*, c.1780.
In this visit to the child's home the wet
nurse is accompanied by her husband.

beth (born 6th May 1603) was] 'nursed at Highgate . . . but lived
above a year, and died there, and was buried at St Pankers church
in the fields by my cozen Toby [88].
From the late 17th century medical writers urged parents, and especially
mothers, to visit their children at nurse (preferably without warning, so
that they could see the true care given to their child [3,13,19,25,37,56,
57]), which confirms that regular parental visits or close supervision
were the exception rather than the norm (plate 5.3). A further confir-
mation lies in the oft-repeated warnings about changelings and children
changed at nurse [6,59,63,71] which would hardly have remained unde-
tected by a mother who visited frequently or regularly.

¶ It is not easy to discover how much wet nurses were paid, since this
was very rarely mentioned in diaries or newspapers, or by authors who
discussed wet nursing. There appears to have been a contract or
arrangement between each woman and the parents of the child as to the
exact amount of money, in addition to any payment in kind, such as
candles, soap, tea or sugar. Where records of payment have been found
they are given as weekly, monthly, quarterly or annual amounts so that
the frequency of payment must also have been arranged between
parents and nurse. Judging from the Dee family in the late 16th century,

Plate 5.3. Painting by George Morland,
1788, *Visit to the child at nurse.*

different nurses either merited or demanded different amounts in the same neighbourhood during the same period. Between 1580 and 1592 these ranged from 4 shillings to 12 shillings a month, plus soap and candles [14]. Sir William Petre of Ingatestone Hall in Essex paid his son's wet nurse 10 pence a week in 1550, whilst her own child was nursed by another woman for 9 pence a week [24]. Between 1602 and 1604 Sir William Herrick paid 2 shillings for one nurse in Surrey, and two shillings and six pence a week for another in Middlesex [88]. Nurses to some wealthy families commanded large salaries in the 17th century; in 1650 the woman who suckled Miss Katherine Paulett, a member of one of the leading families in Somerset, was paid £30 for a year and a half's nursing (seven shillings and nine pence a week) [68], whilst three years earlier a Buckinghamshire wet nurse was paid 4 shillings a week and two loads of wood, for nursing the son of the statesman, Sir Ralph Verney [86].

Payments varied greatly in the 18th century between geographical location and over time. For example, the Somerset physician, Claver Morris, paid 4 shillings a week for his son to be wet nursed near Wells in 1706 [55], while an identical sum was said to be the usual amount to

Table 5.2. Money payments made to wet nurses between 1500
and 1800. For ease of comparison these have all been converted
to weekly amounts, rounded to the nearest penny. (Although not
specified here, additional payment in kind was frequent, sometimes doubling the actual payment [14,32,86].) The increase over
300 years also reflects inflation, particularly in the late 16th
century and during the 18th century.

Date	Amount per week	Location	Source
1550	9d	Essex	Emmison 1964
1550	10d	Essex	"
1552	10d	Christ's Hospital, Counties around London	Pearce 1908
1580	9d	Surrey	Dee 1842
1582	1s/5d	"	"
1583	1s/4d	"	"
1590	1s/4d	"	"
1591	1s/10d	"	"
1591	2s/10d	"	"
1592	2s/7d	"	"
Late 16th C.	8d *to* 1s	Christ's Hospital, Counties around London	Pearce 1908
1602	2s	Surrey	Waters 1887
1603	2s/6d	Middlesex	"
1622	2s/6d	*not known*	Gouge 1622
1644	3s/6d	Essex	Greene 1928–29
1647	4s	Buckinghamshire	Verney 1904
1650	7s/9d	Somerset	Paulett 1650
1706	4s	"	Morris 1934
1711	3s *to* 6s	*not known*	Steele 1711
1737	40s/5d	Royal wet nurse	Caulfield 1931
1742	19s/5d	*not known*	Stone 1977
1748	9s/8d	"	Cadogan 1748
1740s	3s	Foundlings Surrey	Lloyd Hart 1979
1758	2s/6d	Foundlings Wilts	McClure 1981
1757–60	3s/6d	Foundlings Herts	Jones 1978
1768	7s/4d	London	Witkowski 1903
1786	4s	London	Trusler 1786
1795	3s	Foundlings Essex, Herts, Hants, Kent, Surrey	McClure 1981
18th C.	10s/2d *to* 16s/4d	*not known*	Forsyth 1911
18th C.	10s/2d	"	Garrison 1923
Late 18th	10s *to* 12s	"	Forsyth 1911

keep a child at nurse near London in 1786 [84]. Yet Cadogan (1748) quoted £25 a year as the price required for a good wet nurse, in the same decade as Elizabeth Montagu paid £50 a year to the woman who suckled her child [78]. Larger sums could be earned for wet nursing the off-spring of clandestine relationships. Following the birth of a child to the Duchess of Grafton and her lover, Lord Ossery, the accoucheur, Sir William Hunter, deposed in 1768 that he gave the child's nurse a guinea down and a guinea and a half a month [92]. Without stating the source of his information, Forsyth (1911) said that in the 18th century nurses were paid on a sliding scale: from 10 guineas for the first quarter, 16 guineas for two quarters, and 25 guineas for a year, plus a supply of tea and sugar.

The range of wages commanded by wet nurses (table 5.2) is notable for two reasons. First, wet nursing was a comparatively lucrative occupation; dry nurses in the same period were paid only about half as much [14,62,75], and indoor servants even less. Dee paid his dry nurse 11½ pence a week in 1596 [14]; Hertfordshire justices set the wages for indoor maids at 11 to 13 pence a week in 1687 [38]; a London maid cost under 2 shillings a week in 1786, and an indoor servant even less [84]. Secondly, privately-employed wet nurses were paid considerably more than parish 'wet nurses', especially in the 18th century (cf. table 11.4), while wet nurses employed by the Foundling hospital received a sum between the two [44,48]. Therefore, in the pre-industrial period, apart from any physiological advantages in the form of contraception, the occupation of privately-employed wet nurse was clearly a desirable one for women, a fact which appears to have been overlooked by scholars concerned with women's work. For example, in her *Working life of women in the seventeenth century* (1919), Alice Clark hardly mentions wet nursing and certainly does not consider it as an occupation. This may be because of its apparently short-lived nature but, apart from the fact that women nursed many children successively over a period of years, a nurse employed by the wealthier members of society could frequently look forward to continuing concern and care from her employer and/or foster child when her suckling duties were completed. Gifts in later life or in wills were not infrequent [64], and the provision of housing and sometimes a pension were not confined to royal nurses [74]. Although a detailed study of wet nursing as a significant female occupation is beyond the bounds of this book, the subject deserves greater attention than it has yet been accorded.

¶ Wet nursing was a well-established social institution in Britain by the 16th century. Despite a decline in the 18th century, it remained so at least until 1800 and was not confined solely to the children of the aristocracy and higher gentry. The women employed were normally married, living with their husband, had children of their own, and came from the lower, but not poorest, classes of rural society. Their husbands were frequently artisans or tenant farmers who would have had trade links with large towns which facilitated the placing of nurse children. There was possibly an increase in the incidence of wet nursing in the late 17th and early 18th century. Children were normally sent out to be nursed in the nurse's house; it remained relatively rare for wet nurses to be employed within the child's home. Children from cities such as London were sent up to 40 miles away to be nursed in country parishes, whilst families living in the country sent their babies to nearby villages. In neither case were they necessarily visited frequently, or at all, by their parents. The salary of wet nurses varied greatly and was agreed on by employer and nurse for each child; payment was in money and in kind. Privately employed wet nurses were paid considerably more than those employed by the parish and the foundling hospital in the same period, and more than dry nurses and indoor servants, leading to the conclusion that this was a lucrative and desirable occupation for women in pre-industrial Britain.

Country nursing   Town D°

Plate 5.4. George Cruikshank,
Country and town nursing.

REFERENCES

1. Allison, K. J. (1963) An Elizabethan village census *Bulletin of the Institute of Historical Research 36*, 91-103.
2. Armstrong, G. (1771) *An essay on the diseases most fatal to infants*, London, 2nd ed.
3. Barrett, R. (1699) *A companion for midwives, childbearing women and nurses*, London.
4. Baynard, E. (1706) *The history of cold bathing*, London, 2nd ed.
5. Bramston, J. (1845) *The autobiography of Sir John Bramston KB of Skreens in the county of Chelmsford*, London.
6. Brathwaite, R. (1631) *The English gentlewoman*, London.
7. Brooke, H. (1766) *The fool of quality*, London.
8. Cadogan, W. (1748) *An essay upon nursing and the management of children, from their birth to three years of age*, London.
9. Caulfield, E. (1931) *The infant welfare movement in the eighteenth century*, New York.
10. Chamoux, A. (1973) L'allaitement artificiel, *Annales de démographie historique*, Mouton et cie, 410-18.
11. Chamoux, A. (1974) Town and child in eighteenth century Rheims, *Loc. Popul. Stud. 13*, 45-6.
12. Cholmley, H. (1787) *The memoirs of Sir Hugh Cholmley*, London.
13. *Compleat midwife's practice, enlarged, The* (1680), London.
14. Dee, J. (1842) *The private diary of Dr John Dee*, Halliwell, J. O. (ed.), London.
15. D'Ewes, Sir S., *The autobiography and correspondence of Sir Simonds D'Ewes*, Halliwell, J. O. (ed.), London.
16. Defoe, D. (1728-29) *The compleat country gentleman*, Bulbring, K. D. (ed.), London, 1890.
17. De Mause, L. (ed.) (1976) *The history of childhood*, London.
18. Donnison, J. (1977) *Midwives and medical men*, London.
19. Downman, H. (1788) *Infancy or, the management of children*, London, 4th ed.
20. Drake, T. G. H. (1930) Infant feeding in England and France from 1750 to 1800, *Am. J. Dis. Child. 34*, 1049-61.
21. Drake, T. G. H. (1935) Infant welfare laws in France in the 18th century, *Ann. Med. Hist. 7* (N.S.), 49-61.
22. Drake, T. G. H. (1937) Infant nutrition in Paris in the year 1780, *Can. Med. Ass. J. 37*, 595-7.
23. Drake, T. G. H. (1940) The wet nurse in France in the eighteenth century, *Bull. Hist. Med. 8*, 934-48.
24. Emmison, F. G. (1964) *Tudor food and pastimes. Life at Ingateson Hall*, London.
25. *English midwife enlarged, The* (1682), London.
26. Evelyn, J. (1908) *The diary of John Evelyn (1620 to 1706) with an introduction and notes* by Austin Dobson, London.

27. Ferrier, S. (1898) *Memoir and correspondence of Susan Ferrier 1782-1854*, Doyle, J. A. (ed.), London.
28. Fildes, V. A. (1982) *The history of infant feeding 1500-1800*, Unpublished PhD thesis, University of Surrey, Dept of Human Biology and Health.
29. Fildes, V. A. (1984) The English wet nurse and her role in infant care 1538-1800. In press. *Med. Hist.*, 1986.
30. Finlay, R. A. P. (1979) *The population of London 1580-1650*, Unpublished PhD dissertation, University of Cambridge.
31. Flandrin, J-L. (1979) *Families in former times*, trans. Southern, R., Cambridge University Press.
32. Forsyth, D. (1911) The history of infant feeding from Elizabethan times, *Proc. Soc. Med. 4*, 110-41.
33. Freke, E. (1913) *Mrs Elizabeth Freke. Her diary 1671 to 1714*, Carbery, M. (ed.), Cork.
34. Garrison, F. H. (1923) *History of pediatrics*, in Abt. I. A. (ed.), *Pediatrics by various authors*, Philadelphia.
35. Gouge, W. (1622) *Of domestical duties*, London.
36. Greene, J. (1928-29) The diary of John Greene (1635-1657) Symonds, E. M. (ed.), *Eng. Hist. Rev. 43*, 385-94; 598-604; *44*, 106-17.
37. Hamilton, A. (1792) *A treatise on the management of female complaints and of children in early infancy*, Edinburgh.
38. Hardy, W. Le (ed.) (1930) *Hertfordshire county records. Calender to the sessions books, sessions minute books and other sessions records 1658-1700*, vol.VI, Hertford.
39. Hedley, O. (1975) *Queen Charlotte*, London.
40. Hopkirk, M. (1953) *Queen over the water. Mary Beatrice of Modena, queen of James II*, London.
41. Hufton, O. H. (1974) *The poor of eighteenth century France, 1750-1789*, Oxford.
42. Hufton, O. H. (1979) Women, work and the family in eighteenth century France, *Bull. Soc. Soc. Hist. Med. 25*, 7-9.
43. Hyde, M. (1977) *The Thrales of Streatham Park*, Harvard.
44. Jones, A. (1978) *The Foundling Hospital and its arrangements for country nursing 1756-67 illustrated by examples from Hertfordshire*, Unpublished dissertation for Extension Diploma in History, University of London.
45. Lane, M. (1975) *Samuel Johnson and his world*, London.
46. Lara, B. (1791) *An essay on the injurious custom of mothers not suckling their own children; with some directions for chusing a nurse, and weaning of children, etc.*, London.
47. Leinster, E. (1949-57) *Correspondence of Emily, Duchess of Leinster (1731-1814)* Fitzgerald, B. (ed.), Dublin.
48. Lloyd Hart, V. E. (1979) *John Wilkes and the Foundling Hospital at Aylesbury 1759-1768*, Aylesbury.
49. McClure, R. (1981) *Coram's children. The London Foundling Hospital in the eighteenth century*, Yale.

50. MacFarlane, A. (1970) *The family life of Ralph Josselin. A seventeenth century clergyman*, Cambridge.
51. McLaren, D. (1979) Nature's contraceptive. Wet nursing and prolonged lactation: the case of Chesham, Buckinghamshire 1578-1601, *Med. Hist. 23*, 426-41.
52. McMath, J. (1694) *The expert midwife*, Edinburgh.
53. Marshall, D. (1926) *The English poor in the eighteenth century. A study in social and administrative history*, New York. Reprinted 1969.
54. Mettler, C. C. (1947) *History of medicine.* Philadelphia.
55. Morris, C. (1934) *The diary of a west country physician AD 1684-1726*, Hobhouse, E. (ed.), London.
56. Moss, W. (1781) *An essay on the management and nursing of children in the earlier periods of infancy*, London.
57. Nelson, J. (1753) *An essay on the government of children*, London.
58. Newall, F., Personal communication.
59. Newcome, H. (1695) *The compleat mother or, An earnest persuasive to all mothers (especially those of rank and quality) to nurse their own children*, London.
60. Newcome, H. (1852) *The autobiography of Henry Newcome*, Parkinson, R. (ed.), Manchester.
61. Newdigate, A. (1898) *Gossip from a muniment room. Being passages in the lives of Anne and Mary Fitton 1574-1618*, Newdigate-Newdegate, Lady (ed.), London, 2nd ed.
62. Nihell, E. (1760) *A treatise on the art of midwifery*, London.
63. *Nurses guide, The: or the right method of bringing up young children. By an eminent physician* (1729), London.
64. Osborn, M. L. (1979) The rent-breasts: a brief history of wet nursing, *Midwife, Hlth Vis. and Comm. Nurse 15*, 302-6; 347-8.
65. Osborn, M. (1980) Nurses in waiting, *Pulse*, Feb. 16, 43.
66. Osborn, M. (1980) Babes in arms, *Pulse*, March 1, 40.
67. Osborn, M. L. (1979) Hired mothering through the ages in Howells, J. G. (ed.), *Modern perspectives in the psychiatry of infancy*, New York.
68. Paulett papers (1650) SRO. McLaren, D., personal communication.
69. Pearce, E. H. (1908) *Annals of Christ's Hospital*, London.
70. Pollok, L. A. (1983) *Forgotten children; parent-child relations 1500-1900*, Cambridge.
71. Sharp, J. (1671) *The midwives book or The whole art of midwifery discovered*, London.
72. Shorter, E. (1977) *The making of the modern family*, Glasgow.
73. Shorter, E. (1978) *The great transformation of mother-infant relations, eighteenth to twentieth centuries*, Unpublished paper in Library of SSRC Cambridge group for the history of population and social structure, Cambridge.
74. Sibbald, R. (1932) *The memoirs of Sir Robert Sibbald (1641-1722)*, Hett, F. P. (ed.), London.

75. Sloane, Sir H. (1748) *Letter to John Milner, vice president of the Hospital for the maintenance and education of exposed and deserted young children*, 28 October 1748, quoted in full in Brownlow, J. (1847) *Memoranda; or Chronicles of the Foundling Hospital*, London.
76. Steele, R. (1711) On the abuses in nursing children, *The Spectator*, no.246, Wednesday, 12 December.
77. Stone, M. (1976) Middle-class childhood between 1500 and 1800: examples of the lives of artists, musicians, and writers, *J. Am. Acad. Psychoanal. 4*, 545-74.
78. Stone, L. (1977) *The family, sex and marriage in England 1500-1800*, London.
79. Sussman, G. D. (1982) *Selling mothers' milk. The wet-nursing business in France 1715-1914*, Chicago and London.
80. Thiselton-Dyer (1898) *Old English social life as told by the parish registers*, London.
81. Thornton, A. (1875) *The autobiography of Mrs Alice Thornton of East Newton, Co. York*, Jackson, C. (ed.), Durham.
82. *Times index, The* (1790-1800)
83. Trumbach, R. (1978) *The rise of the egalitarian family*, New York.
84. Trusler, Rev. Dr J. (1786) *The London adviser and guide*, London.
85. Underwood, M. (1784) *A treatise on the diseases of children*, London.
86. Verney, F. P. & Verney, M. M. (1904) *Memoirs of the Verney family during the seventeenth century*, London, 2nd ed.
87. Waldman, M. (1972) *The Lady Mary. A biography of Mary Tudor 1516-1558*, London.
88. Waters, R. E. C. (1887) *Parish registers in England. Their history and content*, New edition, London.
89. Wickes, I. G. (1953) A history of infant feeding, *Arch. Dis. Childh. 28*, 151-8; 232-40; 332-40; 416-22; 495-502.
90. Willughby, P. (1630-69) *Observations in midwifery. As also the country midwife's opusculum or vade mecum*. Blenkinsop, H. (ed.), Warwick, 1863.
91. Winchester, B. (1955) *Tudor family portrait*, London.
92. Witkowski, G-J. (1903) *Les seins dans l'histoire*, Paris.

CHAPTER SIX

Wet Nursing:
The Ideal Wet Nurse:
Medical Ideas and Opinions

"Wants a place as a wet-nurse, a healthy young woman, 23 years of age, has not lain-in a fortnight of her first child, has got a good breast of milk, and can be well recommended." *The Times*, 28 October 1793

UNTIL the mid-18th century, medical writers referred repeatedly to wet nurses, and gave copious advice on their choice, qualities, uses and abuses. After this date, wet nursing as a topic in midwifery and paediatric texts was sparingly dealt with, and sometimes completely omitted. This might suggest that wet nurses were declining in popularity, and were less frequently employed than in the two preceding centuries, but it is important that the views of medical authors should not be used as sole evidence for the behaviour of women regarding infant feeding. As will be seen in chapter 12, medical writers did not begin discussing artificial feeding until the late 18th century, whereas evidence from other sources shows that it was practised in Britain well before that date. In the case of infant feeding, evidence from sources such as diaries and memoirs, and from parish records, confirms that though wet nurses were still common in British society in the latter half of the 18th century, and were easily obtainable, the popularity of wet nursing as a means of infant feeding was waning, being gradually superseded by maternal breastfeeding or artificial feeding, or both.

According to the historical sources, to be a good wet nurse a woman ought to have certain qualities of stature, size, colouring and behaviour, in addition to plenty of milk with specific qualities of consistency, colour, taste and smell. These requisites were listed in books on medicine, surgery, midwifery, childcare, early education, household management, and some dietaries, between 1500 and 1800; and the basic qualities remained unchanged from society to society, from the ancient world to the 20th century. They were first fully described by Soranus of Epheseus in the 1st/2nd century AD [79], and remained essentially unchanged in 19th-century textbooks of medicine and paediatrics [31,88]. The desired qualities related to behaviour, health, age, breasts and nipples, complexion and colour of hair, body size, facial appearance, speech, and general appearance. These qualities will now be considered in sequence. The relative importance assigned to particular attributes in different periods is detailed in table 6.1 [27].

Behaviour. The ideal wet nurse should be amiable, cheerful, lively and good-humoured, with strong nerves; not fretful, peevish, quarrelsome, sad or timorous, and free from passions and worries. She should be sober and temperate and not over-indulge in food or any strong drink, in case she should fall asleep and smother the child. It was important that she should have children of her own, preferably two or three, because previous experience with children was important; and some writers also believed that a woman who had several children had a greater flow of breastmilk, and for longer, than a *primipara* [57,60], or that menstruation would recommence sooner after the first than after the subsequent child [92]. She must be chaste and not indulge in light, wanton behaviour or lechery. This factor was connected with worries about menstruation, and will be discussed later. She should have good manners and behaviour, be civil, polite, and courteous, because her manners would be passed on to the child. She should be vigilant and careful, conscientious and watchful at night, and must be wise, discreet, prudent, sensible, and not be foolish or silly, in order to know why the child cried and how to treat him. She must not live in poverty or in a servile condition, her home should be clean and comfortable and she should have the necessities of life, otherwise she could not care properly for the child and her milk would be of poor quality. She should always be laughing, singing and playing or amusing her own child. She should be honest, godly and virtuous, of good reputation and moral character, and preferably a countrywoman because they were healthier and had more milk, although she should not be regularly engaged in heavy, toiling work. Finally, a potential wet nurse must like children.

Health. It was important that this paragon of virtue (plate 6.1) be healthy, strong and active, and free from all diseases, so that she could endure the labour and fatigue of nursing the child, and be able to 'toss and play' with the child when necessary. If she were unhealthy it would affect both her milk and the child, but a healthy nurse would be able to recover a sick child and to correct any bad humours of its mother. In particular, a nurse must not suffer from itch, scab, scurf or running sores; from any deformity, limp or crump shoulder; nor scrofula, consumption or falling-sickness (because the child would not be safe in her arms). Neither the nurse nor her husband should have any venereal infection, because this could be communicated to the child. Her husband, family, parents and lineage in general should be healthy and free of what were believed to be hereditary diseases such as gout, leprosy, falling-sickness, the king's evil, consumption, and bladder stones [27].

169

Plate 6.1. *Nourisse de Monseig.* le Duc de Bourgogne, late
17th C. Presumably an ideal wet nurse since she was
employed by royalty. Note that she is dark, well-built,
and has a good breast of milk.

One surgeon/midwife disagreed with this point; Henry Bracken (1737) thought that the child would not be affected if the nurse's parents suffered from gout, the stone, or falling sickness [9].

Age. Although there was apparently much variation in the recommended age group, most writers wanted a woman neither old nor very young; the idea of what was meant by 'young' or 'middle-aged' seems to vary from period to period. It also depended upon which ancient source was used by the author (Soranus and Aetios favoured women of 20 to 40 years [1,79], while Paul of Aegina and Avicenna preferred them to be 25–35 [4,63]). The age ranges given were always between 18 to 40 years. In general, 17th-century authors preferred nurses of 20 to 40 years, whilst later writers recommended women of 20 to 30 years. Vaguer statements were, that she be young, middle-aged, in the 'flower of her age'; or the same, or nearly the same, age as the mother. At the 'optimum' age the woman was thought to be at her strongest, healthiest and most temperate; her body had finished growing and she would have more milk of a better quality. In contrast, a woman who was too young would have insufficient milk; would be too careless, sleep too soundly at night to hear the child; and would not be prudent or sensible enough to be trusted. If too old she would have less milk of a poor quality because – it was stated – after 35 years the menstrual flow ceases in many [56,62], therefore they must be assumed to have less nutrient for children.

Breasts and nipples. The breasts of a wet nurse should be a good medium size, full, containing plenty of milk. If they were too big it made it difficult for the child to suck, hurt his gums, and might make it develop a crooked nose from being constantly pressed to one side. Breasts that were too small made it difficult for the child to suck, and would hurt its jaws. Some writers, particularly in the 16th and 17th centuries, recommended large broad-breasted women because there was more room for the milk to be made; although this was not essential since (it was said) a small breast could contain as much milk as a large one. Ideally, the breasts should feel firm and fleshy, not hard or contracted, and not too soft, hanging, or 'flaggy'. They were not to be scarred, lumpy or wrinkled, and the blue veins were not to be too large or too small as this indicated too much or too little milk. Other requirements were that they be equal sized, pear shaped, or round. Brouzet (1755) said that they should be positioned so that an equilateral triangle was formed between the nipples, and between each nipple and 'the dimple of the clavicle' (the suprasternal fossa). The wet nurse should have good nipples, sound and of moderate size, not too large or too small, so that the child could suck easily. If they were too large they would hurt the child's gums and make it difficult to swallow the milk. If too small or depressed, they were difficult for the child to grasp. They should be well-perforated with holes, so that milk flowed out in several streams upon gentle pressure. Nipples should not be hard or gristly, not sunk into the breast, and not cracked [27].

Complexion and hair colour. The complexion and colouring referred to in this context is that related to the humoral theory which originated with the Greeks and was an important part of medical theory until the 17th century. Thus the complexion of the nurse was of greater importance to writers in the 16th and 17th centuries than it was in the 18th century. The four complexions were: 1) phlegmatic (cold and moist); 2) melancholic (cold and dry); 3) choleric (hot and dry); 4) sanguine (hot and moist). Children were believed to have varying degrees of hotness and moistness (i.e. sanguine characteristics). Therefore the ideal woman to feed them would have a sanguine complexion, manifested by a brown, ruddy complexion and light brown or chestnut hair. The mention of a 'good complexion' was probably also a reference to the complexion of the woman being suitable or matching that of the child. In addition to agreeing best with the nature of young infants, a sanguine nurse was said to have a better quality and quantity of milk than women of other complexions, whilst the milk of other complexions did not agree with children. Also, sanguine women were usually disease free, and without undesirable qualities. A few authors believed the complexion of the nurse should be as close as possible to that of the mother, so that her milk would 'agree' with the child's [8,19,23,71], or the same as that of the child [25,58]; or – some said – as close as possible to the complexion the parents wished the child to have [5,17]. The colour of the hair was apparently a major indicator of the nurse's complexion, so that extreme colours such as black, white or red hair were frowned upon, and red-haired nurses with freckles were particularly dangerous because they had a bad, rank, strong smell and produced sour, stinking milk; had a bad accent which children would imitate; caused thrush in the child, and generally prejudiced the child's health! This feeling against red-haired nurses originated in the ancient world, probably with Hippocrates, and appears to have been particularly strong in France. It is notable that in the 18th century the requirement of a certain complexion and/or hair colour was confined mainly to continental European writers [7,10,22,46,71]. British medical authors questioned the reasons for the common objection to red-haired women [48, 77,80], and Henry Bracken (1737) stated that it was 'a French idea' that the milk was harmful [9].

Body size and stature. The best nurse was of medium height and weight with a good medium-sized body, because she would perform all functions 'more perfectly', and be able to endure sleepless nights and caring for the child. If she were too thin, this would indicate choler and melancholy, so that she would be a wayward or angry nurse; whilst, if obese, she would be sluggish and sleepy in her movements and probably would have less milk in her breasts. However, if the choice were limited, it was better for a wet nurse to be fat rather than very thin. Some authors believed she should be long-necked, but gave no reason for this preference [27].

Facial appearance. Her skin should be clear without spots and not pock-marked, but most important was the condition of her teeth and mouth. Her teeth should be strong and white with no rotten teeth or bad breath, since it was believed that bad teeth and stinking breath could be communicated to the child's lungs when breathed in, as well as being communicated when the nurse pre-chewed the child's pap. Her eyes were to be clear with no evident soreness, no 'goggle eyes' and, especially, no squint, as the child would become squint-eyed by imitation and by transmission through her milk. Her nose should be straight and not misshapen in any way and with no unpleasant smell since, as with bad breath, the child could breathe it into its lungs. To some writers it was important that she should be comely, or pretty [27].

Speech and education. Concern about the nurse's speech and education was because she was the first person from whom the child learned to speak and would 'pick up' any bad habits. Therefore the nurse must be well educated with a distinct, plain speech and good conversation, and no stammer or speech impediment. Some added that she should not be a foreigner nor use foul language; while the pedagogue, Sir Thomas Elyot (1544) thought that nurses should speak good Latin to the child from an early age! Hugh Downman (1788) was concerned that her voice should not be too harsh. It is interesting that, in the 18th century – see table 6.1 – only two authors thought the nurse's speech of any import, so that the ranking of speech as a quality required fell from 62 per cent in the 17th century to 6 per cent in the 18th.

General appearance. Her general appearance seems to have been of relatively minor importance, only thirteen writers insisting that she should be clean and neat.

¶ The quality of the nurse's milk was discussed in detail by 31 writers from the 16th century to the 18th (table 6.2). What was required was correct consistency, good colour, pleasant sweet taste, and a good smell.

Consistency had been the most important criterion when judging good quality breast milk since the time of the Greeks. The majority of medical writers thought the ideal was a medium consistency, neither thick and sticky nor thin and watery. The reasons for this preference were that thick milk was unnatural and evil, indicating that something was wrong with the blood, and was difficult for the child to digest, so that it became lean and feverish. Milk that was too thin and serous was regarded as 'raw' and passed too quickly through the child without nourishing it sufficiently. In the 18th century, different ideas developed and milk of medium consistency was no longer regarded as ideal. That of a thick consistency was preferred by two writers, but several late 18th-century physicians said that thin milk was best.

Several tests were used to determine the consistency of the woman's milk, the most popular and enduring being the 'nail test' described on p.33. Variations of this test were i) to express milk drops into the hand and see whether they ran off when the hand was turned to one side; ii) to drop milk on to a looking glass and incline it slightly; iii) to drop milk on to a plate and see if it would run off when moved.

A second type of test was to express some breastmilk into a glass, add rennet or myrrh and, after mixing the two together, to allow it to 'set' or coagulate. The ideal milk had equal quantities of the 'cheese' and serous part. If the solid were greater, then the milk should be rejected as too thick. If the serous part predominated then the milk was too thin. This test, described as early as the 4th century AD by Oribasius [63,81], was equally enduring, although less popular with later physicians than the nail test. Nicholas von Rosenstein (1776) and David Spence (1784) gave a variation; expressing milk into a glass, leaving it to stand for several hours, and judging if there were too much cream. Rosenstein also suggested weighing it (the lighter it weighed, the more cream it contained). One test dating at least from the 6th century AD [1] was described only by James McMath (1694). This involved placing a hair into some expressed breastmilk to see if the milk would stick to the hair when withdrawn. If it ran off it was not to be used. The best milk would cling to the entire length of the hair. A final test was to drop breastmilk into the eyes to see whether it would sting. Women's milk had been used for centuries as a treatment for sore eyes, in both adults and children [86] so that this test reflected an additional use of the wet nurse.

Throughout most of our period, the ideal *colour* of human breastmilk was believed to be white. A woman whose milk was streaked, or entirely coloured with black, grey, blue, red, or (particularly) yellow was never to be selected, either because this was a sign of some unnatural defect in the blood, or a tendency towards complexions other than the desirable sanguine; for example, yellow milk was indicative of choler, blue of melancholy, and pale milk of the phlegmatic [29,62]. The aversion to coloured milks was probably related to the fact that infections in the breast, particularly breast abscess, can result in pus of varying shades of yellow, green and black, and blood which may colour the milk. Absence of colours therefore indicated a healthy breast. At the same time as they began to prefer milk of a thinner consistency, physicians in the later 18th century also specified that breastmilk should be bluish or bluish-white in colour rather than white. Since human milk is thinner in consistency and bluer in colour than the milk of other common animals such as cows and goats, this change in preference may reflect the more detailed and scientific observations of breastmilk that were made in the 18th century, particularly after Thomas Young's definitive study *De lacte* [93] was presented in Edinburgh in 1761.

The milk was to have a sweet pleasant *taste*, and milk with any of the following tastes was to be rejected; salty, because it was unwholesome; sour, because it would affect the child's stomach; bitter, because it was unwholesome and 'corrupts the stomach'; and sharp, brackish, hot, or any strong or strange taste. The proper method of tasting was described by La Motte (1746):

> To taste the milk rightly, you must cleanse your mouth well with water, get some of the milk upon a plate, and take several mouthfuls, a little of it not being sufficient to make a right judgment [46].

Again, avoidance of milk which had unpleasant or unusual tastes was equivalent to avoiding women with infections of any degree of severity, particularly of breasts.

'Bad' or infected breastmilk would be detected by an unpleasant strong *odour*, so only women with pleasant-smelling milk were to be selected. A good smell was a sign of a good temperament, for sharp or sour smells indicated a hot and choleric, or cold and melancholy, nature.

The *quantity* of breastmilk was more difficult to judge, and most authors contented themselves with saying that the breasts should feel full, although some suggested that the nurse should have milk left in her breasts after she had suckled, and the child should have passed urine. Burton (1751) suggested examining the child's clouts because strong urine would stain them and indicate insufficient and/or bad milk, whereas plenty of light-coloured urine from the child would show that he was receiving plenty of milk. Too much milk was not thought to be a good thing, because if there were more than the infant required, it could cause problems by stagnating in the breasts and might weaken the nurse; but it was better to have too much than too little, since in the latter case the child would suffer, and the excess could always be given to another child.

¶ The ideal wet nurse would have had two or three children of her own, but there were also specifications about the sex, health and age, especially of her most recent child. The relative importance of these requirements varied at different periods during the 16th and the 18th centuries. The child had to be born at full term, and not have miscarried, as this would be proof of bad blood [56,60]; not born prematurely, since this would be evidence of some default in the nurse's body [29,62]; or have been still-born which, unless due to an accident during delivery, would indicate some fault in the nurse's constitution [30]. Dionis (1719) agreed that a woman whose child was dead should not be allowed to suckle other children, because it would be bad for the child; but if she wanted to be a wet nurse, she had to use a sucking-tube, or have her breasts sucked by a puppy for some days, after which she was presumed fit for employment. Whatever the sex of the child to be nursed, the preferred sex of the nurse's child was male, because the mother of a boy was believed to have better milk, and to make a healthier, stronger nurse. There was also a general belief in the 16th and 17th centuries that the sex of the wet nurse's child would affect her milk, and thus her nurseling. If she had a female child, this would make a male nurseling more effeminate, and vice versa. Moreover, some thought that the nurse's child should ideally be the same sex as the child she was to nurse, so that her milk would be correct for the child [18,43,73]. After the 1730s, neither the term of gestation nor the sex of the nurse's child was regarded as sufficiently important to mention. Henry Bracken (1737) thought the preference for a boy to be 'a vulgar error'; the main concern in the later 18th century was that the nurse's own child be thriving and healthy, and thus a good advertisement for its mother's milk and the quality of her care.

The age of the nurse's own child and therefore the 'age' of her milk was a matter of major interest. The preferred distance of the wet nurse from her own last delivery is of special interest, since it offers confirmatory evidence for the new ideas about neonatal feeding in the 18th century. Until the 1740s, medical writers thought that wet nurses should not be employed until their own child was between one to two months old, and preferably at least two, so that she had recovered from the birth, her lochia had stopped flowing, and her milk was purified; but the majority of 18th-century writers emphasised either that her milk/child should be the same age as the child to be nursed, or should be recently delivered, because the newer – and thinner and more purgative – her milk, the better it was for the child. The maximum age of the nurse's milk was specified, although there were differing opinions about the matter. For example, Mauriceau (1673) thought that the nurse's child/milk should not be older than five to six months; other 17th-century writers suggested that seven to eight or even ten months was best; but Bracken (1737) and the anonymous *Nurse's Guide* of 1729, said that the nurse's child/milk should not be older than three to four months. The reasons given by 18th-century writers for not employing a woman who had been lactating for several months were four-fold. It was believed that breastmilk became thicker and more indigestible the longer a woman lactated, until it stopped altogether [48,59,60,71]; and that breastmilk decreased in quantity the longer she suckled, so that a woman who had been lactating for several months would be unlikely to have sufficient to nurse another child for the required length of time, and the child would therefore have to be weaned early, or a second

/ ... .ss.ons   neeve

CERTIFICAT DE RENVOI POUR LES NOURRICES.

NOUS fouſſignée, Recommandareſſe du Bureau Général rue Quincampoix,
commiſe par M. le Lieutenant General de Police, en vertu du pouvoir à lui donné
par l'Edit du Roi du mois de Juillet 1719, enregiſtré au Parlement le cinq Août ſuivant,
& par celui du 24 Juillet 1769, enregiſtré au Parlement le 28 deſdits mois & an,
atteſtons que *gens .. . veſt –*   Femme de *pierre douiel*
             Nourrice de la Paroiſſe de *ſubley*
Dioèèſe de *vreuse*   – Election de *vreuse*   —
nous a remis entre les mains le Certificat du *Sieur*
Curé de ladite Paroiſſe, portant que le lait de la Nourrice *est de 18 mois*   —
lequel Certificat a été enregiſtré en notre Bureau, conformément à la Déclaration de
Sa Majeſté du 29 Janvier 1715; comme auſſi il nous a été déclaré que l'Enfant
un garçon   né   le *26 avril 1772*   qui a été
cejourd'hui confié à ladite Nourrice, a été baptiſé ſous le nom de *ad rien pierre*
         filſ de *mr. pierre Rene Gromet Cordonnier et ... verge*
& de *barbe elisabeth grimprella* / ſa femme, ſes pere & mere, *...*
demeurant au *...* prise la *proffes*
Paroiſſne *d piarre De montyia* ... en foi de quoi nous lui avons
donné la préſente atteſtation, pour être remiſe par ladite Nourrice à ſon Curé, immédiate-
ment à ſon arrivée chez elle, ſous les peines portées par la Déclaration ſuſdatée. A Paris, ce
24 avril   — mil ſept cent ſoixante- *douze*

venue le ſouse   *Colombe ...*

Nous, THOMAS MOURICAULT, Conſeiller du Roi, Commiſſaire au Châtelet de Paris,
prépoſé par Monſieur le Lieutenant Général de Police, pour l'exécution des Edits & Dé-
clarations de Sa Majeſté concernant les Recommandareſſes; certifions la ſignature ci-deſ-
ſus véritable, en foi de quoi nous avons ſigné; A Paris, les jour & an ſuſdits.

Mouricault

Plate 6.2. French wet nurse's certificate,
1772, stating that, having deposited with
the Nursing Bureau in Paris a form from
her parish priest to the effect that she had
been lactating for 18 months, she had
been entrusted as wet nurse to Adrien
Pierre, son of a shoemaker. The child's
death, at 10 months, is recorded on the
reverse.

nurse might have to be employed later [7,14,22,29,56,59]; the quality of
breastmilk was said to decline after about a year [7,14,59]; and 'old milk'
did not agree with the newborn [10,48] (plate 6.2).

This factor was not always, nor even frequently, observed. James
McMath (1694) said that matching the age of the nurse's milk to the age
of the nursed child 'is mostly neglected, so that one and the same nurse
is sometimes continued still for the next child also'. Hurlock (1742)
described a wet nurse who maintained her milk supply by secretly
suckling a child at night, in order to offer herself as wet nurse to the next
child of her mistress. William Cadogan (1748) said 'It is a common

thing for a woman to suckle two or three children successively with the same milk'. And in the same year, Hans Sloane wrote:

> I think the difference of the age of a wett nurse's milk is not to be so much regarded, having in my family had one wett nurse suckle four children successively, who have been and now are healthy and well.

McLaren's investigation into wet nursing in the parish of Chesham in the late 16th century [52] shows that successive suckling was obviously practised by several women; although sometimes, as in the case of Alice Thornton and her brother in the early 17th century [85], the nurse might have another child between the two sucklings. Clearly if a family found a good, careful and reliable wet nurse, they would continue to employ her for later children, regardless of the age of her milk. Jane Austen was the seventh of the eight children in her family to be suckled by the same wet nurse [82]. Physicians knew that it was rare to find a newly-delivered wet nurse. Brouzet (1755) said that 'in most common cases [she] has suckled her own infant eight or nine months, and always too long for her milk to be perfect'. Sussman (1982) found that, in 323 wet nurses from the Pays de Thelle who took in nurselings between July and September 1732, the median age of their own child was 9 to 10 months [83]. Bracken (1737) said 'Many children do well when nursed by those who have given suck a year'. The nurse of Hugh Cholmley's first child in 1624 had milk that was two years old [15], and in 1709 Samuel Johnson's wet nurse weaned her own child at 18 months in order to suckle the newborn Samuel [47,49]. Although William Hunter recorded that Prince William's wet nurse in 1765 'still kept her own child' [40], doctors did not believe that most women would have sufficient milk to nurse their own child in addition to one, two or more others, or to give them sufficient attention, and this was one indication for supplementing the breast milk with other food. William Moss (1781) insisted:

> Care must be taken the nurse does not give suck to her own child after this time; and that [to prevent it] he be entirely weaned, or put to nurse with another person; as very few women can have milk sufficient for two children, or attend them in other respects as they ought to do.

This belief is fairly widespread in pre-industrial societies, despite physiological evidence that one woman can suckle several children adequately [42]. For example, in the case of twins, the mother is often expected to suckle only one, the second being given to a wet nurse [66]. In mid-17th-century Scotland, when the sister of Andrew Hay, Gentleman, gave birth to twins, she breastfed only one child, the other being wet nursed [67].

Women with certain characteristics or suffering from some medical

178

or physiological conditions were not to be considered for employment as wet nurses. Specifically, there were prejudices against pregnancy, menstruation, red hair, freckles, hereditary diseases, vaginal discharge, addiction to alcohol or tobacco; and – a negative one – not having had smallpox or measles. The views of physicians and midwives are given in table 6.3; and are now analysed in more detail.

Throughout the period, but noticeably less so in the 18th century, physicians and midwives advised parents not to employ *pregnant* women and, if a nurse became pregnant while suckling, advised that the child be weaned (if old enough) or that the nurse be changed immediately. Brouzet (1755) thought it was preferable for the child to suck an animal than a pregnant woman. McMath (1694) was more moderate, provided the nurse became pregnant by her own husband, but he still believed that it was best if she stopped breastfeeding once she knew she was pregnant. The main reason given for this advice was that a pregnant woman had less milk, and of a poorer quality, and that this adversely affected or was the direct cause of illness in the child. Glisson (1651) believed that suckling by a pregnant woman was one cause of congenital rickets. Only the more enlightened Henry Bracken (1737) could not

> see the reason why people should fancy that if a child suck a nurse who happens to be with child herself, such a child will be distemper'd and out of order a long time afterwards.

He claimed that the nursed child suffered only in proportion to the growth of the foetus:

> not by reason of any noxious particles and hurtful principles in the milk itself, but because 'tis thin in substance, and small in quantity.

In fact, some women did carry on suckling until the birth of the next child, with no evidence that the child being breastfed suffered in any way [57,85], although Henry Cholmley (b.1690) said he suffered for many years as a result of his wet nurse not revealing her pregnancy [15]. Today, breastfeeding is usually not advised during a subsequent pregnancy, mainly because of the nutritional demands which are made on the mother. The foetus always has first claim on the mother's bodily resources, so that a woman, particularly if she is in poor health or undernourished, would probably have less breastmilk for her child as her pregnancy advanced; but her milk, as Bracken stated, would not contain any harmful substance. The first person to suffer in such a triad would be the woman; thus the medical advice of the time unintentionally protected the wet nurse.

Employment of a wet nurse who had recommenced *menstruation* was absolutely forbidden by nine writers, with scarcely any change in emphasis between the 17th and 18th centuries. If a wet nurse started to menstruate, parents were advised to change her for another [17,25,53,80] or not to allow her to breastfeed on those days when she was menstruat-

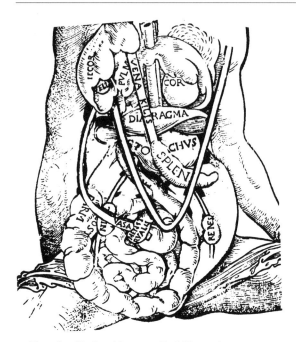

Plate 6.3. Early 16th C. medical illustration
showing the *vasa menstrualis*, which was
believed to carry the menses from the
uterus to the breast during pregnancy
and lactation.

ing [48,71]. If the woman had been nursing the child for several months,
then, if the child were in good health and she still had sufficient milk, it
was all right for her to continue breastfeeding [10,21]; and the French
midwife La Motte (1746) said that children had been observed to do
well even though the nurse menstruated. There were two principal
reasons for this worry. First, it 'spoiled' and reduced the quantity of the
breastmilk [13,17,32,53,56] so that children were less inclined to suck,
received less nourishment, and tended to develop gripes. The woman's
body was said to be 'altered' for two or three days before menstruation,
which also affected the child [21,39]. Secondly, the woman was more
likely to become pregnant, with its accompanying problems of poor milk
and bad effect on the child [17,46]. The reasoning behind the prejudice
was the belief that all the blood which normally was lost during menstruation was removed to the breasts during pregnancy and lactation, and
converted to milk for feeding the child. Both medieval and renaissance
anatomy texts show a lacteal duct leading from the uterus to the breasts

(plate 6.3). Leonardo da Vinci (1492) reasoned that milk must be made in the uterus because 'it is well-known that lactating women do not menstruate' [75]. Thus menstruation 'never happens to good nurses . . . [in whom] all the blood which is retained is dedicated to the nourishment of the infant' [17]. Given this belief, menstruation naturally meant that some milk was lost to the infant. Dionis (1719) made the interesting observation that early onset of menstruation in wet nurses who were employed in the child's home was often due to their having a better diet than they could normally afford at home.

Nurses not infrequently tried to hide the fact that their menses had returned, in order to retain their employment for longer, and royal wet nurses were apparently examined regularly to ensure that they were not menstruating [61].

Some interesting letters were written by Lord Conway in 1659, about an unspecified problem with a wet nurse which eventually resulted in her being changed. Given the concern demonstrated above, it seems quite possible – since it occurred at roughly monthly intervals – that the 'danger' was a menstruating nurse. On 17 May 1659, when his child was three and a half months old, Lord Conway wrote to his brother:

> The child is very well, and hath passed over the same danger which the nurse had before without any disturbances; but, however, my wife is informed that the suck of such a woman is dangerous and brings with it many diseases, and therefore I believe she will wean much sooner than she intended.

One month later, on 14 June, he wrote:

> We . . . are staying here ourselves somewhat longer than we thought of, to provide another nurse. This having injured the child three times, we cannot think it permissible to be borne any longer, and so all my wife's friends advise her [16].

This also illustrates that problems with wet nurses were discussed, and therefore information about them was disseminated, among women by word of mouth. It is relevant to note here that the so-called 'taboo' on intercourse for nurses living in the child's home was because of the belief that intercourse *caused* menstruation, and thus spoiled the nurse's milk and harmed the child [9,25,43,60,62]. Although the electrolyte content of human milk has been shown to change at ovulation [75], no evidence has been found to show that the quantity of breastmilk declines during menstruation. However, breastfeeding mothers today sometimes observe that their children are less inclined to suck, or may become fretful at this time. Such behaviour by infants may have contributed to beliefs in the past that it was harmful for a child to feed at the breast of a menstruating wet nurse. In addition, as modern research shows, if the menses had returned, then this would provide evidence that the woman had not been suckling a child regularly; since regular repeated stimulation of the nipple at short intervals throughout the 24 hours suppresses ovulation and thus delays menstruation [37,74].

Prejudice against red-haired, freckle-faced wet nurses, and those suffering from diseases, has been described above; in addition, women suffering from 'the whites', which was a general name for any type of vaginal discharge, should be avoided, since this was regarded as a sign of a bad constitution or of bad health in the nurse [13,21,22,53,56]. 'The Pox', or venereal infection, if detectable, was also a forbidden condition. This is discussed in chapters 7 and 11. Advice to reject any nurse who had not had smallpox and measles was a protective measure, because she might contract these illnesses and thus communicate them to the baby [30,39]. Although the immunological effects of breastmilk were not understood, the nurse who had had these diseases may have given her nurseling some temporary passive immunity against them [20].

¶ Discussion of wet nursing decreased, and in some instances was not included, in paediatric and midwifery texts after the mid-18th century. Together with evidence from diaries and memoirs this indicates that wet nursing as a means of feeding the wealthier infants in British societies was declining in popularity, and by the end of the 18th century was gradually being superseded by maternal breastfeeding and/or artificial feeding. The main qualities looked for in a good wet nurse were satisfactory behavioural qualities and way of life; good health; an age between 18–40 years, but preferably 20–30 years; with good sized healthy breasts and nipples. Of lesser importance were a medium stature and size; good facial appearance, clear speech and good conversation; and neatness and cleanliness. In the 16th and 17th centuries a sanguine complexion was an important requisite since this matched the child's hot and moist temperament. The nurse's milk was required to be white and of medium consistency until the later 18th century when thin, bluish milk began to be preferred, probably as a result of greater scientific knowledge about milk. Several tests were used to determine consistency, the most popular being the 'nail test'. Women with milk that was 'coloured', with a bad smell or taste (all indicative of infection) were never to be employed as wet nurses. The nurse's most recent child ideally was male, born at full term, and at least 2 months old, because she would have the best milk; after 1730 these requirements were never mentioned, the main criteria being that her child was thriving and either recently delivered or the same age as the child to be nursed. The latter was infrequently observed since parents tended to keep a good wet nurse to feed several of their children successively. Conditions which precluded employment as a wet nurse included pregnancy, venereal infection, women who had recommenced menstruation, and those having red hair and freckles (although this was of more concern to French writers). All were said to have bad milk which would adversely affect the child.

REFERENCES

1. Aetios of Amida (6th century A D) Translated and annotated in Ricci, J. V. (1950), *The gynaecology and obstetrics of the VIth century AD*, Philadelphia.
2. Aitken, J. (1786) *Principles of Midwifery*, London, 3rd ed.
3. Armstrong, G. (1771) *An essay on the diseases most fatal to infants*, London, 2nd ed.
4. Avicenna (10th century A D) in Shah, M. H. (1966) *The general principles of Avicenna's Canon of medicine*, Karachi.
5. Barrett, R. (1699) *A companion for midwives, childbearing women and nurses*, London.
6. Batty, B. (1581) *The christian man's closet*, trans. Louth, W., London.
7. Baudelocque, J-L. (1790) *A system of midwifery*, trans. Heath, J., 3 vols, London.
8. Baynard, E. (1706) *The history of cold bathing: both ancient and modern*, London, 2nd ed.
9. Bracken, H. (1737) *The midwife's companion or, A treatise of midwifery*, London.
10. Brouzet, N. (1755) *An essay on the medicinal education of children; and the treatment of their diseases*, trans. anon., London.
11. Buchan, W. (1769) *Domestic medicine; or The family physician*, Edinburgh.
12. Burton, R. (1621) *The anatomy of melancholy*, Oxford.
13. Burton, J. (1751) *An essay towards a complete new system of midwifery*, London.
14. Cadogan, W. (1748) *An essay upon nursing and the management of children from their birth to three years of age*, London.
15. Cholmley, H. (1787) *The memoirs of Sir Hugh Cholmley*, London.
16. Conway, A. (1930) *Conway letters. The correspondence of Anne, Viscountess Conway, Henry More, and their friends, 1642-1684*, Nicolson, M. (ed.), London.
17. *Compleat midwife's practice, The* (1680), London.
18. Culpeper, N. (1675) *A directory for midwives*, London.
19. Culpeper, N. (1676) *A directory for midwives*, London.
20. Davis, B. D. *et al.* (1973) *Microbiology including immunology and molecular genetics*, Hagerstown, Maryland.
21. Denman, T. & Osborne, W. (1777-78) *Notes abstracted from several courses of lectures in midwifery given by Dr Denman and Dr Osborne.* Taken down by Fran. Kingston. Library of the Wellcome Institute for the History of Medicine, M S 2099.

22. Dionis, P. (1719) *A general treatise of midwifery*, trans. anon., London.
23. Downman, H. (1788) *Infancy or, The management of children*, London, 4th ed.
24. Ebrahim, G. J. (1978) *Breastfeeding the biological option*, London.
25. *English midwife enlarged, The* (1682), London.
26. Elyot, Sir T. (1523) *The book named the governour*, London. Reprinted 1544.
27. Fildes, V. A. (1982) *The history of infant feeding 1500-1800*, Unpublished PhD thesis, University of Surrey, Dept of Human Biology and Health.
28. Foster, E. (1781) *The principles and practice of midwifery*, London.
29. Guillemeau, J. (1612) *Childbirth or The happy deliverie of women. . . . To which is added a treatise of the diseases of infants and young children: with the cure of them*, trans. anon., London.
30. Hamilton, A. (1792) *A treatise on the management of female complaints and of children in early infancy*, Edinburgh.
31. Hamilton, A. (1821) *A treatise on the management of female complaints*, 8th ed., revised and enlarged, Hamilton, J. (ed.), Edinburgh.
32. Hoffmann, F. (c.1740) *A system of the practice of medicine*, vol.2, trans. Lewis, W., London, 1783.
33. Houston, M. *et al.* (1980) The contraceptive effect of lactation, *Nursing Times 10*, July 1980.
34. Houston, M. J. *et al.* (1981) Do breastfeeding mothers get the support they need? *Health Bulletin*, 166-72.
35. Houston, M. J. (1981) Breastfeeding: success or failure, *J. Adv. Nursing 6*, 447-54.
36. Howie, P. *et al.* (1980) How long should a breastfeed last? *Early Human Development 5*, 71-7.
37. Howie, P. *et al.* (1981) Effect of supplementary food on suckling patterns and ovarian activity during lactation, *Brit. Med. J. 283*, 1-7.
38. Hurlock, J. (1742) *A practical treatise on dentition*, London.
39. Hunter, W. (1775) *Lectures anatomical and chirurgical by William Hunter*, Library of the Institute for the History of Medicine, MS 2966. Also dated 1783.
40. Hunter, W. (1908) An obstetric diary of William Hunter, Stark, N. (ed.), *Glasg. Med. J. 70*, 167-77; 241-56; 338-56.
41. James, R. (1746) *The modern practice of physic. As improv'd by . . . H. Boerhaave, and F. Hoffmann . . . Being a translation of the aphorisms of the former with the commentaries of Dr van Swieten*, 2 vols, London.
42. Jelliffe, D. B. & Jelliffe, E. F. P. (1976) *Human milk in the modern world. Psychosocial, nutritional and economic significance*, Oxford.

43. Jones, J. (1579) *The arte and science of preserving bodie and soule in healthe, wisedome, and catholick religion: physically, philosophically and divinely devised*, London.

44. *Ladies dispensatory or, Every woman her own physician* (1740), London.

45. *Ladies physical directory: 7th edition with large additions, alterations, and amendments* (1739), London.

46. La Motte, G., M. de (1746) *A general treatise of midwifery*, trans. Tomkins, T., London.

47. Lane, M. (1975) *Samuel Johnson and his world*, London.

48. Lara, B. (1791) *An essay on the injurious custom of mothers not suckling their own children with some directions for chusing a nurse, and weaning of children, etc.*, London.

49. McHenry, L. C. & MacKeith, R. (1966) Samuel Johnson's childhood illnesses and the King's Evil, *Med. Hist. 10*, 386-99.

50. Mackenzie, C. (1770) *Lectures in midwifery*, Library of the Wellcome Institute for the History of Medicine, MS 3392.

51. Mackenzie, C. (1774) *Mr Mackenzey's Lectures on Midwifery*, ? by D.B., London, Library of the Royal College of Obstetricians and Gynaecologists, unnumbered MS.

52. McLaren, D. (1979) Nature's contraceptive. Wet nursing and prolonged lactation: the case of Chesham, Buckinghamshire 1578-1601, *Med. Hist. 23*, 426-41.

53. McMath, J. (1694) *The expert midwife*, Edinburgh.

54. Mantell, T. (1787) *Short directions for the management of infants*, London.

55. Maubrey, J. (1730) *The female physician*, London.

56. Mauriceau, F. (1673) *The accomplisht midwife*, trans. Chamberlen, H., London.

57. Moss, W. (1781) *An essay on the management and nursing of children in the earlier periods of infancy*, London.

58. Muffet (Moffet), T. (1584) *Health's improvement: or rules comprising the nature, method, and manner of preparing all sorts of food used in this nation. Corrected and enlarged by Christopher Bennet*, London, 1655.

59. Nelson, J. (1753) *An essay on the government of children*, London.

60. *Nurses guide: or the right method of bringing up young children. By an eminent physician* (1729), London.

61. Osborn, M. (1980) Babes in arms, *Pulse*, 1 March, 40.

62. Paré, A. (1575) *The workes of that famous chirurgion Ambrose Parey*, trans. Johnston, T., London, 1634.

63. Paulus Aeginata (7th century AD), *The seven books of Paulus Aeginata. With a commentary*, trans. Adams, F., London, 1844-47, vol.1.

64. Pechey (Peachey), J. (1697) *A general treatise of the diseases of infants and children*, London.

65. Phaire, T. (1545) *The boke of chyldren*, London, reprinted 1955, Edinburgh.

66. Ploss, H. H., Bartels, M. & Bartels, P. (1935) *Woman,* Dingwall, E. J. (ed.), London.
67. Pollock, L. A. (1983) *Forgotten children. Parent-child relations 1500-1900,* Cambridge.
68. *Practice of midwifery by a pupil of the late Dr W. Hunter* (1783), London.
69. Quillet, C. (1655) *Callipaedia or, An art how to have handsome children,* trans. anon., London, 1710.
70. Roesslin the Elder, E. (1540) *The byrth of mankinde,* trans. Jonas, R., London, first published 1512.
71. Rosenstein, N. R. von (1776) *The diseases of children and their remedies,* trans. Sparrman, A., London, first published 1765.
72. Sainte Marthe, S. de (1584) *Paedotrophiae: or The art of bringing up children,* trans. anon., London, 1710.
73. Sharp, J. (1671) *The midwives book or The whole art of midwifery discovered,* London.
74. Short, R. V. (1982) *The biological basis for the contraceptive effects of breastfeeding.* Background document for WHO Workshop on breastfeeding and fertility regulation, Geneva, February 1982.
75. Short, R. V., Personal communication.
76. Sloane, H. (1748) *Letter to John Milner, vice-president of the Hospital for the maintenance and education of exposed and deserted young children,* 28 October 1748. Quoted in full in Brownlow, J. (1847) *Memoranda; or Chronicles of the Foundling Hospital,* London.
77. Smellie, W. (1752) *A treatise on the theory and practice of midwifery,* London, vols 1 and 3.
78. Smith, H. (1774) *Letters to married women on nursing and the management of children,* London, 3rd ed.
79. *Soranus' Gynecology* (1956) Temkin, O. *et al.* (eds), Baltimore.
80. Spence, D. (1784) *A system of midwifery,* Edinburgh.
81. Still, G. F. (1931) *The history of paediatrics,* London.
82. Stone, M. (1976) Middle-class childhood between 1500 and 1800: examples of the lives of artists, musicians, and writers, *J. Am. Acad. psychoanal. 4,* 545-74.
83. Sussman, G. D. (1982) *Selling mothers' milk. The wet-nursing business in France 1715-1914,* Chicago and London.
84. Tansillo, L. (1566) *The nurse. A poem,* trans. Roscoe, M., Liverpool and London, 1800, 2nd ed.
85. Thornton, A. (1875) *The autobiography of Mrs Alice Thornton of East Newton, Co. York,* Jackson, C. (ed.), Durham.
86. Tomsak, R. L. (1978) A brief history of the use of human milk in ocular therapeutics, *Bull. Cleveland Med. Libr. 24,* 12-21.
87. Underwood, M. (1784) *A treatise on the diseases of children,* London.
88. Underwood, M. (1846) *Dr Underwood's treatise on the diseases of children with directions for the management of infants,* 10th ed. with additions by Davies, H., London.

89. Vives, L. (1540) *Instructions for a christian woman,* trans. Byrd, R., London.

90. Wolveridge, J. (1671) *Speculum matricis; or The expert midwives handmaid,* London.

91. Wurtz, F. (1563) *The children's book. Bound with An experimental treatise of surgerie in four parts,* trans. and corrected by Lennerton-Fox, A., London, 1656.

92. Young, T. (late 18th century) *Young's midwifery,* Library of the Wellcome Institute, MSS 5106 and 5107.

93. Young, T. (1761) *De lacte,* cited in Still, G. F. (1931) *The history of paediatrics,* London.

CHAPTER SEVEN

Wet Nursing:
The Wet Nurse as the Cause of
Infantile Diseases and Death

> "Ill, will the bus'ness by that nurse be done,
> Who for another's child neglects her own."
> Ste Marthe, *Paedotrophiae*, c.1584

THE FOLLOWING extracts are representative of medical and religious opinions about wet nurses in the period 1500 to 1800.

I pray you what else is the cause, that many children nursed in the country are so subject to frets, sharpness of urine and the stone; but that their nurses for the most part eat rye bread strong of the leaven and hard cheese, and drink nothing but muddy and new ale.

Thomas Muffet, *Health's improvement*, 1584

In the villages about London, the passing bell hardly ever ceases ringing out the death of infants which have died for the neglect, nastiness, barbarity, or intemperance of their nurses.

Walter Harris, *De morbis acutis infantum*, 1689

'tis a common saying amongst [Welsh] nurses that no child has the rickets unless he has a dirty slut for his nurse.

Sir John Floyer, *The history of cold bathing*, 1706

Hence ye doting train
Of midwives and of nurses ignorant!
Old beldames grey, in error positive,
And still in prejudice, whose fatal care
Oft death attends, or a life worse than death.

Hugh Downman, *Infancy*, 1788

It seems almost obligatory for modern writers to see the wet nurse as the 'ogress' of the pre-industrial period [30,112,113], and some of the cases reported, concerning rural peasant women in some parts of France and Germany seem to support this view. England, too, has contemporary horror stories about wet nurses, some of which are discussed later in this chapter, but these are normally quoted out of the context of medical and popular ideas of the period. Any surrogate mother (witness the traditional wicked stepmother) provides an ideal scapegoat when there is blame to be assigned; but, to understand why contemporary writers blamed wet nurses for everything from bladder stone to bewitchment, some explanation of their role in relation to infant feeding is necessary.

Before 1800, the wet nurse (or the breastfeeding mother) did not just provide nourishment for the baby; she was believed to transmit to the child, along with her ideas, beliefs, intelligence, intellect, diet, and speech, all her other physical, mental and emotional qualities. Effectively, she was seen to be reproducing herself; the child *was* the nurse; an extero-gestate foetus. What affected the nurse affected the child equally. To give food to the nurse was to give that food to the child. Administering physick to the nurse was administering physick to the child. Therefore, when anything (good or bad) happened to the child, no one other than the nurse *could* be responsible. As is the way of the world, ancient and modern, the bad and sensational effects were reported more frequently than the good and commonplace (especially when arguments were needed to support pleas for maternal breastfeeding).

There were four ways in which it was believed that the wet nurse transmitted herself and her good and bad qualities to the child: i) through her milk; ii) through her diet (and then through her milk); iii) by direct contact, such as by touching her skin and inhaling her breath; iv) by imitation.

¶ The idea that the nurse's qualities were transmitted to the infant, through her milk, is very ancient and widespread, and was the reason for the long list of ideal qualities the nurse should possess. It was specifically mentioned by 31 medical and religious authors between 1500 and the mid-18th century, after which time more-enlightened writers began to question its validity. In support of this theory, examples were given of humans who were suckled by animals and grew up with the characteristics of the latter [19,58,93,108]; of the Emperor Tiberius, who was suckled by an alcoholic wet nurse and grew up to become a noted drunkard [11,67,91,92]; and of the Emperor Caligula, remarkable for his cruelty, who had been suckled by a bloodthirsty wet nurse who sometimes daubed her nipples with blood [11,82,91,92]. The natural reaction to this belief was that stated in the *English Midwife Enlarged* of 1682:

> If, then the qualities of the milk pass into those that suck them . . . surely, then, we ought to take no less care of the nurse than of her child; as in her diet, exercise, physick, etc., since whatsoever conduceth to the benefit of the nurse tends to the good and welfare of the infant.

As late as 1728, Daniel Defoe stated categorically that nurture, in the form of breast milk, had more influence on the shaping of the child and his future than all the generating powers of the parents [29]. It was not until Bracken's *Midwife's Companion* of 1737 that this idea was questioned in the English medical and religious literature:

> I cannot acquiesce in this opinion of the Ancients, seeing ... it will not bear scrutiny, neither does experience in the least confirm it ... for a physician to argue that there is so much to be attributed to the milk, as most of them pretend, is much folly and mere quackery.

He believed the child acquired characteristics of the nurse by imitation and habit, and supported his argument by giving the example of unhealthy nurses rearing healthy children:

> It is so far from the milk's having an ill-effect upon children ... that I have observed several times those children who suck'd distemper'd nurses, very healthy, more particularly in the ague; nothing is more common in Lancashire (among the poorer sort) than for them to let their children suck even for years, altho' this troublesome distemper keep its periodical returns, and notwithstanding the nurse looks like a ghost, the child shall appear as a cherub.

He was firmly of the opinion that nature (in the form of the child's parents) was of far greater influence than nurture (in the form of the nurse's milk) [12]. In the later 18th century, transmission of the nurse's qualities through her milk was barely mentioned, yet evidence that the underlying idea was still accepted by physicians and midwives is shown by their concern about the nurse's state of mind.

¶ In the last decade of the 18th century, medical authors were still warning that passions (i.e. worries, shock, grief, anger, etc.) of the nurse would badly affect her milk and cause diseases in the child, particularly epilepsy and convulsions [10,16,59,88,125]. A variety of other diseases were believed to be caused directly by the wet nurse's milk, because the latter happened to be faulty in some way, either in quantity or, more frequently, in consistency or quality (plate 7.1).

They included gastro-intestinal disorders, infant diseases, thrush, ulcers on the head, nightmares, failure to thrive, fevers, and convulsions (table 7.1). Eating unsuitable foods such as onions, garlic and fish was believed to affect the nurse's milk adversely, and the adverse effects thus transmitted to the child. Apart from gastro-enteric upsets, conditions mentioned were infections such as smallpox and measles; bladder stone, rickets and infantile diseases in general.

Physicians believed that if a nurse suffered from *any* disease, whether or not she was aware of it, this would be contracted by the child through close daily contact with her. Thus, one risk of putting the child out to a wet nurse was exposure to diseases which might not be apparent at the time the nurse was hired. In the 16th and 17th centuries speculation on this issue in the literature was restricted to transmission of the pox, but in the 18th century rickets became the principal condition (table 7.2).

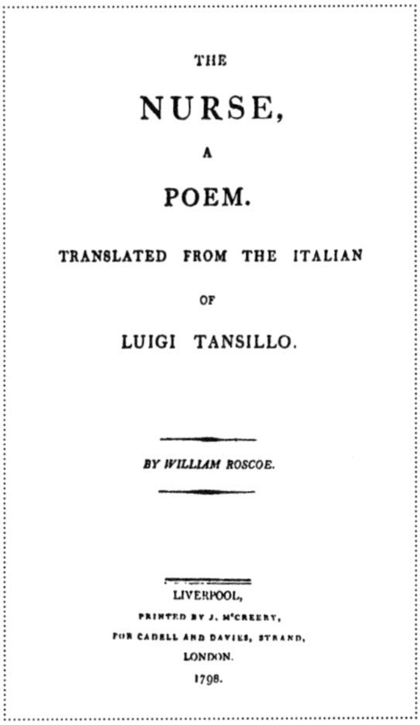

THE

NURSE,

A

POEM.

TRANSLATED FROM THE ITALIAN

OF

LUIGI TANSILLO.

BY WILLIAM ROSCOE.

LIVERPOOL,

PRINTED BY J. M'CREERY,

FOR CADELL AND DAVIES, STRAND,

LONDON.

1798.

Plate 7.1. English translation, 1798, of Tansillo's *La Balia.* Many of the complaints about wet nurses in 16th C. Italy were still valid in late 18th C. England.

When the stated ways in which a wet nurse was believed to cause disease in her nurse child are combined, some indication can be gained of the relative incidence of infantile conditions in children at nurse (conditions caused by imitation were essentially confined to obvious physical deformities in the nurse such as squints, lameness, hump backs, etc. These were normally avoided by such women not being employed as wet nurses). Over the three centuries under review, gastro-intestinal conditions received most prominence, with venereal disease next in ranking (but with a much lower incidence of comment in the 18th century), followed by rickets (table 7.3).

¶ Given such theories about their aetiology, the treatment of diseases in infants-at-nurse was, logically: i) to treat the nurse by administering a purge, physick or other internal remedy; ii) to correct the nurse's diet; iii) to adjust the nurse's milk (usually by correcting her diet) (table 7.4). If these remedies were not effective, then the final resort was to change the nurse or to wean the child from the breast. The reasons for changing the nurse once she had begun suckling were always connected either with some illness in the baby which had not responded to treatment of the nurse (particularly gastro-intestinal upsets, leanness, and failure to thrive), or some obvious illness or defect in the nurse or her milk (especially an infection or fever, menstruation, or pregnancy).

Changing a wet nurse was not easy, particularly when the child had been fed by one woman for several months. Early weaning was also known to be dangerous for the child, but neither was thought to be so life-threatening as allowing an infant to be suckled by a diseased or otherwise undesirable wet nurse.

The methods which might have to be employed when changing to another nurse were described in the anonymous *Nurses' guide* of 1729:

> The child will easily take [to her breasts] if he be not above seven months old: but if he old enough to discern the change, he will not easily admit her. Wherefore 'tis convenient that the new nurse should give him suck for a while in some dark place, 'till he become acquainted with her. But if notwithstanding all her secrecy, and the darkness of the place, he still refuses her milk, she may put a little powder'd sugar on her nipple, and put it to his mouth so often, 'till at last he takes it; or else she may spirt some of her milk upon his mouth, 'till the sweetness of it at last prevails upon him to taste, and swallow it [92].

Sometimes, if the nurse were satisfactory and had only a temporary disability, she was not dismissed, but had to cease breastfeeding for a short period. For example, in 1727, when the son of the 3rd Earl of Cardigan was about 6 months old, his nurse, who was employed in the house, fell:

> and broke both the bones of her own arm about three inches above her right hand. I sent immediately for Dr. Foyer who came and set it before eight. We do not suffer Master Robert to suck for these five or six days, for these things are always attended with a fever.

Robert was cared for by two women of the household and presumably dry-nursed, because three days later the Earl's steward wrote:

> The nurse is entirely free from pain and has not been at all feverish – so that in a day or two the child may suck without any manner of danger. Master Robert has borne the loss of the pap with a great deal of patience.

And, within a day or so, 'Master Robert sucks again for the nurse is very well' [126]. These events illustrate very clearly that a feverish wet nurse was not allowed to suckle (and probably the recognisably-more-dangerous method of handfeeding was preferred) in order to protect the child from harm.

The Pox. A disease which was particularly feared in wet nurses, and was a reason for immediately changing her, was the pox (syphilis), and references to infants contracting this from their wet nurses and passing

Plate 7.2. Frontispiece of the Leyden
edition of Francis Glisson's *Treatise
of the rickets,* 1671.

it to their families occur in the medical literature, as well as the problems
of an affected child infecting a formerly-healthy wet nurse. One reason
for some wealthy families preferring to hand-rear their infants rather
than employ a wet nurse was precisely their fear of poxy women [127,
130]. (The problem of feeding syphilitic infants is discussed in chapter
11.)

Rickets. Another disease for which the wet nurse was an easy scapegoat was rickets, especially if an apparently healthy baby, sent out to
nurse soon after birth, developed rickets in the period during which it
lived with her. This was quite likely, since rickets was observed to occur
after the age of about 9 months [53,62,99] and would become very
evident about the time the child began to walk. Francis Glisson (1651)
(plate 7.2), and most other physicians after 1650, observed that rickets
was more common among the rich than the poor, and there may well
have been some pre-disposing factor involved in wealthy women who
had up to 20 or 30 pregnancies, and a diet which contained little calcium
or vitamin D [2,33,129]. Glisson certainly believed that some infants had
congenital rickets, and recent research among Asian women living in

British cities shows that this could have been an accurate statement [5,37].

There are problems in extrapolating modern information about diseases back to previous centuries, since the nature and severity of some conditions changes over time. This is probably more relevant in relation to diseases caused by bacteria, rickettsia and viruses, in which the organism itself may change [28], than in diseases primarily caused by a dietary deficiency; but even in the latter case the body's ability to adapt to such deficiencies may change [2]. A factor of possibly greater relevance in the 17th and 18th centuries is that the mention of rickets may have increased, as physicians became more aware of it. It was therefore discussed, and possibly diagnosed, more frequently after Glisson's definitive *De rachitide* was published in 1650. It was, however, known to ordinary men and women; from 1637 it appeared regularly in the *Bills of Mortality* as a cause of death [55], and was designated as such, not by qualified medical practitioners, but by the unqualified searchers employed to ascertain causes of death. In 1656, Alice Thornton of Yorkshire blamed her daughter's rickets on the bad milk of two wet nurses [123].

It is possible that the use of a wet nurse who had been lactating for several years, and whose diet was inadequate, could have contributed towards rickets in the early months of life, since the amount of vitamin D present in breast milk would to some extent depend upon the woman's overall dietary state [37,109]. In addition, a bad wet nurse may have concealed the fact that she had little or no breast milk, and fed the child on non-milk substitutes. But, given the climate of opinion of the time, it is more likely that in many cases the wet nurse was simply the obvious scapegoat.

An example of such contemporary thinking is Samuel Johnson, born in Lichfield in 1709. His family, and Johnson himself, believed that he had contracted his general poor health, particularly his poor eyesight and the King's Evil, from his wet nurse, Mrs Marklew. The latter was well known to the family, her husband having been employed by Johnson's father, and she had breastfed her own child uneventfully for 18 months, so presumably the Johnsons knew the state of health of the woman and her child before employing her. Mrs Johnson visited her son every day whilst he was at Mrs Marklew's, so that she was under constant, concerned supervision. Although he was wet nursed for only two and a half months before being weaned and brought home, Mrs Marklew was firmly believed to be the cause of all Johnson's infantile (as well as his lifelong) ailments [73,77]. In a modern investigation of Johnson's childhood illnesses [77] Mrs Marklew has been fairly conclusively exonerated from blame: yet so ingrained was the prejudice about the milk of a wet nurse that her use as a convenient scapegoat was

Plate 7.3. Memorial brass to Anne Consant, who died at nurse aged one month. As an only child, long awaited, she would have been especially precious, yet her parents (her father a parson) followed the custom and put her out to nurse.

'normal' in the 18th century, and was not really questioned for the next two hundred and fifty years.

That there were bad wet nurses as well as good, just as there are good and bad mothers, is not in question, and the contemporary complaints that more children died at nurse than in their own homes were possibly accurate (although, again, this may have been overstated to support arguments for maternal suckling) (plate 7.3).

¶ *Overlaying.* A major cause of death in infants at nurse was said to be 'overlaying'; where an apparently healthy baby was discovered to be dead in the morning. This was normally said to be due to nurses (who often slept in the same bed as their children, for convenience of suckling and warmth, as well as for lack of a cradle) falling asleep on top of their charges and suffocating them. The *Bills of Mortality* recorded at least 100 deaths a year from this cause [52,55] and between 1701 and 1776 almost 4000 infants were described as overlaid [86]. This was said to occur more rarely when mothers nursed their own children [91,131].

Overlaying was mentioned by relatively few medical writers, although it was referred to in contemporary novels, such as Richardson's *Pamela* (1740), and by parents. For example, John Evelyn recorded on 26 March 1664:

> It pleased God to take away my son Richard, now a month old, yet without any sickness or danger perceivably, being to all appearances a most likely child; we suspected much the nurse had overlain him; to our extreme sorrow, being now reduced to one [42].

When a child died in such unexplained circumstances, away from home, it was natural to assume that it had been smothered, although modern research has shown that it is virtually impossible to overlay or suffocate a young baby unless the mother/nurse is drunk, drugged, or otherwise sleeping in an abnormally heavy manner. Some of these infant deaths may indeed have been due to nurses consuming alcohol and falling heavily asleep on top of the child, but accounts of such deaths sound remarkably like the 'sudden infant death syndrome' or 'cot deaths' of today. A similar association has been made for the sudden deaths by overlaying of North American slave children in the 19th century [106], and it is probable that a sizeable proportion of deaths attributed to overlaying at nurse in 17th- and 18th-century Britain were what are today called 'cot deaths'. A proportion of these sudden deaths in young infants may have been due to infections of rapid onset, affecting the respiratory apparatus, which are frequently undetectable even a few hours before they cause death [109].

Overlaying was not restricted to Britain, but was a problem referred to wherever significant numbers of wet nurses were employed. The following description of a device used by Florentine wet nurses in an attempt to avoid the high number of deaths from 'overlaying at nurse', was published in *The Gentleman's Magazine* of January 1746 (and similar descriptions were published in other European journals and newspapers in the mid-18th century, thus demonstrating the size of the problem). However, no evidence has been found to show that the *Arcutio* was ever used or was available in Britain in the 18th century (plate 7.4).

> An extract of a letter from Oliver St. John, Esq: F.R.S. dated from Florence, Nov. 30, 1731. *Philosophical Transact.* No. 412.
>
> When I consider how many are charged overlaid in the bills of mortality, I wonder that the *Arcutios*, universally used here, are not used in England. I send you here the design of one drawn in perspective.
>
> (a) The place where the child lies
> (b) The headboard
> (c) The hollows for the nurse's breasts
> (d) A bed of wood to lean on when she suckles the child
> (e) A small iron arch to support the said bar

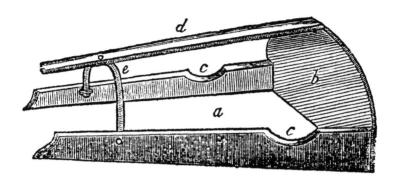

Plate 7.4. The Florentine *arcutio*
(see text for details).

The length about 3 feet 2 inches, and breadth about 1 foot 1 inch
at the head. Every nurse in Florence is obliged to lay the child in
it, under pain of excommunication. The *Arcutio*, with the child
in it, may be safely laid entirely under the bed cloaths in the
winter, without the danger of smothering.

¶ *Infanticide.* It has been said, in some cases very positively [30,112,121,
128], that wet nursing was a form of infanticide, and that nurses could
be employed to overlay their charges. However, this is probably an
example of the type of wet nurse discussed in this chapter being con-
fused with 'wet nurses' employed by the parish, or with those occasionally employed by families wishing to get rid of unwanted infants [133].
Apart from the fact that upper-class families were anxious for heirs
(and used wet nurses as a means of obtaining more children rather than
for disposing of those they already had), a wet nurse employed by a
family of the stature of John Evelyn, for example, could scarcely have
had much motivation for overlaying his child. She was well paid, and
likely to remain so whilst in his employ. Unless she had taken a violent
dislike to the infant or to his family, it would be much less trouble to
remain in the employ of one family than to seek re-employment, and
have to establish breastfeeding with a new infant, whose family she
might find much less amenable. The argument that the wet nurse was
more interested in the money than the child, and could readily find a
new position, does not necessarily mean that it was in the interests of
most privately employed wet nurses to dispose of their charges after
only a few weeks of nursing. Some of the wet-nursing horror stories

produced as evidence for this view [30,121] in fact arose because the
nurse tried either to deal with or to conceal a disease or injury, in order
to maintain herself in employment [13,50,63]. The fact that a nurse tried
to treat her charge is surely evidence of care, however misplaced. It is as
easy to find examples of children with good wet nurses who were highly
regarded. Indeed some parents complained of the children's greater
love for their nurses than for themselves [15,44,107,114].

The mortality of infants, and especially nurse children, was said to be
particularly great in the parishes around London and other large towns
[9,51,54,81]. In 1622 the Puritan William Gouge said:

> It hath been observed in many countrie villages, that the most part
> that from time to time die there, are nurse children.

In 1689 Walter Harris provided this oft-quoted example:

> An observation was made not long ago by a worthy divine, rector of
> a parish 12 miles from London, who with great grief in mind told
> me seriously, that his parish which was not small either in its
> bounds or number of inhabitants, and was situated in a very
> wholesome air, was, when he first came to it, filled with sucking
> infants, and yet in the space of one year, that he had buried them
> all except two, and one of his own, whom being weakly he had
> happily committed to my care from his very birth, and that the
> same number of small infants being soon twice supplied, according
> to the usual custom of hireling nurses from the very great and
> almost inexhaustible city, he had committed them all to their
> parent earth in the very same year. [He went on to warn of the]
> dangers of mercenary nurses, who are greedy only of the profuse
> rewards bestowed on them at the christening, and slight the small
> weekly income that follows; and so being weary of the present
> employment, perform it negligently, while they are looking out for
> a new prey.

This example is one of those used to prove that nurses cared little for
their charges and wished them an early demise in order to look for
re-employment. But in fact this was presented by Harris as part of an
argument in favour of *maternal* suckling [60].

In 1787, the surgeon Thomas Mantell said that the same proportion
of infants in the population died, whether in town or country; but more
infants died in the parishes near large towns than in the parishes within
such towns because of the 'numbers being continually sent to be nursed
in the adjacent country'. There is abundant evidence from parishes
taking in nurse children from London and Oxford [47,79], that a proportion of burials, ranging from 2.3 to 8.6% of all burials, 1580 to 1650,
were nurse children [47]. In some wet nursing parishes, such as Elstree
in Hertfordshire, up to 67% of burials between 1585 and 1742 were
nurse children [46].

Since it is not known what proportion of the parish population consisted of nurse children, it is impossible to know whether more wet-nursed infants died than infants nursed by their own mothers. Even Harris' famous example indeed implied that nearly all infants died, not just those who were wet nursed. There is no way of knowing if the year specified was a typical year in the life of the parish, or was being quoted by the Rector because it was an abnormal event for so many to die. An epidemic of whooping cough or scarlet fever, for example, would not discriminate between infants nursed by their mothers or by hired nurses.

¶ If more infants *did* die at nurse than when breastfed by their own mother, then reasons other than carelessness, ignorance, self-interest, and murder, proposed by contemporaries [8,9,24,39,60,80] and by modern authors, such as Shorter and De Mause, are worthy of examination; these fall under the general headings of physiological and immunological factors, or psychological factors relating to morbidity and mortality of infants at nurse.

Lack of colostrum. The circumstances of wet nursing meant that the newborn infant was unlikely to be put to the breast of the mother (although some mothers did attempt to breastfeed for a few days) and thus would normally receive none of the protective and nutritional benefits of colostrum which were discussed in chapter 2. Since it was unusual for a wet nurse to be employed within a few days of her own delivery, the infant received no colostrum from the wet nurse. If it was breastfed from the first day with breast milk which was several months, or even several years, old (i.e. if the woman had not been delivered of a child for several years), then the protective value of this breast milk in terms of the antibodies it contained would be much less than the milk of a woman delivered within a few weeks of the child's birth [65]. If the child were fed with physick and / or food for a short period before being breastfed by a wet nurse then not only would it not receive the benefits of colostrum but it would also be exposed to the danger of infection from unsuitable and probably unclean foods and utensils.

Entero-mammary circulation. Recent research [34,37,65,111] has shown that the Peyer's patches (lymphatic tissue) in the intestine have B cells of pathogens which the mother has ingested during her life; when a pathogen is ingested by the mother, then these cells break off from this lymphoid tissue and 'home-in' on the mammary glands where, within 24 hours, the relevant immunoglobulin A is secreted in the breast milk. Observation of other mammals shows that if breastfed animals defaecate, and especially if they have diarrhoea, the mother ingests this and secretes the relevant immunoglobulin in her milk. Similarly, mothers in some societies (for example, Australian aborigines) have little regard for hygiene and are often soiled with faeces when they breastfeed. Their infants, however, are unaffected as they are protected by the immunoglobulin A secreted in their mother's milk [111]. Twentieth-century western societies have become so used to extreme cleanliness that this is unacceptable behaviour, but the protective function of ingesting faecal material should not be disregarded when discussing less-developed societies.

When a wet nurse first fed a child from a different environment, she would secrete in her breast milk only the immunoglobulins to those pathogens to which *she* had been exposed. The child would therefore receive no protection, in the form of IgA in the breastmilk, against pathogens to which it, but not its nurse, had been exposed. If the wet nurse lived with and breastfed the child in its own home, then she was likely to be exposed to the same organisms as the child, and would eventually secrete relevant IgA in her milk; but if the child were brought to her home from many miles away, then she would not be exposed to those antigens in the child's environment and therefore would not secrete the appropriate immunoglobulins in her milk. The child would remain unprotected against any infections it might meet between its birth in one environment, during any stay in its own home until sent out to nurse, and to any encountered during the journey from its home to that of the wet nurse.

Transplacental protection. During pregnancy, many antibodies and antitoxins of both major and minor diseases, to which the mother has been exposed, pass into the foetus via the placenta. Thus every child is born with a temporary passive immunity, acquired from the mother, to those infections which have at some time affected its mother. This applies not only to major diseases but also to the potentially pathogenic organisms that commonly occur in the mother's immediate environment or within her body (particularly her intestine) and to which she has developed some measure of immunity [28]. If the child remains with its mother in the same environment, these will offer it a similar degree of immunity to these organisms for a period of several weeks. If the child were wet nursed at home (i.e. in the same general environment) it would be protected against organisms in that environment, but not necessarily against those within or upon the body of the wet nurse, who might have travelled from a considerable distance and have been exposed to a different set of micro-organisms. Thus, organisms to which she was regularly exposed and had become immune would be potentially pathogenic to her nurse-child.

If the child were sent miles away into the country (plate 7.5), to a completely different community, with a different eco-system, where different (or at least different strains) of organisms existed, then the temporary immunity acquired from the mother during uterine life would not protect it against organisms to which the mother had never

Plate 7.5. Greuze, *Le départ de la nourrice,*
c.1780. The mother gives a last kiss to
the baby she may never see again, as the
wet nurse takes it off to the country.

been exposed. There was also the factor of a journey of perhaps up to
40 miles, which in winter was quite likely to take more than one day,
thus exposing a recently-born infant to a whole range of infections en
route, in addition to possible extremes of external temperature. There
are also sufficient contemporary references to the wet nurse's home
being less clean and warm than the child's home [17,20] to raise the
possibility of increased danger of infection from such things as bedding,
clothing and kitchen-ware.

Therefore, the newborn baby sent out to be wet nursed was unprotected from diseases to which the wet nurse, but not the mother, had
been, or currently was, exposed; did not receive the protective, nutritional and immunological substances in colostrum, either from mother
or wet nurse; had to face the mechanical dangers of temperature and of
a microbial environment different from that for which its mother's body

prepared it *in utero*; and did not ingest protective antibodies from the nurse's milk against the pathogens to which it was exposed in the first days of life. Since a major function of colostrum is to protect the infant against diseases of the gastro-intestinal system [34,65], the absence of this, together with any effective protection against gut bacteria in the nurse and her family and environment, give one obvious explanation for gastro-intestinal infections being the major condition mentioned in wet nursed children. When the nurse-child returned to its parents, 6 months to 3 years later, it would have developed its own resistance to organisms and diseases of the community within which it lived, but not necessarily to those in the home environment to which it returned. The danger at this age would be less than to the neonate, but could partly explain the high incidence of illness (especially gastro-intestinal upsets) associated with weaning.

Psychological factors in relation to mortality are much more difficult to assess. Some attempt has been made, particularly by Trumbach (1978), to show that the mortality of aristocratic infants was reduced when, in the later 18th century, the incidence of wet nursing decreased in favour of maternal suckling and/or dry nursing. Psychological problems must have been associated with a close emotional and physical attachment to a wet nurse, initiated and sustained by breast feeding [65,69], which was broken, sometimes for ever, when the child was weaned and returned home. There are examples where nurses were loved by their nurse-children and were cared for into their old age (for example, Robert Sibbald (1641–1722)) [114]; most regarded them as their true mother, disliking or disregarding their biological mother. In the 1740s a Scottish child was so strong-willed that, despite the ridicule of his siblings, he refused to return to live with his parents, but insisted upon living in the poor cottage of his nurse until he was well into his teens [44]. A midwife, Jane Sharp (1671), advocated that children should be encouraged to repay the nurture of their wet nurse by caring for her in later life.

This situation of two homes and two mothers must have caused conflict in the child, but this was more likely to affect it at or after weaning than as a small infant. The evidence produced by modern authors, that infants would have been less attached to wet nurses than to their mothers because the former did not care for, or about, them [112, 113,124] is not borne out by writings of the period. Some 17th-century authors claimed that nurses did not want to part with their nurse children and would go to great lengths in order to keep them, this being one reason for not disclosing that their milk supply had declined or otherwise become unsuitable [8,24,39]. A similar wish by nurses to keep their nurse children has been noted in foundling hospital nurses in the 18th century [66,76] and in those who nursed young infants from Christ's Hospital in the 16th century [95].

Contemporary medical complaints that nurses fed their infants with unsuitable foods and gave them medicines and spirits are not necessarily indicative either of poor care or poor emotional relations betwen nurse and child. Nurses might well have thought that they were doing their best for the child. Is there any material difference between modern mothers who give gripe water, aspirin, and phenergan to their fretful sleepless infants and the nurses and mothers who administered the 17th- and 18th-century equivalents – gin, brandy, and poppy-juice? In addition, it is not infrequently observed by health professionals today that children who are considered to have been abused or uncared for, nevertheless may have a close loving relationship with their mother or foster mother. The evidence for poor psychological attachment between wet nurses and their charges is therefore tenuous, and not sufficiently strong to account alone for any fall in infant mortality, once wet nursing went out of fashion (as Trumbach (1978) has suggested [124]). A more plausible explanation is the physiological benefits to the child of being fed by his own mother, or at least remaining in an environment against which he had some immunological protection; and avoidance of the physical contrasts between the homes of his two 'mothers', which were said to differ so much in social status, diet, temperature, clothing, activity and cleanliness.

¶ The nurse child was regarded as an extero-gestate foetus to whom the nurse's milk carried all her physical and mental qualities, her emotions, her food and drink, and her diseases; the nurse was therefore seen as the cause of most infantile diseases and any treatment was given to her rather than to the child, since it would pass to the child through the milk. The child was also believed to contract diseases by direct contact with the nurse. The diseases most frequently transmitted by, or contracted from, wet nurses, were said to be gastro-intestinal infections, syphilis, rickets, thrush and convulsions. Illness or defect in the nurse or her milk was the most common reason for changing a wet nurse. This was done for the safety of the child even though it was recognised to be difficult to replace a woman who had fed a child for several months.

In some cases of illness or death of a child at nurse, the wet nurse was probably used as a scapegoat. Although there must have been bad wet nurses, most would have had little motivation to get rid of the nurse-children who were their livelihood. The readiness of historians to accept the horror stories about wet nurses in Britain has resulted in a biased, and probably false, picture of the majority of these women. Many deaths attributed to overlaying at nurse may have been due to what today are called cot deaths; a proportion may have been caused by respiratory infections of rapid onset. It is unlikely that the upper and upper-middle strata of British society in the pre-industrial era sent their children out to nurse as a means of infanticide, since this was incompatible with their desire to conceive more heirs. If mortality of infants at nurse was higher in Britain than that of infants fed by their own mother then this was probably related to lack of the protective benefits of colostrum, and the inappropriateness of both the IgA secreted in the nurse's milk and the temporary passive immunity, acquired from the mother, when a very young baby was taken to a new and distant environment and fed by a woman who had been exposed to different infections from the mother.

Psychological factors associated with wet nursing included close nurse-child relationships which were broken when the child had to be returned to his own home, although some children loved and cared for their wet nurses for the rest of their lives. There is no evidence that the majority of wet nursed infants were maltreated or formed poor psychological attachments to their nurses; therefore the fall in infant mortality at the same time as wet nurses were going out of fashion, is unlikely to have been due to improved emotional attachment alone, but is more probably related to immunological and environmental factors.

REFERENCES

1. Allen, John (1733) *Synopsis medicinae: or A summary view of the whole practice of physick*, London, 2 vols, vol.1.

2. Appleby, A. B. (1979) Diet in sixteenth-century England: sources, problems, possibilities in Webster, C. (ed.), *Health, medicine, and mortality in the sixteenth century*, Cambridge.

3. Arbuthnot, J. (1732) *Practical rules of diet in the various constitutions and diseases of human bodies*, London.

4. Armstrong, G. (1771) *An essay on the diseases most fatal to infants*, London, 2nd ed.

5. *Artificial feeds for the young infant* (1980) DHSS report on health and social subjects, no.18, London.

6. Astruc, J. (1746) *A general and complete treatise on all the diseases incident to children from their birth to the age of fifteen*, trans. anon., London.

7. Shah, M. H. (ed.) (1966) *The general principles of Avicenna's Canon of Medicine*, Karachi.

8. Barrett, R. (1699) *A companion for midwives, childbearing women and nurses*, London.

9. Baynard, E. (1706) *The history of cold bathing: both ancient and modern, Part II*, London, 2nd ed.

10. Baudelocque, J.-L. (1790) *A system of midwifery*, trans. Heath, J., 3 vols, London.

11. Boaistuau, P. (1566) *The theatre or Rule of the world*, trans. Alday, J., London.

12. Bracken, H. (1737) *The midwife's companion or, A treatise of midwifery*, London.
13. Bramston, J. (1845) *The autobiography of Sir John Bramstone, K.B. of Skreens in the County of Chelmsford*, London.
14. Brathwaite, R. (1631) *The English gentlewoman*, London.
15. Brooke, H. (1766) *The fool of quality or, The history of Henry, Earl of Moreland*, London.
16. Brouzet, N. (1755) *An essay on the medicinal education of children; and the treatment of their diseases*, trans. anon., London.
17. Buchan, W. (1769) *Domestic medicine; or The family physician*, Edinburgh.
18. Bullein, W. (1595) *The governement of health*, London.
19. Burton, R. (1621) *The anatomy of melancholy*, Oxford.
20. Cadogan, W. (1748) *An essay upon nursing and the management of children, from their birth to three years of age*, London.
21. Cheyne, G. (1724) *An essay of health and long life*, Bath.
22. Clark, W. (1751) *The province of midwives in the practice of their art*, Bath and London.
23. Clinton, E. (1622) *The Countesse of Lincolne's nurserie*, Oxford.
24. *Compleat midwife's practice, enlarged, The* (1680), London.
25. Cooke, J. (1768) *Some necessary directions in the care of infants*, in *A collection of pieces relative to inoculation for the smallpox*, Dublin.
26. Culpeper, N. (1675) *A directory for midwives*, London.
27. Culpeper, N. (1676) *A directory for midwives or, A guide for women, in their conception, bearing and suckling their children*, London.
28. Davis, B. D. *et al*. (1973) *Microbiology including immunology and molecular genetics*, Hagerstown, Maryland.
29. Defoe, D. (1728-29) *The compleat English gentleman*, Bulbring, K. D. (ed.), London, 1890.
30. De Mause, L. (ed.) (1976) *The history of childhood*, London.
31. Dionis, P. (1719) *A general treatise of midwifery*, trans. anon., London.
32. Downman, H. (1788) *Infancy or, The management of children*, London, 4th ed.
33. Drummond, J. C. & Wilbraham, A. (1957) *The Englishman's food. A history of five centuries of British diet*, London.
34. Ebrahim, G. J. (1978) *Breastfeeding the biological option*, London.
35. Ebrahim, G. J. (1978) *Mother and child health in developing countries*, London.
36. Ebrahim, G. J. (1979) *Care of the newborn in developing countries*, London.
37. Ebrahim, G. J. (1983) *Nutrition in mother and child health*, London.
38. Elyot, Sir T. (1523) *The boke named the governour*, London.
39. *English midwife enlarged, The* (1682), London.

40. Erasmus, D. (1526) The whole familiar colloquies of Erasmus of Rotterdam, trans. Bailey, N., Glasgow, 1877.
41. Ettmueller, M. (1699) *Etmullerus abridged: or a complete system of the theory and practice of physic,* trans. anon., London.
42. Evelyn, J. (1908) *The diary of John Evelyn (1620 to 1706) with an introduction and notes by Austin Dobson,* London.
43. Exton, B. (1751) *A new and general system of midwifery,* London.
44. Ferrier, S. (1898) *Memoir and correspondence of Susan Ferrier 1782-1854,* Doyle, J. A. (ed.), London.
45. Fildes, V. A. (1982) *The history of infant feeding 1500-1800,* Unpublished PhD thesis, University of Surrey, Dept. Human Biology and Health.
46. Fildes, V. A. (1984) The English wet nurse and her role in infant care 1538-1800. In press. *Med. Hist.* 1986.
47. Finlay, R. A. P. (1976) *The population of London 1580-1650,* Unpublished PhD dissertation, University of Cambridge.
48. Floyer, Sir J. (1706) *The history of cold bathing: both ancient and modern. Part I,* London, 2nd ed.
49. Foster, E. (1781) *The principles and practice of midwifery,* London.
50. Freke, E. (1913) *Mrs Elizabeth Freke. Her diary 1671 to 1714,* Carbery, M. (ed.), Cork.
51. *Full view of all the diseases to children* (1742), London.
52. *Gentleman's magazine, The* (1765) Anonymous writer, *On some of the causes that occasion the mortality of children under two years of age. In answer to queries in the public papers, concerning the cause of the great mortality of infants in this metropolis under that age,* London, December 1765.
53. Glisson, F. (1651) *A treatise of the rickets, being a disease common to children,* trans. Armin, P., London.
54. Gouge, W. (1622) *Of domestical duties,* London.
55. Graunt, J. (1676) *Natural and political observations on the Bills of Mortality. Much enlarged,* London, 5th ed.
56. Griffith, M. (1633) *Bethel: or a forme for families,* London.
57. Guazzo, M. S. (1581 and 1586) *The civile conversation,* trans. Pettie, G. & Young, B., in *The Tudor translations,* 2nd series *8,* Webley, C. (ed.), London.
58. Guillemeau, J. (1612) *Childbirth or The happie deliverie of women.... To which is added a treatise of the diseases of infants, and young children: with the cure of them,* trans. anon., London.
59. Hamilton, A. (1792) *A treatise on the management of female complaints and of children in early infancy,* Edinburgh.
60. Harris, W. (1689) *A treatise of the acute diseases of infants,* trans. Martyn, J., London.
61. Hoffmann, F. (c.1740) *A system of the practice of medicine,* vol.2, trans. Lewis, W., London, 1783.
62. Hunter, W. (1775) *Lectures anatomical and chirurgical by William Hunter,* Library of the Wellcome Institute for the

References

History of Medicine, MS 2966. Also dated 1783.

63. Hurlock, J. (1742) *A practical treatise upon dentition*, London.
64. James, R. (1746) *The modern practice of physic. As improv'd by ... H. Boerhaave and F. Hoffmann. ... Being a translation of the former with commentaries of Dr van Swieten*, 2 vols, London.
65. Jelliffe, D. B. & Jelliffe, E. F. P. (1978) *Human milk in the modern world. Psychosocial, nutritional and economic significance*, Oxford.
66. Jones, A. (1978) *The Foundling Hospital and its arrangements for country nursing 1756-67 illustrated by examples from Hertfordshire*, Unpublished dissertation for Extension Diploma in History, University of London.
67. Jones, J. (1579) *The arte and science of preserving bodie and soule in healthe, wisedome, and catholicke religion: physically, philosophically and divinely devised*, London.
68. Johnstone, J. (1657) *The idea of practical physick in twelve books*, trans. Culpeper, N. & W. R., London.
69. Klaus, M. H. & Kennell, J. H. (1982) *Parent-infant bonding*, St Louis, 2nd ed.
70. *Ladies dispensatorie or, Every woman her own physician*, 1740, London.
71. *Ladies physical directory: by a physician, 7th edition with large additions, alterations, and amendments*, 1739, London.
72. La Motte, G., M. de (1746) *A general treatise of midwifery*, trans. Tomkins, T., London.
73. Lane, M. (1975) *Samuel Johnson and his world*, London.
74. Lara, B. (1791) *An essay on the injurious custom of mothers not suckling their own children; with some directions for chusing a nurse, and weaning of children, etc.*, London.
75. Leinster, E. (1949-57) *Correspondence of Emily, Duchess of Leinster (1731-1814)*, Fitzgerald, B. (ed.), Dublin.
76. McClure, R. (1981) *Coram's children. The London Foundling Hospital in the eighteenth century*, Yale.
77. McHenry, L. C. & MacKeith, R. (1966) Samuel Johnson's childhood illnesses and the King's Evil, *Med. Hist. 10*, 386-99.
78. Mackenzie, C. (1774) *Mr Mackenzey's Lectures on midwifery*, ? by D.B., London, Library of the Royal College of Obstetricians and Gynaecologists, unnumbered MS.
79. McLaren, D. (1979) Nature's contraceptive. Wet nursing and prolonged lactation: the case of Chesham, Buckinghamshire 1578-1601, *Med. Hist. 23*, 426-41.
80. McMath, J. (1694) *The expert midwife*, Edinburgh.
81. Mantell, T. (1787) *Short directions for the management of infants*, London.
82. Maubray, J. (1730) *The female physician*, London.
83. Mauriceau, F. (1673) *The accomplisht midwife*, trans. Chamberlen, H., London.

207

84. Mears, M. (1797) *The midwife's candid advice to the fair sex; or The pupil of nature*, London.
85. Memis, J. (1765) *The midwife's pocket companion*, London.
86. Mettler, C. C. (1947) *History of medicine*, Philadelphia.
87. Morley, D. (1973) *Paediatric priorities in the developing world*, London.
88. Moss, W. (1781) *An essay on the management and nursing of children in the earlier periods of infancy*, London.
89. Muffet (Moffet), T. (1584) *Health's improvement: or Rules comprising the nature, method, and manner of preparing all sorts of food used in this nation. Corrected and enlarged by Christopher Bennet*, London, 1655.
90. Nelson, J. (1753) *An essay on the government of children. Under three general heads: viz Health, manners and education*, London.
91. Newcome, H. (1695) *The compleat mother or, An earnest persuasive to all mothers (especially those of rank and quality) to nurse their own children*, London.
92. *Nurses guide: or the right method of bringing up young children. By an eminent physician*, London, 1729.
93. Paré, A. (1575) *The workes of that famous chirurgion Ambrose Parey*, trans. Johnston, T., London, 1634.
94. Paulus Aeginata (7th C. AD) *The seven books of Paulus Aeginata. With a commentary*, trans. Adams, F., London, 1844-47, vol.i.
95. Pearce, E. H. (1908) *Annals of Christ's Hospital*, London.
96. Pechey (Peachey), J. (1697) *A general treatise of the diseases of infants and children. Collected from the best practical authors*, London.
97. Pemell, R. (1653) *De morbis puerorum, or a treatise of the diseases of children*, London.
98. Phaire, T. (1545) *The boke of chyldren*, London. Reprinted 1955, Edinburgh.
99. *Practice of midwifery, by a pupil of the late Dr W. Hunter* (1783), London.
100. Quillet, C. (1655) *Callipaediae or, An art how to have handsome children*, trans. anon., London, 1710.
101. Radbill, S. X. (1973) Mesopotamian pediatrics, *Episteme 7*, 283-8.
102. Richardson, S. (1740) *Pamela*, London.
103. Roesslin the Elder, E. (1540) *The byrth of mankynde*, trans. Jonas, R., London, first published 1512.
104. Rosenstein, N. R. von (1776) *The diseases of children and their remedies*, trans. Sparrman, A., London, first published 1765.
105. Sainte Marthe, S. de (1584) *Paedotrophiae: or The art of bringing up children*, trans. anon., London, 1710.
106. Savitt, T. L. (1975) Smothering and overlaying of Virginia slave children: a suggested explanation, *Bull. Hist. Med. 49*, 400-4.

107. Shakespeare, W. (c.1594) *Romeo and Juliet*, Act 2, scene I, in *The complete works of William Shakespeare*, Alexander, P. (ed.), London and Glasgow.

108. Sharp, J. (1671) *The midwives book or The whole art of midwifery discovered*, London.

109. Shaw, J. C. L., Personal communication.

110. Short, R. V. (1982) *The biological basis for the contraceptive effects of breastfeeding*. Background document for WHO Workshop on breastfeeding and fertility regulation, February 1982, Geneva.

111. Short, R. V., Personal communication.

112. Shorter, E. (1977) *The making of the modern family*, Glasgow.

113. Shorter, E. (1978) *The great transformation of mother-infant relations, eighteenth to twentieth centuries*, Unpublished paper in the library of SSRC Cambridge Group for the History of Population and Social Structure, Cambridge.

114. Sibbald, R. (1932) *The memoirs of Sir Robert Sibbald (1641-1722)*, Hett, F. P. (ed.), London.

115. Sloane, H. (1748) *Letter to John Milner, vice-president of the Hospital for the maintenance and education of exposed and deserted young children*, 28 October 1748. Quoted in full in Brownlow, J. (1847) *Memoranda: or, Chronicles of the Foundling Hospital*, London.

116. Smith, Henry (1597) *The sermons of Maister Henrie Smith gathered into one volume*, London.

117. Smith, H. (1774) *Letters to married women on nursing and the management of children*, London, 3rd ed.

118. *Soranus' Gynecology* (1956) trans. Temkin, O. *et al.*, Baltimore.

119. Spence, D. (1784) *A system of midwifery*, Edinburgh.

120. Steele, R. (1711) On abuses in nursing children, *The Spectator*, no.246, Wednesday, 12 December 1711.

121. Stone, L. (1977) *The family, sex and marriage in England 1500-1800*, London.

122. Tansillo, L. (1566) *The nurse. A poem*, trans. Roscoe, W., Liverpool and London, 1800, 2nd ed.

123. Thornton, A. (1875) *The autobiograhy of Mrs Alice Thornton of East Newton, Co. York*, Jackson, C. (ed.) Durham.

124. Trumbach, R. (1978) *The rise of the egalitarian family*, New York.

125. Underwood, M. (1784) *A treatise on the diseases of children*, London.

126. Wake, J. (1953) *The Brudenells of Deene*, London.

127. Wentworth, T. (1883) *The Wentworth papers 1705-1739*, Cartwright, J. (ed.) London.

128. Wickes, I. G. (1953) A history of infant feeding. *Archs Dis. Childh. 28*, 151-8, 232-40, 332-40, 416-22, 494-502.

129. Wilson, C. A. (1976) *Food and drink in Britain. From the stone age to recent times*, Harmondsworth.

130. Willughby, P. (1630-69) *Observations in midwifery. As also the country midwife's opusculum or vade mecum,* Blenkinsop, H. (ed.), Warwick, 1863.

131. Wolveridge, J. (1671) *Speculum matricis; or The expert midwives handmaid,* London.

132. Wooley, P. V. (1945) Mechanical suffocation during infancy, *J. Pediat. 26,* 572-3.

133. Wrightson, K. (1975) Infanticide in earlier seventeenth century England, *Loc. Popul. Stud. 15,* 10-22.

134. Young, T. (late 18th century) *Young's midwifery,* Library of the Wellcome Institute for the History of Medicine, MSS 5106 and 1507.

Mixed or Supplementary Feeding

Limewood statue of Virgin and Child,
16th C. Jesus is holding a sucking bag.

Plate 8.1. Simon de Vallambert's book on the
feeding and management of children, 1565.

CINQ LIVRES,
De la maniere de nourrir
ET GOUVERNER
LES ENFANS DES LEVR
NAISSANCE.

PAR

*M. Simon de Vallambert, Medecin de madame
la Duchesse de Sauoye et de Berry, et
depuys peu de temps, de monsei-
gneur le Duc d'Orleans.*

A POICTIERS,
Par les de Marnefz, & Bouchetz, freres.
1 5 6 5.

CHAPTER EIGHT

Mixed or Supplementary Feeding: The Foods Used for Mixed or Supplementary Feeding

"Now when he springs, and spreads his little arms,
And smiles, and utters sounds which strike thine ear
With wondrous pleasure. Tho' we now permit
Some added food, its quality regard
As of important consequence."
Hugh Downman, *Infancy*, 1788

THE MAIN foods used for mixed feeding during the period 1500–1800 were pap and panada, or variants of these. Pap was said to date from the mid-15th century, and consisted of flour or breadcrumbs cooked in water or milk; panada was of more ancient origin, and consisted of bread, broth (sometimes with legumes, oil or butter) or milk; eggs were occasionally added [20]. To some extent the terms pap and panada were interchangeable. This chapter will identify the ingredients and method of preparation of these infant foods, to put into context the following two chapters in which some assessment will be made of attitudes towards their use.

Of the medical texts relating to England and France in this period, 38 have been found which contain descriptions of infant foods, recommended or said to be in common use. When these were extracted, and the main ingredients listed, 73 recipes were obtained: pap (40), panada (14), and alternative substances which were similar to, but not specifically named as, pap or panada (19). Nine of these were from the 16th century, 14 from the 17th century, and 50 from the 18th century (table 8.1). Authors often gave more than one recipe [26]. The French physician Simon de Vallambert (1565), who has been credited as the first to give recipes both for pap and panada [20], has one recipe for pap and four different ways of making panada. James McMath (1694) gives three versions of pap, and Smellie (1752) two versions of panada. A list of all the recipes is given at the end of this chapter. These have been analysed to discover i) the principal constituents, and ii) whether boiling was employed during preparation. The quantities and proportions of ingredients and/or the amount of food actually given to children were rarely stated, so it is not possible to assess the calorific/metabolic value taken in by the child, but analysis of these common foods does allow some estimation to be made of their nutritional value to infants.

The main ingredients of the 40 pap recipes are listed in table 8.2 [26]. It appears from these that pap, whether of the kind recommended by physicians, or said to be in common use by nurses, had three major components: i) a liquid, most frequently milk; ii) a cereal; iii) additives. The additives may be further divided into those which were added for flavouring, such as spice or sugar; and those which had a significant protein or fat content, such as eggs. Like pap, panada also had three major components (table 8.3), but these were less varied in type: i) a liquid, most frequently broth; ii) breadcrumbs; iii) additives which were a) flavouring, and b) nourishing.

All but two of the remaining 19 recipes were recorded in the 18th century, and all after 1748, when there was some general disapproval of pap and panada as popularly made and administered. These alternative recipes were, however, very similar in composition to what were called pap and panada in the 16th and 17th centuries (table 8.4). After 1748, recipes often give alternatives to the cereal or grain component, the most common being forms of bread or rice; 88% of authors mentioned some variety of bread as an alternative or sole ingredient and 41% mentioned rice as an alternative to bread [26]. The main component of these recipes were: i) a protein-containing liquid; ii) a cereal or grain; iii) flavouring additives. Additives such as eggs or butter were not mentioned by any of the authors giving these recipes.

¶ When all 73 recipes were studied, in order to obtain an idea of gross changes in composition over three centuries (table 8.5) [26], the main components were i) a liquid, most frequently milk or broth; ii) a cereal or grain, most frequently bread or breadcrumbs; iii) additives a) flavouring and b) nourishing.

The changes in composition which were of most significance to the health of the child apparently started in the 17th century, when liquids of little food value, such as ale or water, were recommended in place of protein-containing liquids, such as milk or meat broth, which had been more usual in the 16th century. This trend continued into the 18th century, with a third of all the infant food recipes containing no milk or other nourishing liquid.

At the same time the use of eggs or egg yolks as an additive, and the inclusion of butter or other fat in infant foods apparently greatly declined. The decreased use of dairy foods or 'white meats' is significant, because these would have been the main source of vitamins A and D, first-class protein, calcium, and, in the case of eggs, iron [50]. The cereal component, whether bread or meal, was not highly processed in this period [22] so that some protein, calcium and iron would have been obtained from this source, but the fat-soluble vitamins A and D are not present in the other constituents of these recipes. This would not have been a problem for children who were still receiving breastmilk but, for those who were fed on paps or panadas as a substitute for milk, or who received only small quantities of breastmilk from a woman with a failing milk supply, it would eventually have led to vitamin-deficiency diseases such as rickets. The use of meat or pulse broths rather than milk would not have rectified this deficiency, since neither meat nor legumes contain significant amounts of vitamins A or D [50].

Rickets was first recognised in England about 1620 [33] and, possibly partly because it was diagnosed or named more frequently, became an increasing problem during the 17th and 18th centuries [27,38,81]. The incidence of rickets during the 17th and 18th centuries was probably partly related to the infant diet, since by the 18th century only just over 40% of these infant foods contained a source of vitamin D, although this would have been more of a problem where the pap was used as a replacement rather than as a supplement for breastmilk.

The incidence of 'the stone' was high in pre-industrial England and was a problem in all age groups from infancy to old age, but small children were particularly affected [24]. Since the incidence of bladder stones has been connected with a diet high in calcium and low in vitamin A [22] and with diets low in animal products but high in vegetable proteins [24], the use of predominantly cereal-containing foods in infancy may well have been a contributory factor to this condition.

Scurvy was endemic in the winter months during the 16th and 17th centuries [22,37,85] and infantile scurvy was also well known [33,77]. It is clear that none of the ingredients listed above were good sources of vitamin C. Only the milk of cows and goats fed on grass during the summer months would have contained it [22,50]. The variable amounts of the vitamin in the milk would have been reduced if the milk were not used when fresh, or if it were boiled during preparation [50]. As will be shown in the following section, before the mid-18th century most of the infant food recipes were boiled, so that, although the use of milk rather than other liquids was more common in the 16th and 17th centuries, the amount of vitamin C available to the child was probably insufficient in the summer months, and absent from October to March [50]. Any such deficiency would not have been remedied even if the child were still being suckled, because the amount of vitamin C present in human milk is dependent on the dietary intake of the mother [42]. At a time when the diet of the mass of the population contained little or no fruit or vegetables during the winter [22,85], and many adults suffered from at least mild degrees of scurvy, it is unlikely that during the winter months lactating women would have secreted milk which contained significant amounts of vitamin C.

It is unlikely that there was any deficiency of the B group of vitamins associated with the intake of these infant foods, since these water-soluble vitamins are present in cereal foods and yeast, both of which were always common ingredients, although the prolonged cooking that some recipes demanded may have destroyed up to half of the vitamins contained in the uncooked cereals [50]. Unlike rickets and scurvy, diseases such as beri-beri and pellagra do not feature in the history of medicine in Britain [22].

Increased use of breadcrumbs in preference to meal was partly a reflection of the adult diet, breadcrumbs being the most popular thickening agent at this time [22,85]. This must have been less so in Scotland, where the mass of the population until at least the mid-19th century had small access to wheat flour, The staple diet of the population was oats, barley, and potatoes. It is significant that three Scots medical writers, McMath (1694), Buchan (1769), and Spence (1784) all specify 'bread', 'loaf bread', and 'white bread' thus clearly addressing their advice to the upper class of Scottish society, or to a southern audience. Uncooked flour or meal was frowned upon, because it was thought to be indigestible [4,25,54] and, although the use of flour for making pap was continued in France [4,7,18], bread or associated products such as rolls or rusks were preferred in Britain [2,9,56]. The introduction after 1748 of rice or of other farinaceous substances, such as tapioca, may have been due to the increased availability of such grains at this time [22]. An alternative explanation is that its use had been suggested – possibly as a personal preference – by William Cadogan (1748) whose views were then repeated for the next half century [12,53]. It is noteworthy that no evidence has been found that children actually had any rice in their broth, or that it was commonly given; it appears only as a recommended infant food.

The increased use of sweetening agents reflected adult tastes, since sweet puddings were a feature of the adult British diet. Until the 17th century honey was the main sweetening ingredient, but later on sugar became cheaper and more widely available [85]. The decreased use of spices could have been associated with the move towards simplicity in infant foods, advocated by John Locke (1693) [48] and vehemently recommended by Cadogan (1748), although this explanation is weakened by the fact that the addition of sugar to paps and panadas was condemned just as greatly as the addition of spice [9,56,57].

¶ The method of preparation for each recipe is given at the end of this chapter. The issue discussed here is whether infant foods were boiled, either as a whole, or at any point during the preparation; and whether changes occurred in this practice during the period considered (tables 8.6–8.13).

From the analysis it is apparent that, in the 16th and 17th centuries, at least 64–89% of the infant foods discovered were recommended to be boiled during preparation, and no distinction was made between boiling milk or any other liquid ingredient. In the 18th century the advice of the nutritionists changed quite radically. At least two-thirds of all recipes involved boiling, but when milk was part of the food it was rarely boiled, usually being added after the water, or water and cereal, had been boiled. In only 14% of the 21 18th-century baby foods described here was the milk boiled. Since boiling is the simplest effective method of destroying micro-organisms in food, although not completely sterilising most substances [35], its employment during food preparation in the past can be taken to provide a very approximate estimate of the 'cleanliness' of infant foods.

There are several pitfalls in attempting to assess how far infant foodstuffs were responsible for transmitting diseases such as tuberculosis or, particularly, gastro-intestinal infections to small babies, before the need for sterilisation began to be understood in the 19th century. There is little doubt that gastro-intestinal upsets were extremely common in infants, and often led to death, since almost all medical authors alluded to the problem [56,57,74]. How much this was due to lack of knowledge, care and cleanliness in preparation of the food itself, can only be guessed at, despite the assumption of some writers on infant feeding that these foods, dismissed – without real study – as totally bad and unsuitable, were the cause of infantile 'tummy upsets' [21,28,49,69]. Other unknown factors to be taken into account before such judgments are made include: i) the degree of cleanliness of the utensils used to store and administer the foods to babies; ii) the length of time which elapsed between boiling the food and its administration to the infant; iii) the degree of freshness and freedom from bacterial contamination of the milk used in making paps, etc., whether or not it were boiled; iv) how far boiling the water, known by contemporaries to be generally contaminated [22,24], was effective in destroying those pathogenic organisms carried in water.

The above factors are likely to have been different for each child. Whilst cleanliness was upheld as something desirable among the upper and, later, the middle classes [29,53], and among women involved in dairy work [13], the scrubbing and washing of utensils would have been of little use if the water used were contaminated; and among the very poor there is no evidence of such conventions of cleanliness. Similarly, insisting that a recipe should contain 'new milk' [18,44] was of small effect if the cow were infected with tuberculosis or brucellosis. In recipes which specified that pap be made 'in bulk', and small amounts used as needed [5,78], contamination may have occurred between its preparation and its being fed to the child, particularly in hot weather.

No firm conclusions can therefore be drawn from the knowledge that recommended infant foods were generally boiled during the 16th and 17th centuries but not in the 18th century. The most which can be said is that, if the food were given soon after preparation, were given in a receptacle thoroughly washed in fresh spring water rather than river water, and contained fresh milk from a disease-free animal, it was less likely to have transmitted disease organisms to the child in the 16th century than in the 18th century. It is also possible that the 16th- and early 17th-century baby was more likely to be given fresh milk than an infant in the 18th century, when the individual ownership of cows was less, and the milk supply in towns was known to be very poor, inefficient, and was usually sour, skimmed and contaminated [22,56,79]. It might be expected that such an important change in preparation, if generally observed, would be accompanied by a rise in infant mortality. In fact no such rise has been noted after 1748 [45,46,83,84] (tables 2.8 and 2.9) but this does not necessarily mean that there was no increased mortality from this cause, since any rise could have been counteracted by other factors, such as decreased use of wet nurses; improvements in maternal nutrition; changes in neonatal feeding practices; and unknown environmental changes.

The idea that the milk component of infant foods should not be boiled seems to have originated in the medical literature with William Cadogan (1748), the basis of his opinion being that milk was changed in some way by boiling, and that boiled milk would therefore be harmful to infants [9]. Like the rest of his opinions on infant feeding, most of which were sound, this belief was repeated throughout the 18th century. Only a few physicians towards the end of that century began to say it was all right for mothers and nurses to boil milk [61,74]. Significantly, Hugh Smith (1774) said that milk could be boiled, especially if the child had gripes; so, apparently, some physicians had noted that boiling milk prevented or cured 'the gripes', thus implying that the use of unboiled milk in infant foods was related to some cases of gastro-intestinal upsets.

¶ Three main types of infant foods were used for mixed feeding in the period 1500–1800. Pap consisted of a liquid (usually milk), a cereal, and additives for flavouring or adding nourishment. Panada consisted of a liquid (usually broth), breadcrumbs and various additives. Eighteenth-century alternative recipes contained a protein-containing liquid, a cereal or grain, and various flavourings. Sixteenth-century infant foods were apparently relatively nutritious substances, since the only nutrient consistently absent or poorly supplied was vitamin C. Panadas made with meat or pulse broths rather than milk or dairy products were deficient in vitamins A and D. The foods described in the 17th century were slightly less nutritious, due principally to the reduced use of eggs

218

and meat broth. In the 18th century there was a definite decline in the nutritional value of infant foods, when compared to the 16th century, with 58% containing no milk or dairy products and, of these, 34% containing no animal protein, vitamins A, D or C, and possibly low in fat, calcium and iron. The foods recommended or commonly given to infants, sometimes from birth, and often as a substitute for the breast, became less nutritious over the 300 years, and this could have been associated with the apparently increased incidence of rickets, the continuing incidence of infantile scurvy, and the high incidence of bladder stone in young children. The great majority of infant foods were boiled during preparation in the 16th and 17th centuries but in the 18th century – apparently from Cadogan's belief that boiled milk was changed in composition and could harm infants – the milk used in infant foods was not boiled, usually being added after the cereal and water had been boiled. Because of various unknown factors, no firm conclusions as to the effects of this practice on infants can be made, although it is possible that 18th-century infants suffered more gastro-intestinal problems because of this practice than did their 16th- and 17th-century counterparts.

REFERENCES

1. Adams, S. F. (1959) Use of vegetables in infant feeding through the ages, *J. Am . Diet. Ass. 35*, 692-703.
2. Armstrong, G. (1771) *An essay on the diseases most fatal to infants*, London, 2nd ed.
3. *Artificial feeds for the young infant* (1980) DHSS report on health and social subjects no.18, London.
4. Baudelocque, J-L. (1790) *A system of midwifery*, trans. Heath, J., 3 vols, London.
5. Bonet, T. (1684) *A guide to the practical physician*, trans. anon., London.
6. Bracken, H. (1737) *The midwife's companion or, A treatise of midwifery*, London.
7. Brouzet, N. (1755) *An essay on the medicinal education of children; and the treatment of their diseases*, trans. anon., London.
8. Buchan, W. (1769) *Domestic medicine; or The family physician*, Edinburgh.
9. Cadogan, W. (1748) *An essay upon nursing and the government of children, from their birth to the age of three years*, London.
10. Cone, T. E. (1976) *200 years of feeding infants in America*, Columbus, Ohio.
11. Cone, T. E. (1979) *History of American pediatrics*, Boston.
12. Cooke, J. (1768) *Some necessary directions in the care of infants*, in *A collection of pieces relative to inoculation for the smallpox*, Dublin.

13. Crawford, P., Personal communication.
14. Culpeper, N. (1675) *A directory for midwives*, London.
15. Culpeper, N. (1676) *A directory for midwives or, A guide for women, in their conception, bearing and suckling their children. Corrected from many gross errors*, London.
16. De Claubry, C. D. G. (1783) *Nouvel avis aux mères qui veulent nourir*, Paris. Partially translated by Drake, T. G. H. (1931) Pap and panada, *Ann. Med. Hist. 3* (N.S.), 289-95.
17. De Vallambert, S. (1565) *Cinq livres, de la manière de nourir et gouverner les enfants des leur naissance*, Poictiers. Also the partial translation, in Drake, T. G. H. (1931) Pap and panada, *Ann. Med. Hist. 3* (N.S.), 289-95.
18. Dionis, P. (1719) *A general treatise of midwifery*, trans. anon., London.
19. Downman, H. (1788) *Infancy or, The management of children*, London, 4th ed.
20. Drake, T. G. H. (1931) Pap and panada, *Ann. Med. Hist. 3* (N.S.), 289-95.
21. Drake, T. G. H. (1932-33) Antiques of pediatric interest, *J. Pediat. 1*, 502-3, 764-5; *2*, 68-9; *3*, 374-5, 639-40, 779-80.
22. Drummond, J. C. & Wilbraham, A. (1957) *The Englishman's food. A history of five centuries of British diet*, London.
23. Ebrahim, G. J. (1983) *Nutrition in mother and child health*, London.
24. Ellis, H. (1969) *A history of bladder stone*, Oxford and Edinburgh.
25. Ettmueller, M. (1699) *Etmullerus abridg'd: or A complete system of the theory and practice of physic*, trans. anon., London.
26. Fildes, V. A. (1982) *The history of infant feeding 1500-1800*, Unpublished PhD thesis, University of Surrey, Dept. Human Biology and Health.
27. Fildes, V. A. (1984) *'The English disease'; infantile rickets and scurvy in pre-industrial England*. Paper presented at the tenth British Congress on the History of Medicine, Swansea, 6-8 April. In press.
28. Forsyth, D. (1911) The history of infant feeding from Elizabethan times, *Proc. Soc. Med. 4*, 110-41.
29. Furnivall, F. J. (ed.) (1868) *Early English meals and manners*, London.
30. Gardien, C. M. (1807) *Traité d'accouchemens de maladies des femmes, de l'éducation médicinale des enfants*, Paris, vol.3. Partially translated in Drake, T. G. H. (1931) Pap and panada, *Ann. Med. Hist. 3* (N.S.), 289-95.
31. *Gentleman's magazine* (1765) Unsigned writer, *On some of the causes that occasion the mortality of children under two years of age*, London.
32. Glass, D. V. & Eversley, D. E. C. (1974) *Population in history, Essays in historical demography*, London.

33. Glisson, F. (1651) *A treatise of the rickets, being a disease common to children*, trans. Armin, P., London.

34. Guillemeau, J. (1612) *Childbirth or The happie deliverie of women. . . . To which is added a treatise of the diseases of infants, and young children: with the cure of them*, trans. anon., London.

35. Hawker, L. E. *et al.* (1967) *An introduction to micro-organisms*, London.

36. Hedley, O. (1975) *Queen Charlotte*, London.

37. Hess, A. F. (1920) *Scurvy past and present*, Philadelphia.

38. Hess, A. F. (1929) *Rickets including osteomalacia and tetany*, Philadelphia.

39. Hopkirk, M. (1953) *Queen over the water. Mary Beatrice of Modena, Queen of James II*, London.

40. Hunter, W. (1908) An obstetric diary of William Hunter, Stark, J. N. (ed.), *Glasg. Med. J. 70*, 167-77, 241-56, 338-56.

41. James, R. (1746) *The modern practice of physic. As improv'd by . . . H. Boerhaave and F. Hoffmann. . . . Being a translation of the aphorisms of the former with commentaries of Dr van Swieten*, London.

42. Jelliffe, D. B. & Jelliffe, E. F. P. (1978) *Human milk in the modern world. Psychosocial, nutritional and economic significance*, Oxford.

43. Johnstone, J. (1657) *The idea of practical physick in twelve books*, trans. Culpeper, N. & W. R., London.

44. Jones, J. (1579) *The arte and science of preserving bodie and soule in healthe, wisedome, and catholick religion: physically, philosophically and divinely devised*, London.

45. Jones, R. E. (1976) Infant mortality in rural north Shropshire 1561-1810, *Popul. Stud. 30*, 305-17.

46. Jones, R. E. (1980) Further evidence on the decline in infant mortality in pre-industrial England: North Shropshire 1561-1810, *Popul. Stud. 34*, 239-50.

47. Leroy, A. (1807) Recipe included in Gardien, C. M. (1807) *Traité d'accouchements de maladies des femmes, de l'education médicinale des enfants*, Paris, vol.3.

48. Locke, J. (1693) *Some thoughts concerning education*, London.

49. Lyon, A. B. (1933) History of infant feeding, *Am. J. Dis. Child. 46*, 359-74.

50. *McCance and Widdowson's The composition of foods* (1978), revised and extended Paul, A.A. & Southgate, D. A. T. (eds), London, 4th ed.

51. MacKenzie, C. (1770) *Lectures in midwifery*, Library of the Wellcome Institute for the History of Medicine, MS 3392.

52. McMath, J. (1694) *The expert midwife: a treatise of the diseases of women with child, and in child bed . . . with fit remedies for the various maladies of newborn babes*, Edinburgh.

53. Mantell, T. (1787) *Short directions for the management of infants*, London.

54. Maubray, J. (1730) *The female physician containing all the diseases incident to that sex... together with the diet and regimen of both the mother and child,* London.

55. Mauriceau, F. (1673) *The accomplisht midwife, treating of the diseases of women with child, and in childbed... with fit remedies for the several indispositions of newborn babes,* trans. Chamberlen, H., London.

56. Moss, W. (1781) *An essay on the management and nursing of children in the earlier periods of infancy,* London.

57. Nelson, J. (1753) *An essay on the government of children,* London.

58. *Nurses guide: or The right method of bringing up young children. By an eminent physician* (1729), London.

59. O'Hara-May, J. (1977) *Elizabethan dyetary of health,* Kansas.

60. Orrery (1903) *The Orrery papers,* Cork and Orrery, Countess of (ed.), London, vol. 1.

61. Osborne, W. & Denman, T. (1776) *Sketches of the practice of midwifery. From the lectures of Drs Osborne and Denman,* Library of the Wellcome Institute for the History of Medicine, MS 2098.

62. Paré, A. (1575) *The workes of that famous chirurgion Ambrose Parey,* trans. Johnston, T., London, 1634.

63. *Present day practice in infant feeding* (1974) DHSS report on health and social subjects no.9, London.

64. Raulin (1769) *De la conservation des enfants,* Paris, vol. 2. Partially translated in Drake, T. G. H. (1931) Pap and panada, *Ann. Med. Hist. 3* (N.S.), 289-95.

65. *Recommended intakes of nutrients for the United Kingdom* (1973) DHSS reports on public health and medical subjects no.120, London.

66. Rosenstein, N. R. von (1776) *The diseases of children and their remedies,* trans. Sparrman, A., London.

67. Sainte Marthe, S. de (1584) *Paedotrophiae: or The art of bringing up children,* trans. anon., London, 1710.

68. Schofield, R. & Wrigley, E. A. (1979) Infant and child mortality in the late Tudor and early Stuart period, in Webster, C. (ed.), *Health, medicine and mortality in the sixteenth century,* Cambridge, 61-95.

69. Schwab, M. G. (1979) The rise and fall of the baby's bottle, *J. Hum. Nutr. 33,* 276-82.

70. Sharp, J. (1671) *The midwives book or The whole art of midwifery discovered,* London.

71. Shaw, J. C. L., Jones, A. & Gunther, M. (1973) Mineral content of brands of milk for infant feeding, *Brit. Med. J.,* 12-15.

72. Smellie, W. (1752) *A treatise on the theory and practice of midwifery,* London, vols 1 and 3.

73. Smerdon, G. T. (1950) Daniel Whistler and the English disease. A translation and biographical note, *J. Hist. Med. 5,*

397-415.
74. Smith, H. (1774) *Letters to married women on nursing and the management of children. The 3rd edition, revised and considerably enlarged,* London.
75. Spence, D. (1784) *A system of midwifery,* Edinburgh.
76. Still, G. F. (1931) *The history of paediatrics,* London.
77. Still, G. F (1935) Infantile scurvy; its history, *Archs Dis. Childh. 10,* 211-18.
78. Trumbach, R. (1978) *The rise of the egalitarian family,* New York.
79. Trusler, Rev. Dr J. (1786) *The London adviser and guide,* London, 2nd ed.
80. Underwood, M. (1784) *A treatise on the diseases of children,* London.
81. Vahlquist, B. (1975). A two-century perspective of some major nutritional deficiency diseases in childhood, *Acta Paediat. Scand. 64,* 161-71.
82. Van Helmont, J. B. (1662) *Oriatrike or, Physick refined,* trans. J.C., London.
83. Wrigley, E. A. (1968) Mortality in pre-indstrial England: the example of Colyton, Devon, over three centuries, *Daedalus 97,* 564-80.
84. Wrigley, E. A. & Schofield, R. (1981) *The population history of England,* London.
85. Wilson, C. A. (1976) *Food and drink in Britain. From the stone age to recent times,* Harmondsworth.
86. Wood, C. B. S. & Walker-Smith, J. A. (1981) *MacKeith's Infant feeding and feeding difficulties,* Edinburgh and London, 6th ed.
87. Young, T. (late 18th century) *Young's midwifery,* Library of the Wellcome Institute for the History of Medicine, MSS 5106 and 5107.

Recipes for pap, panada and similar
substances used for infant feeding
1500–1800

RECIPES are given in chronological order under: a) pap; b) panada; c) foods similar to pap and panada.

Those given first appear in the tables of the preceding chapter. Additional recipes are given for comparison and interest. The number in brackets following the author's name and date denotes the number of recipes extracted from the description and included in the analysis. The ingredients of each recipe are summarised at the foot of each quotation.

N.B. The concern about alum which recurs throughout the 18th-century recipes refers to the practice, particularly common in London, of adulterating white bread with alum to make it appear whiter.

RECIPES FOR PAP

Simon de Vallambert, 1565 (1)
'The flour of which it is made nowadays the greater part of the nurses pass simply through a sieve without other preparation. Others cook it in the oven in a leaded or vitrified earthen pot after the bread is drawn, to finally take away the viscosity which is in the crude flour. The milk mixed with the flour is commonly from the goat or cow, that of the goat is better. When one intends to add more nourishment one adds finally an egg yolk, when one wishes to guard against constipation one adds honey.'
Flour, Milk, Egg yolk, Honey.

Ambroise Paré, 1575 (1)
'Pap hath these three conditions, so that it be made with wheaten flower, and that not crude but boiled. Let it be put into a new earthen pot or pipkin, and so set into an oven at the time when bread is set therein to be baked, and let it remaine there untill the bread bee baked and drawne out: for when it is so baked it is less clammy and crude. Those that mixe the meale crude with the milke, are constrained to abide one of these discommodities or other, either to give the meale grosse and clammy unto the childe, if that the pap be only first boiled over the fire in a pipkin or skillet for so long as shall be necessary for the milk, . . . or else they give the child the milk despoiled of its butterish and wheyish portion, and the terrestriall and cheeselike or curdlike remaining, if the pap be boiled so long as is necessary for the meale: for the milke requireth not so great, neither can it suffer so long boyling as the meale. Those that doe use crude meale, and have no hurt by it, are greatly bound to nature for so great a benefit.'
Wheatmeal, Milk.

John Jones, 1579 (1)
'Take of new milke a pinte, put therein of fine wheate flower, so much,
as being boiled, will make it thicke. Add to it the biggenesse of a
chestnut of almond butter, or of sweete butter, one ounce of the beste
sugar not faulted in the sunning, and then it will bee the better to digest,
and the refuse not turned to the nourishment of the bodye, the sooner
and earlier emptied. For that made of the milke and floure alone, is
somewhat slow in distribution, and therefore binding.'
New milk, Fine wheat flour, Almond butter or sweet butter, Sugar.

Scévole de Sainte Marthe, 1584 (1)
'With milk and bread the sooty tin they fill,
Stir it together o'er the fire, and boil,
They try it with a touch, the spoon they dip,
Blow it, and put it to his craving lip.'
Bread, Milk.

John Johnstone, 1657 (1)
'Pap made of wheat meale and milk, usual amongst us; which because
it breeds gripings and obstructions, the wheat flour must be dried in an
oven . . .'
Wheatmeal, Milk.

Jane Sharp, 1671 (1)
'Barley bread steeped a while in water and then boiled in milk.'
Barley bread in water, Milk.

François Mauriceau, 1673 (1)
'Give him pap, made of flower and milke . . . put the meal in an earthern
pan, into an oven as soon as the bread is drawn, stirring it often, to dry
it equally. Pap made of this flower, besides that it is sooner concocted,
is much better than the ordinary, which is heavier, clammier, and not so
easy of digestion; for being made with raw flower, 'tis very difficult to
boil it well, without consuming the best part of the milk, leaving only the
grossest part behind, and losing by the long boiling both its goodness
and taste.'
Flour, Milk.

Nicholas Culpeper, 1676 (1)
'Make a pap of barley-bread steept in water, and boyled in milk.'
Barley bread in water, Milk.

James McMath, 1694 (4)
'Pap of new milked milk, clear ale, or yet water, and meal well dryed to
be less viscid and crud: or rather crumbs of white bread gently boiled to
a moderate consistence (though some order the milk raw as being of a
cleansing quality, easier of digestion and excellent to prevent all convul-

sions and griping pains of the stomach) . . . adding a little sugar, butter, or powdered anis.'
1) *Meal, New Milk.*
2) *Meal, Clear Ale.*
3) *Meal, Water.*
4) *White breadcrumbs, Milk, Sugar, Butter, Anis powder.*

Michael Ettmueller, 1699 (4)
'It ought to consist of white bread dry'd and beaten small, yolks of eggs and aniseed boil'd in milk or water to the consistence of a thin pulp. That which is made of flower and milk or water is fitter for paste than anything else: for it lies heavy in the child's stomach, and degenerates into a viscous tough crudity: whereas the bread being already fermented, is sooner and more easily digested.'
1) *White bread, Milk, Egg yolks, Aniseed.*
2) *White bread, Water, Egg yolks, Aniseed.*
3) *Flour, Milk.*
4) *Flour, Water.*

Pierre Dionis, 1719 (1)
'There's scarce a woman who knows not how to make pap' but few take care to dry the flour sufficiently which makes it heavy and viscous and difficult to digest. It must be made of new milk and not too thick.
Flour, New milk.

The Nurses Guide, 1729 (1)
'Pap . . . ought to be made with a little fine flower, boil'd in a great deal of milk adding to it a little salt. . . . But before this flower is boil'd in the milk, it must first be put into some vessel, and afterwards into an oven with a batch of house-hold-bread, and not be taken out till the bread is quite baked; for otherwise the flower will not be sufficiently boil'd along with the milk, because it takes a much longer time to boil than the milk: and then it will produce a crude chyle. . . . But if as much time be allow'd to boil the flower in the milk, as the flower requires, then the milk, by having its serous parts evaporated, grows thick, and is turn'd to a kind of cheese, and so produces flatulencies, and causes obstructions.'
Fine flour, Milk, Salt.

John Maubray, 1730 (4)
Pap 'is commonly made of flower and milk, or ale, with a little sugar and butter: but because flower is of itself humid and viscid . . . it ought to be first well dryed in a new or clean earthen pot in an oven: or, what is better, the pap made be made of the crumb of loaf.'
1) *Flour, Milk, Sugar, Butter.*
2) *Flour, Ale, Sugar, Butter.*
3) *Breadcrumbs, Milk, Sugar, Butter.*
4) *Breadcrumbs, Ale, Sugar, Butter.*

Henry Bracken, 1737 (1)
'. . . soft water with old manchet-bread (which has not much barm or yest in its composition) grated into it and boil'd well, afterwards adding a little canary or tent wine, I think is of the better sort.'
  Stale manchet breadcrumbs, Soft water, Canary or tent wine.

Robert James, 1746 (2)
'. . . well-fermented bread reduced to a soft pulp, by an affusion of milk, or flesh-broth, may be properly used.'
  1) *Bread, Milk.*
  2) *Bread, Meat broth.*

James Nelson, 1753 (2)
'It is usual to feed it with nothing but water pap, that is, bread and water boil'd together, without the addition of milk' but it should have 'bread and water boil'd lightly together, and milk added to it.'
  1) *Bread, Water.*
  2) *Bread, Water, Milk.*

N. Brouzet, 1755 (2)
'Pap or wheatflour, diluted in milk or water, and made of a certain consistence is the first solid aliment given to young children.' A better pap is made from the flour of wheat malt such as is used in France for brewing ale.
  1) *Wheat flour, Milk.*
  2) *Wheat flour, Water.*

Raulin, 1769 (2)
'One makes pap with light bread well baked and well fermented . . . one prepares it by boiling bread broken into morcels in water into which one puts a little oil or butter following the usage of the country. One reduces it over a gentle fire to the consistence of a jelly or of a light panada. The bread ought not be freshly baked: it is better when three or four days old. One ought to smooth the pap with brown sugar or honey or indeed with loaf sugar if the infants are threatened with diarrhoea. . . . One also makes pap with wheat biscuit, which one knows under the name of sea biscuit. One cooks it with pure water in an earthen vessel stirring with a wooden spoon until the material is reduced to a jelly. In place of biscuit one slices well fermented bread and dries these slices at the fire. One powders it and keeps it in bottles or other vessels in a dry place. When one wishes to serve this powder suitable to the quantity of pap which one wishes to prepare, one softens it with lukewarm water and reduces it over a low fire to the consistence of jelly. One regards with reason the flour of malted wheat as very good to make pap. It is prepared like the preceding. One ought to fear that pap made by the admixture of milk would become more likely to cause colics than it is by itself.'

1) *Stale bread, Water, Oil or butter, Sugar or honey.*
2) *Sea biscuit / dried powdered bread, Oil or butter, Water, Sugar or honey.*

Colin Mackenzie, 1770 (1)
'If the bread pap is made the bread should be cut into slices and some boiling water poured upon it and after standing for some time sh^d be poured off by which means you'll wash off the alum. Pap made of tops and bottoms is better. Some give biscuit pap but this is nearly the same as flower and water and consequently improper.'
   Bread or tops and bottoms, Water.

George Armstrong, 1771 (2)
'Crumb of bread boiled in soft water, to the consistence of what is commonly called pap, or a thin panada. The bread should not be new baked, and, in general, I think roll is preferable to loaf bread; because the former is commonly baked with yeast only, whereas the latter is said to have alum sometimes mixt with it. . . . This pap should be sweetened with soft, or lisbon sugar, unless the child is of a lax habit of body, in which case the finest loaf sugar should be used; and in this case too, the pap should be made with biscuit instead of roll. It should not be made sweeter than new milk; for too much sugar both palls the appetite and grows sour upon their stomachs. . . . If the infant is to be bred up by hand from the birth, it ought to have new cow's milk mixed with its victuals as often as possible. . . . The victuals should be made fresh twice a day . . . and three times in summer, and the milk must never be boiled with the pap but by itself, and added to the pap every time the child is fed; otherwise it will curdle, and grow sour on the child's stomach. It can hardly be necessary to mention, that when new milk is made use of, it must not be boiled at all.'
   1) *Breadcrumbs, Soft water, Sugar.*
   2) *Breadcrumbs, Soft water, New milk, Sugar.*

William Moss, 1781 (5)
'The food which is almost universally given; namely panada and pap, which is composed of bread and water, boiled and sweetened with brown sugar; to which is, sometimes, added a small quantity of milk; or oatmeal and water, in the form of thin water gruel, with the same additions. . . . Care is necessary in the choice of the bread; it should not be too fine nor too coarse . . . the first may make it binding; the latter too loosening. The bread should be made with yeast, without butter, or any kind of seeds, and very light; so that, when mixed in the food, it may be as smooth and free from lumps as possible. . . . When bread of any kind is put into the food, it ought to be boiled sufficiently in water first, and the milk put to it afterwards without being boiled. When all sorts of bread have disagreed with a child, I have sometimes found that a piece

of upper crust boiled whole in water, and the water poured off clear and mixed with the milk would agree very well.'
1) *Bread, Water, Sugar.*
2) *Bread, Water, Milk, Sugar.*
3) *Oatmeal, Water, Sugar.*
4) *Oatmeal, Water, Milk, Sugar.*
5) *Bread, Water, Milk.*

Jean-Louis Baudelocque, 1790 (1)
'Pap made from boiled flour, the use of which seems so generally adopted, is never less fit for a child than in the earlier periods of its existence. . . . It may be rendered a little less viscous, and more easy of digestion, by first baking the flour with which it is prepared.'
Flour, Water.

Additional recipes
Théophile Bonet, 1684 (4)
'The usual food of children . . . is Pap, made of flour, wheaten especially, and milk, of a middle consistence between a solid and a liquid, although it came nearer the former; for it cannot be supped . . . a food difficult of concoction. Some endeavour to amend this fault by long boiling. . . . Others, by mixing it well, and stirring it, make pap with a gentle boiling. . . . But neither thus is the mischief avoided, for the flour remains crude, incoctible, and insuperable . . . this is the way to make it not only proper for children, but for the use of the kitchin, of which an easie dish may be made, by mixing it with milk, broth, etc. Take barley, or oaten-flower, put it in a bag of thick cloth, boil it in a kettle for twelve hours, so as that the water may be always above it, keeping down the bag, by laying a weight upon it. When the flower is taken out, set it in an hot oven, after the bread is taken out, and keep the mass for use.' Theodorus Zwingerus, 1680, disapproved of 'making pap this common way. The matter, saith he, of pap, is flower and milk; nay, and often instead of this it is made of water, of which things, without fermentation, a paste is made only by simple boiling, with which they cram children every day.'
1) *Wheat flour, Water.*
2) *Barley or oat flour, Water, Milk.*
3) *Barley or oat flour, Water, Broth.*
4) *Flour, Milk.*

Descriptions of the paps, etc. given to James, Prince of Wales, 1688 [39]
'At first [English Children] are given nothing but boiled milk and crumbs of bread, and soon after, more solid food.' *Barillon*
'They feed [him] on boiled bread, according to the decision to give him neither milk nor a wet nurse.' *Terriesi*
'The said aliment, called "water-gruel" is composed of barley-flour,

water and sugar, to which a few currants are sometimes added.' *D'Adda*
'A species of paste made of oatmeal, barley and water.' *Terriesi*
1) *Breadcrumbs, Milk.*
2) *Bread, Water.*
3) *Barley flour, Water, Sugar.*
4) *Barley flour, Oatmeal, Water.*

Reference to the pap given to George, Prince of Wales, 1762 [40]
'The Princess [of Wales] desired a little milk to be put into the pap.'
Aug. 13.
'We found that the pap was without milk, the Princess having said as the child is well let there be no change.' Aug. 16.
'Pap made with chicken broth.' Sept. 16.

Recipe passed from Lady Spencer to her daughter-in-law, 1760s [78]
'Take a white half-penny role, such as are sold at country bakers, piqued at each end, and let all the crust be pared off very thin (that is the outward crust of all), and then put the rest of the roll into a pint of very fine spring-water, which must boil till it looks like a jelly, it must then be strained into a china or earthern bowl through a lawn sieve, this if rightly done, will be of the consistency of a jelly when it is cold; it is to be taken out in small quantities as is wanted, to be warmed and mixed with a little milk, and the milk should be mixed into every cupful, when it is warmed, and not into the whole quantity.'
Bread roll, Water, Milk.

RECIPES FOR PANADA

Simon de Vallambert, 1565 (4)
'One grates a crumb of bread very small, then one puts it in a bouillon of good flesh in a small glazed earthern pot and puts it to cook on a small charcoal fire without smoke. Sometimes it is cooked in a bouillon of peas or other legumes, with oil or butter, and more often it is cooked with goats or cows milk or milk of sweet almonds. Others mix with the panada an egg yolk or the entire egg.'
1) *Breadcrumbs, Meat broth, (sometimes egg/yolk).*
2) *Breadcrumbs, Pulse broth, Oil or butter, (sometimes egg/yolk).*
3) *Breadcrumbs, Goats' or cows' milk, (sometimes egg/yolk).*
4) *Breadcrumbs, Milk of sweet almonds, (sometimes egg/yolk).*

Johannes Baptista Van Helmont, 1662 (1)
'Made of bread boyled so long in thin ale, with clarified honey, if not, with sugar, until they shall come together in the likeness of a mucilage, or glew or jelly: then as much thin ale is mingled with, and washed on this jelly, as is sufficient for it to serve instead of drink.'
Bread, Weak ale, Clarified honey or sugar.

William Smellie, 1752 (2)
'. . . loaf bread and water, boiled up together, in form of panada, and mixed with the same quantity of new cow's milk; and sometimes with the broth of fowl or mutton. . . . The food . . . ought to be light and simple . . . such as thin panada mixed with cows milk, and sweetened with sugar: or should the child be costive, instead or sugar, honey or manna may be used.'
   1) *Loaf bread, Water, New milk, Sugar or honey.*
   2) *Loaf bread, Meat broth, Water, Sugar or honey.*

N. Brouzet, 1755 (1)
'. . . a kind of panada, made of bread slightly boiled in small beer, and sweetened with clarified honey or sugar, the whole being reduced to the consistence of a jelly, and at length diluting it with a sufficient quantity of smallbeer, to the end that this preparation may also serve to drink.'
   Bread, Smallbeer, Clarified honey or sugar.

C. D. G. De Claubry, 1783 (2)
'Panada is made in different fashions with bouillon and bread, and also is made with water, butter and bread to which one sometimes adds an egg yolk and a little sugar. One puts the whole to boil in a glazed earthern pot which is used only for this purpose and cooks well over a small fire stirring gently with a spoon.'
   1) *Bread, Broth.*
   2) *Bread, Water, Butter, Egg yolk, Sugar.*

David Spence, 1784 (1)
Thin panada sweetened with raw sugar and a little wine or spirits occasionally added. Do not use newly baked bread. Loaf bread preferable to rolls as bread in Scotland 'grow lighter and lighter everyday, and continue fit for the purpose of making panada longer than any other bread we have'.
   Bread, Sugar, Wine or spirits (liquid not given).

Michael Underwood, 1784 (1)
'The first addition of any kind . . . ought to be broth (preferably the diluted juices from roast beef or mutton) which with a little bread beat up in it in the form of panada, will be at once an agreeable and wholesome change and prepare them for further advances.'
   Bread, Meat broth.

Alphonse Leroy, late 18th century (Gardien, 1807) (1)
'One commences first by making a bouillon with a piece of veal and 2 or 3 ounces of beef. One next takes the crust of bread which has been well-boiled and one adds the bouillon according as it swells, one ought also to add aromatics. One salts this bouillon only with sugar.'
   Bread, Meat broth, Water, Sugar, Aromatics.

C. M. Gardien, 1807 (1)
(Cream of bread, a type of panada recommended by the Faculty of Medicine, Paris.)
'The manner to make this cream consists in taking a wheaten loaf which one divides in the centre to dry by baking: next one steeps it in water for six hours. It is then pressed in a cloth. It is placed in a pot and is boiled in a sufficient quantity of water for eight hours taking care to stir the whole from time to time with a spoon and to dilute with warm water as it is thickened by the fire. One adds a pinch of anis and a little sugar in the proportion of 59 grains of anis and an ounce of sugar per pound of bread. Finally one passes the whole through a hair sieve. When this cream is served for the nourishing of infants one should take care to reheat each time only the necessary quantity.'
Bread, Water, Sugar, Anis.

Additional recipes
From Colonial America* [10, 11]
'Set a little water on the fire with a glass of white wine, some sugar, and a scrape of nutmeg and lemon peel; meanwhile grate some crumbs of bread. The moment the mixture boils up, keeping it still on the fire, put the crumbs in and let it boil as fast as it can. When of a proper thickness just to drink, take it off.'
Breadcrumbs, Water, White wine, Sugar, Nutmeg, Lemon peel.

Chicken panada*
'Boil it till three parts ready in a quart of water, take off the skin, cut the white meat off when cold, and put into a marble mortar; pound it to a paste with a little of the water it was boiled in, season with a little salt, a grate of nutmeg, and the least bit of lemon peel. Boil gently for a few minutes to the consistency you like; it should be such as you can drink though tolerably thick.'
Chicken meat, Water, Salt, Nutmeg, Lemon peel.

* These two recipes were not included in the analysis as it is unclear whether these were intended for infants or as invalid foods for adults.

RECIPES FOR INFANT FOODS SIMILAR TO PAP AND PANADA

Scévole de Sainte Marthe, 1584 (1)
'The soft bread that's in the broth infus'd.'
Bread, Broth.

John Johnston, 1657 (1)
'White bread crumbs moistened with hens broath.'
Bread crumbs, Meat broth.

William Cadogan, 1748 (3)
'A little bread and water boil'd almost dry, and then mixed with fresh milk, not boiled. . . . One half of infants diet [should] be thin, light broths [made from full grown animals such as young ox or wild animals] with a little bread or rice boiled in them.'
  1) *Bread, Water, Fresh, unboiled milk.*
  2) *Bread, Meat broth.*
  3) *Rice, Meat broth.*

William Smellie, 1752 (1)
'Thick water-gruel, mixed with milk, and sweetened [with sugar or honey].'
  Water gruel, Milk, Sugar or honey.

Gentlemans Magazine, 1765 (3)
'Nothing is so good as cows-milk, but not to be boiled, with some of the biskets called tops and bottoms, or rusks, by which we are sure to avoid that pernicious thing called alum . . . half their diet should be thin, light broths, a little with bread or rice boiled in them.'
  1) *Tops and bottoms/rusks, Milk.*
  2) *Bread, Broth.*
  3) *Rice, Broth.*

John Cooke, 1768 (2)
'Half their diet should be thin, light broths, with a little well-baked bread, biscuit or rice in it.'
  1) *Bread/Biscuit, Broth.*
  2) *Rice, Broth.*

William Buchan, 1769 (1)
'One of the best methods of preparing [bread] is to boil it in water, afterwards pouring the water off, and mixing with the bread a proper quantity of new milk unboiled. Milk is both more wholesome and nourishing this way than boiled, and is less apt to occasion costiveness.'
  Bread, Water, New Milk.

Nils Rosén von Rosenstein, 1776 (1)
'Unboiled milk mixed with a little rye-biscuit, which is tender and well-fermented, being previously soaked in warm water.'
  Rye biscuit, Water, Milk.

William Osborne and Thomas Denman, 1776 (1)
'Tops and bottoms, or rusks, as being very well baked and free of alum. When used they should be provisionally steeped a night in water and then boiled up with skimmed milk, and a small proportion of sugar, a few carraway seeds may also be boiled with ye food so as to give it a slight aroma.'
  Tops and bottoms/rusks, Water, Skimmed milk, Sugar, Carraway seeds.

C. D. G. De Claubry, 1783 (1)
'The crèmes of rice, barley, oats, semolina, vermicilla are the farinaceous substances which are most proper for the nourishment of the infant given well cooked in bouillon.'
Rice/farinaceous substances, Broth.

Michael Underwood, 1784 (1)
'Boil a piece of roll, together with the upper crust, in a good deal of water, till it be very soft; by which the bread will part with some of its ascescent quality: the water should then be strained off, and the bread mixed up with some milk, which ought to be boiled if the child be very young, or inclined to be purged.'
Bread roll, Water, Milk.

Thomas Mantell, 1787 (1)
'Milk of cows, asses, or goats, and weak broths joined with some farinaceous substance, as bread, flour, biscuit, rice or semolina, is the most proper food . . . vary it, in the farinaceous part.'
Farinaceous substances/bread etc., Broth.

Hugh Downman, 1788 (1)
'Bread well fermented, unadulterate with deleterious alum, this with milk and with the limpid element decoct.'
Bread, Milk, Water.

Thomas Young, late 18th century (2)
In Paris infants are fed on flour and milk 'well-baked bread a lighter food, with milk and water and a little sugar. . . . Paste of flour and water will remain long undissolved in water; but yeast and fire makes it light, as bread, easily dissolved.'
1) *Bread, Milk, Water, Sugar.*
2) *Flour, Milk.*

CHAPTER NINE

Mixed or Supplementary Feeding:
Medical Ideas and Opinions about the Foods used for Mixed or Supplementary Feeding

"Who in the world, endued with the faculty of
reason, can imagine that such a tough substance
as flesh can agree with infants before Nature has
provided them with teeth to chew it?"
Walter Harris, *De morbis puerorum*, 1689

ALTHOUGH the previous chapter dealt with specific types of baby
foods, these were not the only foods recommended, or necessarily
given, to all infants. Physicians in particular had strong opinions about
which substances were suitable and which were not. From the foods
that they recommended, and from those that were condemned as
unsuitable for infants, it is possible to gain a picture of what *some* infants
were given for their first solid food. In order to give a clear view of
opinions throughout the period 1500 to 1800, the 52 authors who
discussed the subject are considered separately for each century [23]
(tables 9.1–9.3).

In the 16th century, only one author out of five recommended the use
of meat, and another claimed that the use of pre-chewed foods was
common. A century later, two writers out of twelve recommended meat
and one said its use was common. In the 18th century, three out of
thirty-five listed meat, and three claimed it was in common use. Fruit
and vegetables are noticeably lacking throughout. In general pap, bread,
broth, gruel, and milk-based foods remained dominant, but (tables
9.1–9.3) there was no close relationship between the substances recommended by medical writers and those said to be in common use in the
same period.

A closer analysis of recommendations, condemnations, and observations by medical writers of the common practice merely confirms the
picture, but brings out the extent to which, with the passing of time,
increasing numbers of medical writers turned against the use of pap and
ceased to recommend it as a baby food (tables 9.4–9.6) [23]. By the late
18th century more and more alternatives were suggested to pap, as it
was said to be commonly made, the most popular of which were bread

or rice in broth and panada, which (as was seen in chapter 8) was usually a bread and broth mixture. Despite this recommendation, broth was not apparently in common use, and panada, although increasingly recommended over time, does not seem to have been a very popular food at any period, compared to pap.

The fact that certain foods were singled out as being *unsuitable* for young babies indicates that these foods must have been in fairly common use. In some cases an author explicitly condemned the use of a food which he said was in common use. For example, James Nelson (1753), an anonymous writer in the *Gentleman's Magazine* (1765), and John Cooke (1768), decried the use of water-pap which they said was normally given to infants. Tea and opiates apart, unsuitable foods listed by some writers included sugar, bread, meat, and alcohol.

Since the nutritional composition and preparation of pap has been shown to have deteriorated after the 16th and early 17th centuries, it is probable that the increasing condemnation of this substance by concerned medical authors was linked to this fact, especially since those writing from Cadogan (1748) onwards gave recipes for milk mixtures and broth mixtures which were more like the paps of the 16th century.

The remaining substances were frequently mentioned by only one or two authors and reflect more the individual preferences of the men concerned, particularly in the 18th century, than the diet of actual children. Hunter (1908), Heber (1936), Hopkirk (1953), Hedley (1975) and Trumbach (1978) all described late 17th- and 18th-century children who were fed on various forms of pap as their first solid food. Possible exceptions to this were pre-chewed foods and the concern with alcoholic drinks and opiate drugs used for sedating infants, such as *Godfrey's cordial* (plate 9.1).

Alcoholic drinks and opiates. The consumption of easily available and very cheap gin during the 18th century was a serious social problem among the poor [27,40] and, as can be seen on the far right of Hogarth's *Gin Lane* (plate 9.2), it was obviously not uncommon for infants to be given tots of gin to keep them quiet. James Nelson said in 1753:

> There is a practice among the vulgar still more shocking . . . that of giving drams to the children themselves, even while infants; they . . . pour the deadly poison down the poor babe's throat even before it can speak [56].

William Buchan (1769) said: 'Some parents teach their children to guzzle ale, and other strong liquors, at every meal' but, in a time when water was not commonly drunk, he approved of 'fine smallbeer, or a little wine mixed with water' [12]. Both of these were of low alcoholic content and were 'watered-down' versions of what the adult population normally drank.

Walter Harris (1689) had been the first to draw attention to this

236

Dr. Benjamin Godfrey's Cordial.

WHICH is a medicine that plainly anfwers to its name, having a general tenden-cy to the curing many difeafes; for in all fharp pains where through vehemen-cy of anguifh, the fick are almoft deftroyed, as in the Cholic, griping of the guts, all forts of fluxes and loofeneffes, and to correct or ftop the violent working of any vomit or purge whatfoever, in any cafe, when dangerous, it is moft happily ad-miniftered.

Alfo in Hic-cough, Pleurify, Rheumatifm, Catarrhs, or defluction of humours, upon the Lungs, which caufe tickling Coughs, they are all flayed by the ufe of it in a wonderful manner.

This Cordial I recommend as the greateft help to weakly women, when they are with child, to prevent mifcarriage, by keeping off thofe wearifome pains which tire them before the time of true labour; and immediately after delivery, take two fpoonfuls of this Cordial, to keep off thofe intolerable after-pains fome women are incident to have; in this cafe it is a certain and fpeedy cure, even to admiration; and if the pains follow greatly, then take two fpoonfuls every two hours, till they abate; in this cafe it proves an incomparable medicine.

In the Bloody Flux, as alfo of the griping of the guts, attended with vehement vomiting, and a continual loofenefs, it effects fo much beyond the force of other medicines as is fcarcely credible.

This Cordial is of excellent ufe for young children that are weakly and refilefs; for it quieteth froward children, and thofe that are greatly troubled with gripes, vomitings, or loofeneffes, it gives prefent eafe.

It is of great ufe to thofe children that breed their teeth hardly; alfo for thofe that are inclined to Rickets, or any otherwife inclined to be weakly; this is in fuch cafes a ftrengthening medicine. And in all fevers, fmall-pox, and meafles, it is highly ferviceable.

It is with fafety and good fuccefs given to thofe troubled with burftennefs, efpe-cially in time of great pain, being very powerful for the expulfion of wind, and that to admiration; it affuages the torment and griping of the ftomach and bowels, and drives out the wind both upwards and downwards, which is often the caufe of gripings.

So great is the ufe of this Cordial, that thofe who have made experience of it, will have recourfe to it in the greateft ftraits.

The manner of taking for children.—A large tea-fpoonful at night, to one a year old; half a tea-fpoonful to one half a year old; and fo in proportion to younger children. Be fure always to begin with the leaft dofe at firft, which afterwards may be increafed if occafion be. Men and women may take two fpoonfuls at bed-time, or every two hours, as occafion is. Shake the glafs, that all the confection which remains at the bottom be mixed.

Note. To prevent the public from being impofed upon by counterfeits, I have put my Name to the top of the bottles, (as here) there being counterfeit forts fold with the title of Godfrey's Cordial on the top of the bottles. Prepared and fold at the great wholefale warehoufe in London, where likewife is fold, with great allowance to all fhopkeepers, &c. The Original Dr. Boerhaave's Antifcorbutic Leyden Pills, Daffy's Elixir, Dr. Boftock's Elixir, Bateman's Drops, Scot's Pills, Britifh Oil, Hungary Water, Lavender Water, Aqua Mcllis or the King's Honey Water, &c.

Dr. Benjamin Godfrey's Cordial

Plate 9.1. Late 18th-C. advertisement for the notorious Godfrey's cordial, an opiate-based panacea for all child ailments.

practice when he complained about the monthly nurses (women who cared for the mother and infant for the first month after delivery) who make no scruple to give wine or even brandy sweetened with sugar to newborn infants as often as they cry immediately, to pacify them, as they say, and keep themselves easy.

Plate 9.2. Hogarth, *Gin Lane,* 1751 (detail).
An infant is being dosed with gin, and
two young girls are sipping it.

He also complained that children were commonly given opiates in the
form of cordials 'which are less safe, nay downright noxious to children'
[32]. John Cooke made a similar complaint in 1768 when he referred to
that wicked custom of forcing opiates . . . down their throats, to
compel them to lie quiet, while the lazy nurse may sleep and forget
them [15].

¶ The pre-chewed foods said to be in common use were foods, often of
the adult diet, which were chewed by the nurse or mother to a fine
consistency before being placed in the infant's mouth. This was an
ancient and very widespread practice and may have been so common
that it was not considered worthy of mention by most authors. Pre-
chewed food was discussed by several ancient medical writers, beginning with Soranus of Ephesus in the 1st/2nd century AD. It must have
been a common custom since he condemned the habit, for 'the morsels
which the wet-nurse has formed by munching are harmful because of
being combined with phlegm' [72]. However, Galen, in the next century,
recommended pre-chewing, and again indicated that it was a common

238

practice: 'as women taught by experience do: first bread and then vegetables and meat and other such things, grinding them before putting them into the babies' mouths' [25].

Avicenna, in the 10th century, also recommended pre-chewing, as did the medieval midwife, Trotula of Salerno [74].

A Swiss surgeon, Felix Wurtz (1563), described the method when used for pap:

> In some places children are fed in this manner; they take a spoonful of pap out of the pan, put it into the mouth, then put it again into the spoon, then they give it to the child [79].

In Colonial America, a minister stated in 1750 that 'the nurse puts the meat first into her own mouth and chews and feeds her child with it' [14]. Brouzet (1755) said that foods were pre-chewed because it was believed that infants were incapable of chewing and that it was common

> in many countries very distant from each other: it is used in Italy, in Turkey, and in almost all Asia; it is also found in America, and is used in the Caribee Islands, at Canada, etc.

Brouzet's main complaint was that the 'saliva of nurses is sometimes vicious, many of them have rotten and stinking teeth, foul gums, etc.' (quite possibly due to scurvy) [11]. Despite increasing condemnation, the practice survived at least until the 19th century in England, and is still general in many parts of the world today [51,53,62].

Pre-chewing foods of the adult diet would have mechanically reduced the size of the food particles and produced a slight degree of pre-digestion of starches by mixture with the *ptyalin* in the saliva of the nurse, the actual food value of the substance remaining unchanged. The idea of pre-chewing paps and foods, athough distasteful to modern western societies, is widely accepted as normal among less developed peoples [51,53]. It may have jeopardised the health of the infant if the mother or nurse were, as Brouzet stated (1755), diseased or had an infection of the mouth and gums, but was probably a lesser source of infection than feeding a baby with an unwashed or poorly-cleaned feeding vessel.

If pap and pre-chewed foods of the adult diet were the substance most commonly given to infants as their first solid foods, then the nutritive value of those given to each child would have varied greatly, depending upon: i) the particular recipe and method employed in making the pap; ii) the quality of the diet of the family concerned; iii) whether only certain foods were selected from the adult diet to be pre-chewed for infants, or whether the baby partook of all the foods eaten by the family. Brouzet (1755) said that women gave them most of the foods they ate themselves [11], and Hurlock (1742) said that he was told by the mother of a young child that 'at about a quarter old she would begin to give them anything that she ate or drank herself, and that her

Plate 9.3. Hogarth, *Strolling actresses in a barn,*
1738 (detail). Note baby being spoonfed.

children care not for spoon victuals' [38].

Given such variables, it can only be concluded that the nutritional
value of infant foods reflected the diet and material circumstances of the
family in which the child lived for the first months of his life (plate 9.3).

¶ There was no close relationship between the foods recommended by
medical writers and those said to be in common use in the same period.
The most common food given to infants was pap. Sixteenth-century
writers thought this a suitable food but after the 17th century many
medical authors condemned its use and ceased to recommend it, preferring alternative recipes of bread or rice in broth or panada. This change
in attitude may have been related to the changing composition and
method of making pap. It was apparently common to give infants
alcoholic drinks (particularly gin or brandy) especially during the late
17th and the 18th century. This practice was condemned by medical
writers. Some, possibly many, infants were given foods pre-chewed by
the nurse or mother, a custom which excited increasing disapproval
from medical writers.

Many unknown factors relating to the methods of preparing foods, the quality of the family diet, and the variation of diet given to infants, make impossible any detailed assessment of the nutritional quality of the foods given to babies.

REFERENCES

1. Adams, S. F. (1959) Use of vegetables in infant feeding through the ages, *J. Am. Diet. Ass. 35*, 692-703.
2. Aitken, J. (1786) *Principles of midwifery*, London, 3rd ed.
3. Allen, J. (1733) *Synopsis medicinae: or, A summary view of the whole practice of physick*, London, vol.2.
4. Arbuthnot, J. (1732) *Practical rules of diet in the various constitutions and diseases of human bodies*, London.
5. Armstrong, G. (1771) *An essay on the diseases most fatal to infants*, London, 2nd ed.
6. Astruc, J. (1746) *A general and complete treatise on all the diseases incident to children from their birth to the age of fifteen*, trans. anon., London.
7. Avicenna (10th century AD) in Shah, M. H. (1966) *The general principles of Avicenna's Canon of medicine*, Karachi.
8. Barrett, R. (1699) *A companion for midwives, childbearing women and nurses. Directing them how to perform their respective offices*, London.
9. Baudelocque, J-L. (1790) *A system of midwifery*, trans. Heath, J., 3 vols, London.
10. Bracken, H. (1737) *The midwife's companion or, A treatise of midwifery*, London.
11. Brouzet, N. (1755) *An essay on the medicinal education of children; and the treatment of their diseases*, trans. anon., London.
12. Buchan, W. (1769) *Domestic medicine; or The family physician*, Edinburgh.
13. Cadogan, W. (1748) *An essay upon nursing and the management of children, from the birth to three years of age*, London.
14. Caulfield, E. (1952) Infant feeding in Colonial America, *J. Pediat. 41*, 673-87.
15. Cooke, J. (1768) Some necessary directions in the care of infants, in *A collection of pieces relative to inoculation for the smallpox*, Dublin.
16. Culpeper, N. (1675) *A directory for midwives*, London.
17. Culpeper, N. (1676) *A directory for midwives or, A guide for women, in their conception, bearing and suckling their children. Corrected from many gross errors*, London.
18. Dionis, P. (1719) *A general treatise of midwifery*, trans. anon., London.
19. Downman, H. (1788) *Infancy or, The management of children*, London, 4th ed.
20. Drummond, J. C. & Wilbraham, A. (1957) *The Englishman's food. A history of five centuries of British diet*, London.

21. Ettmueller, M. (1699) *Etmullerus abridg'd: or A complete system of the theory and practice of physic*, trans. anon., London.
22. Exton, B. (1751) *A new and general system of midwifery*, London.
23. Fildes, V. A. (1982) *The history of infant feeding 1500-1800*, Unpublished PhD thesis, Dept of Human Biology and Health, University of Surrey.
24. *Full view of all the diseases to children containing a translation of Dr Harris' book upon the acute diseases of infants, and the eminent Dr Boerhaave's treatise upon all their diseases*, (1742), London.
25. Galen (2nd century AD) *A translation of Galen's 'Hygiene' (De sanitate tuenda)*, trans. Green, R. M., Springfield, Illinois, 1951.
26. *Gentleman's Magazine* (1765) Unsigned writer, *On some of the causes that occasion the mortality of children under two years of age*, London, December.
27. George, M. D. (1966) *London life in the eighteenth century*, Harmondsworth.
28. Glisson, F. (1651) *A treatise of the rickets, being a disease common to children*, trans. Armin, P., London.
29. Guillemeau, J. (1612) *Childbirth or The happie deliverie of women. . . . To which is added A treatise of the diseases of infants, and young children: with the cure of them*, trans. anon., London.
30. Gowing, L. (1971) *Hogarth*, London.
31. Hamilton, A. (1792) *A treatise on the management of female complaints and of children in early infancy*, Edinburgh.
32. Harris, W. (1689) *A treatise of the acute diseases of infants*, trans. Martyn, J., London.
33. Heber (1936) *Dear Miss Heber. An eighteenth century correspondence*, Bamford, F. (ed.), London.
34. Hedley, O. (1975) *Queen Charlotte*, London.
35. Hoffmann, F. (c.1740) *A system of the practice of medicine*, vol.2, trans. Lewis, W., London, 1783.
36. Hopkirk, M. (1953) *Queen over the water. Mary Beatrice of Modena, Queen of James II*, London.
37. Hunter, W. (1908) An obstetric diary of William Hunter, Stark, J. N. (ed.), *Glasg. Med. J. 70*, 167-77, 241-56, 338-56.
38. Hurlock, J. (1742) *A practical treatise upon dentition*, London.
39. James, R. (1746) *The modern practice of physic. As improv'd by . . . H. Boerhaave and F. Hoffmann. . . . Being a translation of the aphorisms of the former with commentaries of Dr van Swieten*, 2 vols, London.
40. Jarrett, D. (1976) *England in the age of Hogarth*, Frogmore, Herts.
41. Johnston, J. (1657) *The idea of practical physick in twelve books*, trans. Culpeper, N. & W. R., London.
42. Jones, J. (1579) *The arte and science of preserving bodie and soule in healthe, wisedome, and catholicke religion: physically, philosophically and divinely devised*, London.

43. *Ladies dispensatorie or, Every woman her own physician*, (1740), London.

44. La Motte, G. Marquest de (1746) *A general treatise of midwifery*, trans. Tomkins, T., London.

45. Mackenzie, C. (1770) *Lectures in midwifery*, Library of the Wellcome Institute for the History of Medicine, MS 3392.

46. McMath, J. (1694) *The expert midwife: a treatise of the diseases of women with child, and in child bed . . . with fit remedies for the various maladies of newborn babes*, Edinburgh.

47. Mantell, T. (1787) *Short directions for the management of infants*, London.

48. Marshall, D. (1926) *The English poor in the eighteenth century. A study in social and administrative history*, New York, reprinted 1969.

49. Maubray, J. (1730) *The female physician containing all the diseases incident to that sex . . . together with the diet and regimen of both the mother and child*, London.

50. Mauriceau, F. (1673) *The accomplisht midwife, treating of the diseases of women with child, and in childbed . . . with fit remedies for the several indispositions of newborn babes*, trans. Chamberlen, H., London.

51. Mead, M. (1935) *Sex and temperament in three primitive societies*, New York, 3rd ed., 1963.

52. Mears, M. (1797) *The midwife's candid advice to the fair sex; or The pupil of nature*, London.

53. Mondot-Bernard, J. M. (1977) *Relationships between fertility, child mortality and nutrition in Africa. A tentative analysis*, Paris.

54. Moss, W. (1781) *An essay on the management and nursing of children in the earlier periods of infancy*, London.

55. Muffet (Moffet), T. (1584) *Health's improvement: or Rules comprising the nature, method, and manner of preparing all sorts of food used in this nation. Corrected and enlarged by Christopher Bennet*, London, 1655.

56. Nelson, J. (1753) *An essay on the government of children*, London.

57. Newcome, H. (1695) *The compleat mother or, An earnest persuasive to all mothers (especially those of rank and quality) to nurse their own children*, London.

58. *Nurses guide: or The right method of bringing up young children* (1729), London.

59. Osborne, W. & Denman, T (1776) *Sketches of the practice of midwifery. From the lectures of Drs Osborne and Denman*, Library of the Wellcome Institute for the History of Medicine, MS 2098.

60. Paré, A. (1575) *The workes of that famous chirurgion Ambrose Parey*, trans. Johnston, T., London, 1634.

61. Pechey (Peachey), J. (1697) *A general treatise on the diseases of infants and children. Collected from the best practical authors*, London.

62. Ploss, H. H., Bartels, M. & Bartels, P. (1935) *Woman,* Dingwall, E. J. (ed.), London, vol.3.
63. Porter, R. (1982) *English society in the eighteenth century,* Harmondsworth.
64. *Present day practice in infant feeding* (1974) DHSS report on health and social subjects no.9, London.
65. Rodin, A. E. (1981) Infants and gin-mania in 18th-century London, *J. Am. Med. Ass. 245* (12), 1237-9.
66. Rosenstein, N. R. von (1776) *The diseases of children and their remedies,* trans. Sparrman, A., London.
67. Sainte Marthe, S. de (1584) *Paedotrophiae: or The art of bringing up children,* trans. anon., London, 1710.
68. Sharp, J. (1671) *The midwives book or The whole art of midwifery discovered,* London.
69. Sloane, H. (1748) *Letter to John Milner, vice-president of the Hospital for the maintenance and education of exposed and deserted young children,* 28 October. Quoted in full in Brownlow, J. (1847) *Memoranda,* London.
70. Smellie, W. (1752) *A treatise on the theory and practice of midwifery,* London, vols 1 and 3.
71. Smith, H. (1774) *Letters to married women on nursing and the management of children. The 3rd edition, revised and considerably enlarged,* London.
72. Soranus (1st/2nd century AD) *Soranus' Gynecology,* trans. Temkin, O. *et al.,* Baltimore.
73. Spence, D. (1784) *A system of midwifery,* Edinburgh.
74. Trotula of Salerno (11th century AD) *The diseases of women. A translation of Passionibus mulierum curandorum,* Mason-Hoyl, E., New York, 1940.
75. Trumbach, R. (1978) *The rise of the egalitarian family,* New York.
76. Underwood, M. (1784) *A treatise on the diseases of children,* London.
77. Watney, J. (1976) *Mother's ruin. A history of gin,* London.
78. Wilson, C. A. (1976) *Food and drink in Britain. From the stone age to recent times,* Harmondsworth.
79. Wurtz, F. (1563) *The children's book.* Bound with *An experimental treatise of surgerie in four parts,* trans. and corrected Lennerton-Fox, London, 1656.
80. Young, T. (late 18th century) *Young's midwifery,* Library of the Wellcome Institute for the History of Medicine, MSS 5106 and 5107.

CHAPTER TEN

Mixed or Supplementary Feeding:
The Practice of Mixed Feeding

"We may be well assured, there is a great mistake either in
the quantity or quality of children's food, or both, as it is
usually given them; because they are made sick by it."
William Cadogan, *An essay upon nursing,* 1748

THREE factors of infant nutrition will be discussed in this chapter:
the *age* at which foods other than breastmilk were introduced: the
amount of food given; and the disorders and *diseases* which were associated with the introduction of solid foods.

¶ *Age.* This was not a topic with which medical authors were particularly
concerned, possibly because it was assumed that women would give
additional foods either when a child appeared to be ready for them, or
according to the custom among family and friends. Royal infants apart,
little evidence has been discovered about the age of commencement of
mixed feeding among most children. This section is therefore confined
to the recommendations of medical authors.

Between 1500 and 1800 about thirty writers discussed the introduction of mixed feeding, and the two main factors which they thought
were important when considering the time to begin were: the age of the
child, and the appearance of the first incisor teeth [26]. Twenty mentioned a specific age at which infants should be given additional foods
(table 10.1). Although in the 16th century 7–9 months was the favoured
time to introduce mixed feeding, there was a change that began in the
late 17th century towards much earlier introduction of additional food.
Sixty-five per cent of 17th- and 18th-century writers thought that this
should be given at 2–5 months, with the majority favouring 2–4 months.

The age of the child was not the only criterion of the majority of
authors. Often several other factors were taken into account [26] (table
10.2), relating to the appearance of first teeth, availability of breastmilk,
the health of the child and the wish to habituate it early to solids. They
included the following: i) if the milk supply of the nurse or mother were
insufficient [9,14,35,60]; ii) to get the child used to other foods early

Plate 10.1. Etching by A. von Ostade, 1648.
Against a typical peasant interior a father
spoonfeeds the baby while the small child
sups its pap or gruel.

[4,32,64]; iii) if the child were particularly lusty and strong [19,67,75]; iv) if the child were unable to suck [35]; v) if the nurse were menstruating [64] (cf. chapter 6, p.179).

The idea that the appearance of the child's first teeth was the signal for mixed feeding to begin went back at least as far as the 2nd century AD, when Galen suggested it [28], and it was repeated by Avicenna in the 10th century [7]. Soft foods such as pap were probably given earlier (plate 10.1), and the cutting of the first teeth (with the implication that the child was then able to chew) was the sign that more varied foods than paps and panadas could begin to be given in preparation for weaning. Similarly, some of the authors, who thought it a good idea to get the child used to foods early on, had in mind the eventuality that early weaning might be necessary [4,32,53,64].

Two definite references from Europe have been found to verify this. Heronymus Mercurialis, an Italian physician from Padua, is quoted as saying in 1552 that Nature intended milk to last into the second or third year, but 'he was bound to admit that these modern women do start giving sopped bread as early even as the third month' [54]. Hunt (1972) quotes de Vallambert (1565) as saying:

Long before the first teeth appear, even before the age of three months . . . the women of the countryside, and the poor women of the towns [give bouilli to their children] because if the latter took no other nourishment beside milk, they would not be able to go so long without sucking as they do, during the time when mothers are absent and held down by their work. . . . Because of their continued labour and poor life [these mothers] do not have a lot of milk, so that they would not be capable of feeding the child if he did not take other nourishment in addition to milk from the breast [20,37].

This was also reported to be the case in 17th-century Scotland:

There are many women who give pap to their children as soon as they are born, and nurses who have little milk ordinarily do so, to hinder their crying as they will do when they are hungry [47].

The problem of an inadequate supply of breastmilk was not confined to the very poor, since pap was also given to the future King Louis XIII in 1601, at the age of 18 days, because his physician thought the nurses had insufficient milk to satisfy his hunger [49].

The only indication of general practice about the introduction of mixed feeding in the late 18th century comes from Thomas Young, who admitted that although breast milk only was usually advised for 8–9 months, women 'oft begin to give it [i.e. pap] much earlier nowadays' [77], and in 1762, the future George IV was given pap, in addition to milk from his wet nurse, within a few days of his birth [34,38].

This seems to have been a normal custom, since there is no indication that it was an exceptional procedure, or that his wet nurse had insufficient breastmilk. In view of these comments, the late age (7–9 months) recommended by Jones (1579) and Ste Marthe (1584) probably bore little relation to the practice of the majority of mothers and nurses and, if age were ever taken as an absolute requirement, the much earlier age advised from the late 17th century onwards was probably closer to reality. It is similar to that advised and practised today in Britain [63], although modern pre-industrial societies vary in the time at which they begin giving additional food, ranging from 0–4 months to 12 months and over, depending upon the custom of their particular society or ethnic group [55].

In pre-industrial Britain, women probably took several factors into account when deciding to supplement their breastmilk, not least their own ability to satisfy their child's hunger. The recommendations of physicians would not have reached the mass of the population, although possibly they influenced the upper and middle classes [58,74], so that this decision was undoubtedly made by each individual woman according to the needs of herself, her child, and her family, and related to the common practices she observed around her.

¶ Evidence for how much and how often additional foods were given to infants is difficult to find, since few writers before the 18th century mention the matter, and those who were concerned with the quantity or frequency of feeding tended to have individual and differing opinions from which a coherent picture of practice could not be composed. There was a division of recommendations, and possibly practice, following the appearance of Cadogan's *Essay* [14] (plate 10.2), so the periods discussed here will be: i) 1500–1747; ii) 1748–1800.

Frequency. i) During the period 1500–1747, 9 authors discussed this point, and the majority suggested that additional food be given only once a day at first [26]. John Maubray (1730) specified that the morning was the best time, whilst the anonymous *Nurses' guide* (1729) suggested feeding the child at noon. This could then be increased to twice a day [31,47,51], although the *Nurses' guide* warned against giving pap too often. John Jones (1579) was exceptional in recommending that children be fed at mealtimes, presumably indicating three times a day. Two authors recommended frequent or demand feeding of foods [39,66], although Ste Marthe (1584) said that this was only if the child really were crying for food. As a variant of demand feeding, McMath (1694) suggested that the frequency of feeding could be varied according to the needs of the individual child.

The quantity of food was rarely discussed, although Mauriceau (1673) said that only a little should be given at first, and 5 writers warned against overfeeding. Harris (1689) said that feeding infants with meat too early was inseparable from over-feeding. Over-feeding

(16)

more fubftantial, and the Appetite ever precede the Food ; not only with regard to the daily Meals, but thofe Changes of Diet, which opening, increafing Life requires. But this is never done in either Cafe, which is one of the greateft Miftakes of all Nurfes. Thus far Nature, if fhe be not interrupted, will do the whole Bufinefs perfectly well; and there feems to be nothing left for a Nurfe to do, but to keep the Child clean and fweet, and to tumble and tofs it about a good deal, play with it, and keep it in good Humour.

BUT now the Child (I mean when it is about three Months old) requires more folid Suftenance, we are to enquire what, and how much, is moft proper to give it. We may be well affured, there is a great Miftake either in the Quantity or Quality of Childrens Food, or both, as it is ufually given them; becaufe they are made fick by it. As to Quantity, there is a moft ridiculous Error in the common Practice; for it is generally fuppofed, that whenever a Child cries, it wants Victuals; and it is accordingly fed, ten, twelve, or more times in a Day and Night. This is fo obvious a Mifapprehenfion, that I am furprized it fhould ever prevail. If a Child's Wants and Motions are diligently and judicioufly attended to, it will be found that it never cries but from Pain : Now the firft Senfations of Hunger are not attended with Pain ; accordingly a Child (I mean this of a very young one) that is hungry, will make a hundred other Signs of its Want, before it will cry

(17)

cry for Food. If it be healthy and quite eafy in its Drefs, it will hardly ever cry at all. Indeed thefe Signs and Motions, I fpeak of, are but rarely to be obferved; becaufe it feldom happens that Children are ever fuffered to be hungry. In a few, very few, whom I have had the Pleafure to fee reafonably nurfed, that were not fed above two or three times in four and twenty Hours, and yet were perfectly healthy, active and happy; I have feen thefe Signals, which were as intelligible as if they had fpoke.

THERE are many Faults in the Quality of their Food : It is not fimple enough. Their Paps, Panada's, Gruels, &c. are generally enriched with Sugar, Spice, and fometimes a Drop of Wine; neither of which they ought ever to tafte. Our Bodies never want them : they are what Luxury only has introduced, to the Deftruction of the Health of Mankind. It is not enough that their Food be fimple, it fhould be alfo light. Several People, I find, are miftaken in their Notions of what is light; and fancy that moft kinds of Paftry, Puddings, Cuftards, &c. are light, that is, light of Digeftion. But there is nothing heavier in this Senfe than unfermented Flour and Eggs boil'd hard, which are the chief Ingredients of thofe Preparations. What I mean by light, to give the beft Idea I can of it, is any Subftance that is eafily feparated, and foluble in warm Water. Good Bread. is the lighteft thing I know; the Power of due Fermentation, in which confifts the

C

Plate 10.2. W. Cadogan, *Essay upon nursing,*
1748. These pages refer to the introduction of mixed feeding.

very young infants was not said to be common during this long period. Hurlock (1742) alone quoted an example. A child who, throughout her first year, frequently had calf's head, pig, turkey, etc., and

for a good part of the summer had half a handsome chicken daily dressed for dinner; the flesh of which, was all, except for the skin and sinews, constantly eat up by the child, and liked better roasted than boiled: besides which, she eat her pannikin of milk victuals for breakfast; again, at the Nurses breakfast time, tea with toast and butter; and about eleven in the morning some bread and butter, or else broth; these with the addition of the several feedings between noon and night etc. may well be supposed to have bred ill juices in the blood of so young a child [39].

This description was presented as exceptional, the result of the ignorance of the parents about dieting young infants, according to Hurlock. The warnings of others against over-feeding were because of the diseases it was said to cause. These included vomiting, indigestion, distension and pain in the belly [42,47,66]; gripes, colic, and diarrhoea [15,47], difficulty in breathing [42], and ultimately death [47,66]. These would even today be the expected consequences of gross over-feeding, but there is no evidence that these were anything but warnings against over-indulgence rather than reflections of actual practice. Many of the above are also symptomatic of salmonella and other gastro-intestinal infections as well as protein-calorie deficiency (kwashiorkor), so that there *may* have been factors here other than simple over-feeding, but in the absence of sufficient evidence these must remain hypothetical.

From the lack of interest shown by medical writers in the frequency and quantity of additional foods which were to be given to infants, this was apparently a matter left to the woman involved in child care and the mother or nurse used her own judgement and/or experience, based upon what she observed as usual around her.

ii) In the period 1748–1800, 11 authors discussed how frequently food should be given to the child and, as in the preceding period, it was suggested that infants should be fed at first only once or twice a day; that by the age of 5 or 6 months 2–3 times a day was appropriate and certainly not more than 4 times in 24 hours [26]. George Armstrong (1771) thought that feeds should be frequent at first, and Brouzet (1755) indicated that this may have been common practice since, he said, nurses gave food whenever their babies cried. Again, this may have been related to a woman's milk supply, since Moss (1781) said additional food could be given as often as necessary when the nurse or mother had insufficient milk.

It was in this period that the first mention was made of adhering to set times when feeding very young infants [14], and authors were insistent that they should not be fed at night (which suggests that this may have been a fairly common occurrence). However, Armstrong (1771) disagreed, and recommended that additional foods should first be given *only* at night, so that the mothers's rest was not disturbed. Moss (1781) thought there was nothing wrong in the advice to stick to regular feeding times, but claimed that it was difficult to accomplish in practice.

The quantity of food to be given was rarely mentioned. Cadogan (1748) said that it should be ruled by the child's appetite, whilst Underwood (1784) thought that it depended upon the strength and circumstance of the child. Mantell (1787) stated that the quantity should be gradually increased. No medical attention was paid to the balance of the different foods in the child's diet, and it is possible that small children could have suffered malnutrition by being over-fed with certain foodstuffs (such as water pap) whilst not receiving sufficient of all essential nutrients. A less likely possibility (given the concern about over-feeding) is that subnutrition frequently occurred.

A main concern of authors in the second half of the 18th century was over-feeding, and 15 authors discussed this problem (table 10.3) [26]. The adverse effects of over-feeding were said to be:

i) gastro-intestinal disorders, such as vomiting, distended painful belly, indigestion, gripes and colic [4,13,14,57,69];

ii) death [16,22,57,75];

iii) nearly all childhood diseases [14,22];

iv) difficulty in breathing [64];

v) fevers and convulsions [16].

These differed little from ill-effects noted by earlier writers. The addition of all childhood diseases, fevers, etc. was a reflection of the current views of the aetiology of children's disorders such as rickets, in which over-feeding was thought to be a major causative factor [30].

The over-feeding of infants in the past has been presented as a problem by writers discussing infant feeding, but it is important to note that, throughout the 300-year period, this was the topic within the context of mixed feeding with which the fewest number of writers was concerned. Only 20 writers (i.e. 35% of those discussing mixed feeding) thought it worthy of mention. Therefore, although it may have been a problem which increased, or became more apparent, in the second half of the 18th century, this is by no means certain. Those discussing it were almost all physicians with practices among the fashionable and wealthy [26], among whom over-feeding may well have been a problem; it is unlikely that it was so among the poor [36,50]. Also, with the exception of Clark (1751) and Cooke (1768), all of them were major writers on infant feeding and gave a very full discussion of the different aspects of infant nutrition, of which over-feeding was only one. Thus over-feeding was not necessarily as prevalent as has been assumed, since, as one topic within the whole subject of infant feeding, it received relatively little attention, and probably applied only to the children of the rich and to those whose nurses and families could afford to indulge their infants. This opinion may be reinforced by the fact that, whilst evidence from the present day indicates that young babies fed on the large amounts of food described by 18th-century authors rapidly become visibly overweight [41,63], portraits, caricatures, and other pictorial evidence of the period, very rarely depict young babies or children as obese, or even moderately plump (plate 10.3).

The relative lack of interest in the actual practice of mixed feeding by both medical and non-medical authors (the latter ignored the subject), was almost certainly because it was considered to be outside the realm of physicians or midwives, and among the wealthy was also outside the family proper. When a child was newly-born, midwives, men-midwives and sometimes physicians would all be involved around the time of the birth and the puerperium. They would thus be concerned with such

Plate 10.3. Mixed feeding. Engraving by
Charles Martin, 1778.

matters as neonatal feeding, whether the child was to be put out to nurse
or to stay within the family home. In wealthy homes, once the child had
left the lying-in chamber and either entered the home of a wet nurse or
been consigned to a distant nursery, its care became the responsibility
of women (plate 10.3); and the midwives, surgeons and physicians
(who wrote the books) were no longer involved. Similarly, the time of
weaning was one which was discussed and noted by diarists and scholarly writers because it was a moment of some anxiety, and marked the
transition from infancy to childhood. If it were wet nursed, it also
marked the child's return home. Thus it was a subject important
enough for discussion. But what happened in the period between birth
and weaning was the concern of women, and was therefore rarely
recorded unless something abnormal occurred. The acceptance of
mixed feeding as being the province of women is probably the reason
why so little information was given about the frequency and amount of
supplementary foods, and the age at which they were introduced. Quite
simply, men did not know, and did not regard it as their concern.

¶ In the 17th and 18th centuries medical writers increasingly associated the intake of foods other than breastmilk (particularly pap) with the occurrence of certain diseases (table 10.4) [26]. Most authors only specified improper foods as causative agents, but nearly half the writers who discussed the subject specifically indicted pap – particularly if it was not properly cooked and/or was given at too early an age (table 10.5) [26].

The only other foods which were singled out as causative agents were: i) sugar as a cause of 'looseness' [57]; ii) eating flesh meat too early as a cause of worms [2,33]; iii) sweet foods, cakes, and sweetmeats as a cause of worms [6] and a cause of death [14]; iv) alcoholic drinks as a cause of convulsions [10]. These were essentially the foibles of individual physicians. Although worms could have been taken in by eating contaminated pork (the meat most commonly eaten by the poor) [23], Harris (1689) and his followers were more concerned that infants should not eat meat before they had cut their first teeth and thus tended to blame all childhood ills on its consumption.

Gastro-intestinal upsets, particularly gripes and looseness, were the main problems which these authors associated with mixed feeding, and this has a modern parallel in the condition known in the Third World as weanling diarrhoea. This condition was originally investigated and named in the Punjab, India, in 1963, and several confirmatory studies have been done, particularly in Latin America, which have established it as an epidemiological entity [24,41,56]. Such diarrhoea in infants is closely connected with the introduction of foods other than breastmilk, and is thought to be the result of several interacting factors during the early weaning period including: i) enteral infection, associated with a sudden change in intestinal microflora or with large doses of environmental bacterial contamination; ii) the effects of malnutrition, such as diminished intestinal enzymes; iii) a diet of indigestible, ill-cooked foods which may be poorly absorbed or irritant. In the Punjab, the observed death rate was relatively low in the first 6 months of life (20.6 per 1000), more than doubled in the second 6 months of life (53.6 per 1000), and decreased thereafter until children were completely weaned from the breast by the beginning of the third year of life [41].

Since, in the 17th and 18th centuries, all three of these contributory factors would have been present among the poor, especially in times of poor harvests and famine [3], and at least two, (i and iii) among the more well-fed infants, it seems that there existed a similar, if not identical, condition to the weanling diarrhoea of the 20th century. This condition could explain not only the reported gastro-intestinal symptoms and deaths, but possibly the many cases of convulsions were also the result of diarrhoea and consequent *hypernatraemia* (an abnormally high concentration of sodium in the blood) [68].

The association of mixed feeding with rickets was first explicitly stated by Glisson in his definitive treatise of 1650/1 [30]. He observed that children were not affected while they were fed on breastmilk alone, thus implicating mixed feeding and weaning from the breast as one cause of the disease. However, Guillemeau (1612) made the observation that

> to give him any other nourishment than milke or dishmeate, before he hath teeth, . . . often times doe cause the child to have bunches, or contusions, about his backbone and ribs [31].

He attributed a similar observation to Avicenna in the 10th century [7] and Soranus of Ephesus also noted this phenomenon [70]. This has been taken as an early reference to the disease of rickets as known in the 17th century. Brouzet (1755) made the interesting comment that rickets was very common in Paris where infants were normally fed on pap, but was rare in Languedoc, where the usual food given was panada [12]. He attributed this to the use of malted flour in the preparation of the latter, but probably a more relevant factor was that infants in Languedoc were exposed to more sunlight than in urban Paris, and that (as has been seen in chapter 8) panada was more likely than pap to contain milk, especially in a country region.

The very few references to leanness [13,59], and fatness or bloatedness [58,69] in connection with mixed feeding implies that protein-calorie malnutrition, such as is seen in some pre-industrial societies today [41], was not a great problem in pre-industrial Britain except possibly at times of severe famine [3], but insufficient evidence has been found to confirm or refute this point.

The fact that 16th-century authors did not relate mixed feeding to infantile disorders was possibly a reflection of the general lack of interest in the treatment of children's ailments in that period [65,72], when physicians rarely were consulted about children [46], and books devoted specifically to children's diseases were rare [72]. Although there may have been a lower incidence of gastro-intestinal upsets because the foods offered were more suitably prepared, this is a less plausible explanation given the general level of hygiene at the time since, as shown in other parts of this study, the connection between infant management and feeding and the health of children was increasingly made as medical interest in the causes and treatment of the diseases of children increased.

¶ In the 16th century the ideal age for introducing mixed feeding was 7–9 months, but during the late 17th and 18th centuries the much earlier age of 2–4 months was favoured. The age at which foods other than breastmilk were first given was probably earlier than the time recommended by physicians and midwives, depending upon the custom of each woman. Age and the cutting of the first teeth were the two main considerations when starting infants on a mixed diet. Medical authors made few references to the frequency and quantity of additional foods, probably because this was thought to be the concern of women. In the second half of the 18th century there was some discussion of over-feeding although this was almost certainly confined to the children of the wealthy.

Sixteenth-century authors did not relate infantile disorders to the introduction of mixed feeding but those of the 17th and 18th centuries described several conditions which resulted from giving 'improper food', particularly pap. The level of concern of medical authors in this aspect of feeding reflected the increased interest of physicians in childhood diseases, especially in the 18th century. Disorders of the gastrointestinal tract were a major problem; these were probably a variety of the disease which today is recognised as 'weanling diarrhoea'. Other conditions, mentioned by relatively few writers, included rickets and worms.

REFERENCES

1. Aitken, J. (1786) *Principles of midwifery*, London, 3rd ed.
2. Allen, J. (1733) *Synopsis medicinae: or, A summary view of the whole practice of physick*, London, vol.2.
3. Appleby, A. B. (1973) Disease or famine? Mortality in Cumberland and Westmorland, *Econ. Hist. Rev. 26*, 403-32.
4. Armstrong, G. (1771) *An essay on the diseases most fatal to infants. To which are added rules to be observed in the nursing of children: with a particular view to those who are brought up by hand*, London, 2nd ed.
5. *Artificial feeds for the young infant* (1980) D H S S report on health and social subjects no.18, London.
6. Astruc, J. (1746) *A general and complete treatise on all the diseases incident to children from their birth to the age of fifteen*, trans. anon., London.
7. Avicenna (10th century A D) In Shah, M. H. (1966) *The general principles of Avicenna's Canon of medicine*, Karachi.
8. Barrett, R. (1699) *A companion for midwives, childbearing women and nurses. Directing them how to perform their respective offices*, London.
9. Baudelocque, J-L. (1790) *A system of midwifery*, trans. Heath, J., London.
10. Baynard, E. (1706) *The history of cold bathing: both ancient and modern, part II*, London, 2nd ed.
11. Bracken, H. (1737) *The midwife's companion or, A treatise of midwifery*, London.

12. Brouzet, N. (1755) *An essay on the medicinal education of children; and the treatment of their diseases*, trans. anon., London.
13. Buchan, W. (1769) *Domestic medicine; or The family physician*, Edinburgh.
14. Cadogan, W. (1748) *An essay upon nursing and the management of children, from their birth to three years of age*, London.
15. Cheyne, G. (1724) *An essay of health and long life*, Bath.
16. Clark, W. (1751) *The province of midwives in the practice of their art*, Bath and London.
17. Cooke, J. (1768) *Some necessary directions in the care of infants*, in *A collection of pieces relative to inoculation for the smallpox*, Dublin.
18. Culpeper, N. (1675) *A directory for midwives*, London.
19. Culpeper, N. (1676) *A directory for midwives; or, A guide for women, in their conception, bearing and suckling their children. Corrected from many gross errors*, London.
20. De Vallambert S. (1565) *Cinq livres, de la manière de nourir et gouverner les enfants des leur naissance*, Poictiers. Also the partial translation in Drake, T. G. H. (1931) Pap and panada, *Ann. Med. Hist. 3* (N.S.), 289-95.
21. Dionis, P. (1719) *A general treatise of midwifery*, trans. anon., London.
22. Downman, H. (1788) *Infancy or, The management of children. A didactic poem in six books*, London, 4th ed.
23. Drummond, J. C. & Wilbraham, A. (1957) *The Englishman's food. A history of five centuries of British diet*, London, revised ed.
24. Ebrahim, G. J. (1983) *Nutrition in mother and child health*, London.
25. Ettmueller, M. (1699) *Etmullerus abridg'd: or A complete system of the theory and practice of physic*, trans. anon., London.
26. Fildes, V. A. (1982) *The history of infant feeding 1500-1800*, Unpublished PhD thesis, University of Surrey, Dept. Human Biology and Health.
27. *Full view of all the diseases incident to children containing a translation of Dr Harris' book upon the acute diseases of infants and the eminent Dr Boerhaave's treatise upon all their diseases* (1742), London.
28. Galen (2nd century AD) *A translation of Galen's 'Hygiene' (De sanitate tuenda)*, trans. Green, R. M., Springfield, Illinois.
29. *Gentleman's magazine* (1765) Unsigned writer, *On some of the causes that occasion the mortality of children under two years of age. In answer to queries in the public papers, concerning the cause of the great mortality of infants in this metropolis under that age*, London, December.
30. Glisson, F. (1651) *A treatise of the rickets, being a disease common to children*, trans. Armin, P., London.
31. Guillemeau, J. (1612) *Childbirth or The happie deliverie of women. . . . To which is added a treatise of the diseases of infants,*

     and young children: with the cure of them, trans. anon., London.
32. Hamilton, A. (1792) *A treatise on the management of female complaints and of children in early infancy*, Edinburgh.
33. Harris, W. (1689) *A treatise of the acute diseases of infants*, trans. Martyn, J., London, 1742. Also see *Full view*.
34. Hedley, O. (1975) *Queen Charlotte*, London.
35. Hoffmann, F. (c.1740) *A system of the practice of medicine*, vol.2, trans. Lewis, W., London, 1783.
36. Hufton, O. H. (1974) *The poor of eighteenth century France, 1750-1789*, Oxford.
37. Hunt, D. (1972) *Parents and children in history: the psychology of family life in early modern France*, New York and London.
38. Hunter, W. (1908) An obstetric diary of William Hunter, Stark, J. N. (ed.), *Glasg. Med. J. 70*, 167-77, 241-56, 338-56.
39. Hurlock, J. (1742) *A practical treatise upon dentition*, London.
40. James, R. (1746) *The modern practice of physic. As improv'd by . . . H. Boerhaave and F. Hoffmann. . . . Being a translation of the aphorisms of the former with the commentaries of Dr van Swieten*, 2 vols, London.
41. Jelliffe, D. B. & Jelliffe, E. F. P. (1978) *Human milk in the modern world. Psychosocial, nutritional and economic significance*, Oxford.
42. Johnston, J. (1657) *The idea of practical physick in twelve books*, trans. Culpeper, N. & W. R., London.
43. Jones, J. (1579) *The arte and science of preserving bodie and soule in healthe, wisedom, and catholicke religion: physically, philosophically and divinely devised*, London.
44. *Ladies dispensatorie or, Every woman her own physician*, (1740), London.
45. *McCance and Widdowson's The composition of foods* (1978) revised and extended Paul, A. A. & Southgate. D. A. T. (eds), London, 4th ed.
46. MacDonald, M. (1981) *Mystical Bedlam. Madness, anxiety and healing in seventeenth-century England*, Cambridge. Also Personal communication.
47. McMath, J. (1694) *The expert midwife: a treatise of the diseases of women with child, and in child bed . . . with fit remedies for the various maladies of newborn babes*, Edinburgh.
48. Mantell, T. (1787) *Short directions for the management of infants*, London.
49. Marvick, E. W. (1974) Childhood history and decisions of state: the case of Louis XIII, *Hist. Childh. Quart. 2*, 135-80.
50. Marshall, D. (1926) *The English poor in the eighteenth century. A study in social and administrative history*, New York, reprinted 1969.
51. Maubray (Mowbray), J. (1730) *The female physician containing all the diseases incident to that sex . . . together with the diet and regimen of both the mother and child*, London.

52. Mauriceau, F. (1673) *The accomplisht midwife, treating of the diseases of women with child, and in childbed . . . with fit remedies for the several indispositions of newborn babes,* trans. Chamberlen, H., London.
53. Mears, M. (1797) *The midwife's candid advice to the fair sex; or The pupil of nature,* London.
54. Mercurialis, H. (1552) *Nomothesaurus seu ratio lactandi infantes,* Padua. Cited in Still, G. F. (1931) *History of Paediatrics,* London.
55. Mondot-Bernard, J. M. (1977) *Relationships between fertility, child mortality and nutrition in Africa. A tentative analysis,* Paris.
56. Morley, D. (1973) *Paediatric priorities in the developing world,* London.
57. Moss, W. (1781) *An essay on the management and nursing of children in the earlier periods of infancy,* London.
58. Nelson, J. (1753) *An essay on the government of children,* London.
59. *Nurses guide: or the right method of bringing up young children. By an eminent physician,* London, 1729.
60. Paré, A. (1575) *The workes of that famous chirurgion Ambrose Parey,* trans. Johnston, T., London, 1634.
61. Pechey (Peachey) J. (1697) *A general treatise of the diseases of infants and children. Collected from the best practical authors,* London.
62. Phaire, T. (1545) *The boke of chyldren,* London. Reprinted 1955, Edinburgh..
63. *Present day practice in infant feeding* (1974) DHSS report on health and social subjects no.9, London.
64. Rosenstein, N. R. von (1776) *The diseases of children and their remedies,* trans. Sparrman, A., London.
65. Ruhrah, J. (1925) *Pediatrics of the past,* New York.
66. Sainte Marthe, S. de (1584) *Paedotrophiae: or The art of bringing up children,* trans. anon., London, 1710.
67. Sharp, J. (1671) *The midwives book or The whole art of midwifery discovered,* London.
68. Shaw, J. C. L., Jones, A. & Gunther, M. (1973) Mineral content of brands of milk for infant feeding, *Br. Med. J.,* 12-15. Also Shaw, J. C. L., Personal communcation.
69. Smith, H. (1774) *Letters to married women on nursing and the management of children. The 3rd edition, revised and considerably enlarged,* London.
70. Soranus of Ephesus (1st/2nd century AD) *Soranus' Gynecology,* trans. Temkin, O. *et al.,* Baltimore.
71. Spence, D. (1784) *A system of midwifery,* Edinburgh.
72. Still, G. F. (1931) *The history of paediatrics,* London.
73. *Trace elements in human nutrition* (1973) WHO technical report series no.532, Geneva.
74. Trumbach, R. (1978) *The rise of the egalitarian family,* New York.

75. Underwood, M. (1784) *A treatise on the diseases of children. With directions for the management of infants from the birth: especially such as are brought up by hand,* London.
76. Wood, C. B. S. & Walker-Smith, J. A. (1981) *MacKeith's Infant feeding and feeding difficulties,* Edinburgh and London, 6th ed.
77. Young, T. (late 18th century) *Young's midwifery,* Library of the Wellcome Institute for the History of Medicine, MSS 5106 and 5107.

Artificial Feeding

CHAPTER ELEVEN

Artificial Feeding:
The Incidence of, and Reasons for,
Handfeeding

"The children as soon as they were borne, were delivered
to the men to nourysshe up with milke, and such other
things as theyr tendrenes required . . . if a wench was born
they streight scarred ye pappes, that they might not growe
to hindre them in the warres. Therefore the Grecians
called them Amazones, as ye would saie, Pappeless."
Johannes Boemus, 1555

MEDICAL WRITERS have habitually paid less attention to artificial feeding than to any other aspect of infant nutrition. This has been
assumed, wrongly, to indicate that artificial feeding was scarcely practised before the late 18th or 19th century. Use of a range of sources
extending beyond medical texts, however, shows that it was a well-
known and long-established technique for rearing certain groups of
children, and had been practised in and since antiquity. Numbers of
feeding vessels have been found in infant graves from 4000 B C onwards
(plate 11.1), and analysis has shown some to contain residues of milk
[61]. The use to which such vessels were put is recorded in illustrations,
while literary references range from artificial nipples in the Roman
Empire [103] to animal horns in the dry-nursing of some medieval saints
[67], from sucking-bottles in 15th-century Germany to the widespread
custom of handfeeding in 19th-century Europe and North America
[35]. Whether such utensils were used for supplementary feeding only,
or whether – and how often – babies were artificially fed from birth, is
impossible to determine, but there must always have been infants for
whom no breastmilk was available: children of mothers who died during
or soon after childbirth; children of overworked, poorly-nourished
mothers who consequently had insufficient breastmilk; abandoned children, especially females, whose families did not wish to rear them;
foundlings in institutions; infants with deformities of the mouth or
pharynx whch rendered them incapable of sucking in the normal way;
and infants with congenital syphilis, for whom no wet nurse would risk
her health. These are valid and, until the recent past, relatively common

Plate 11.1. Sudan, 1st millennium
BC. Grave of twin babies, showing
two spouted feeding vessels and small
bowl found in the grave. (Addison,
Jebel Moya, London 1949.)

reasons for dry nursing babies; whilst in particular regions in certain
periods the vagaries of fashion or ingrained local custom caused infants
not to be breastfed, even if breastmilk was available. Thus there were
four grounds for raising infants by hand in pre-industrial Europe and its
American colonies: i) *custom*; ii) *necessity*, which could affect children
from all social groups; iii) *institutions*, which cared for foundlings,
orphans and the very poor; iv) *passing fashions* in dry nursing, which
affected mainly the wealthier social classes.

¶ In certain regions of pre-industrial Europe infants were rarely or never breastfed, whether by the mother or by a wet nurse, but from birth were raised by artificial means. Children were reared in this way in parts of Germany, particularly Southern Bavaria, Wurttemberg, Baden and Saxony [4,56,57]; in Bohemia [60]; in the Basel region of Switzerland [6,121]; in parts of Russia [7,14], Austria and Northern Italy, particularly the Tyrol [60,88,100]; and in some regions of Scandinavia, especially in Sweden, Finland and Iceland [7,60,62,97,122]. The practice dated in some areas from at least the 15th century and was probably of more ancient origin, though why this custom arose is still obscure. Perhaps it was to allow peasant women to return quickly to work in the fields, unencumbered by a suckling; but in the Tyrol it was said to be related to the tight-fitting dresses worn by all classes [88]. It was certainly a deeply-ingrained social custom, and any woman who attempted breast-feeding was reviled by women in general, as can be seen from the following example from the Oberbayern district of Bavaria:

> A woman who came from Northern Germany and wanted according to the customs of her homeland to nurse her infant herself was openly called swinish and filthy by the local women. Her husband threatened he would no longer eat anything she prepared, if she did not give up this disgusting habit [56],

In the Middle-European areas, the food used in place of breastmilk was 'meal pap' [56,58]. A French physician, Joseph Raulin (1708–84) [94], wrote that in Germany, Switzerland and France a pap made of cows' or sheep's milk and barley flour was given every four hours, with intermediate feedings of water in which raspings of deer horn, ivory, or anise seeds had been boiled. If children did not thrive on this diet they were fed on meat juice, the yolk of egg, and bread or toast reduced to a powder and mixed with milk or meat juices [6].

How many infants died as a direct result of artificial feeding from birth is unknown; it is by no means certain that more infants died in such non-breastfeeding regions than in those where maternal breastfeeding or wet nursing was the norm. Some 18th-century writers thought the former did better. In Basel, where foundling infants were fed a pap made from milk and flour, and given water to drink, Raulin claimed they did not die any more frequently than those brought up differently; nor were their diseases more dangerous [6,94]. Brouzet, the physician to King Louis xv, stated, in 1755, that in Muscovy and Iceland

> it is universally allowed that these people are stronger, and less subject to disease, than the southern nations. This . . . does not prove that they owe these advantages to the nourishment they receive in their infancy; but it, at least, evidently proves, that this food is not prejudicial [7].

Children in these northern areas were fed on animal milk rather than the meal pap used elsewhere [14], as Brouzet describes:

> The practice of giving women's milk to infants is wholly unknown in Muscovy and Iceland . . . soon after they are born [infants] are left all day, by their mothers, lying on the ground, near a vessel filled with milk or whey, in which is placed a tube, the upper extremity of which the infant knows how to find, and putting his mouth to it, sucks whenever he is oppressed with hunger or thirst . . . the infants of this savage country much more frequently escape the dangers of infancy, than amongst us . . . it is certainly true that their method of feeding children with the milk of animals is evidently not dangerous, and that it is, at least, attended with as happy effects as that of giving them women for wet nurses [7].

Mortality figures from a later period have been used to assess the effects of breastfeeding versus artificial, in different areas of Bavaria [59]. The figures show that although infant mortality (0–1 year) was higher in the non-breastfeeding regions, child mortality (1–5 years) was much lower; perhaps indicating that 'survival of the fittest' occurred in non-breastfeeding areas, where infants exposed from birth to a variety of organisms transmitted in food and drink either quickly succumbed or rapidly developed resistance. The maternally-breastfed child, though initially protected by passive immunity from his mother, at a later date met the disease organisms associated with eating contaminated foods, as weaning commenced. Perhaps, also, areas with a centuries-long tradition of artificial feeding had discovered by trial-and-error the best methods of preparing and administering artificial foods. It is notable that all the foods mentioned consisted partly or entirely of milk, and there is evidence that it was usual in Germany and Switzerland for drinking water for young infants to be boiled [6,75].

Climate was another factor that affected the success of artificial feeding, especially when milk-based foods were used. All the non-breastfeeding regions identified to date are in Northern Europe, have a cold dry climate, and many are in mountainous terrrain. Artificial feeding was more likely to succeed in such a climate than in warm, temperate zones or in Mediterranean countries, where milk and other foods rapidly become sour and contaminated, making infants more susceptible to gastro-intestinal disease. Brouzet guessed that climate might have been a factor in the success of the hand-rearing peoples, and his opinion that wet nurses were more harmful to infant lives is also pertinent. Wet nursing was virtually non-existent in non-breastfeeding areas [7,60] so that each infant remained under the care of the parents, and was not therefore prey to the bad practices said to be perpetuated by wet nurses in continental Europe [100,101].

¶ Four conditions made artificial feeding essential for children from any level of society: i) lack of breastmilk; ii) congenital defect or birth injury; iii) prematurity; iv) congenital or acquired infantile syphilis.

i) *Lack of breastmilk.* Some children were raised by hand because their mother died during or soon after childbirth, or had badly scarred nipples or breasts from feeding other infants, or her milk did not 'come in'; all in circumstances where there was no other lactating woman who could wet nurse the child. This occurred more frequently in the colonies or on board an emigrant ship, where there were relatively few females [13], than in any English village, where there were certain to be some lactating women who could wet nurse a child for a short time at least [23,66]. In a case from Maryland, in 1658, a Lucie Stratton gave birth to a bastard and 'most unnaturally dried up her milke through which actions the infants life mought have bin in danger'. The father asked a neighbour to suckle his child. She was unable to agree as she thought she was pregnant but said 'if hee would have it drie nurst she would do her best endeavour for it'. The father decided that if anyone 'could bring it up by hand Lucie Stratton should' and the said Lucie received thirty lashes as punishment for her 'unnatural behaviour' [13]. This illustrates not only that lack of breastmilk could be tantamount to infanticide but also the attitude of a puritan community in the mid-17th century towards such behaviour.

That many infants in the American colonies were wholly or partially dry nursed for lack of breast milk, is evidenced by a thriving trade in sucking bottles in the 17th and 18th centuries, and by occasional diary references by English colonists to hand-feeding [13]. A related occurrence was that of multiple births, where the mother had insufficient milk for more than one child. For example, in 1736, the loss of two milch cows was a problem for a father of 10 children under 17, plus 2-month-old triplets: 'cows on which we had considerable dependence for the support of my family, and especially my infants' [13].

Famine was another reason for women having insufficient milk to breastfeed a child. A sequence of bad harvests occurred in parts of northern England and in Scotland in the 16th and – even more – in the 17th century, and hit the poorer members of society most of all [2]. Perhaps it is significant that the first specific mention in British medical literature of artificial feeding was published by James McMath, an Edinburgh apothecary and physician, soon after a severe famine in the Edinburgh area. Pieter Breugel's drawings of 1563 offer contemporary illustration of the effects of famine or extreme poverty on the ability of women to breastfeed (see plate 13.2). Compare these with 'Oxfam' pictures of the 20th century, showing a starving child sucking vainly at the shrunken breasts of his mother.

ii) *Congenital defects or birth injury.* If a baby had a deformity or injury of the face, mouth or palate which made it unable to suck normally, then the only course was to spoon feed or bottle feed it, either with expressed breast milk or with substitutes such as pap. The most common deformities were hair lip and cleft palate [45], but the craft of midwifery, as practised in pre-industrial Europe, resulted in more facial injuries during difficult deliveries than is the case today [28,118]. Unless some form of surgical correction was performed, these handfed infants usually died. In 1612 a French surgeon, Jacques Guillemeau, described

> . . . little children that have been nourish'd by a sucking bottle, the space of two or three months: but at length they have died: because the milke ran out by the nose, it being a very hard thing to make an artificial pallet, that should keep it from going forth: nevertheless, I would counsel the chirurgion to make one, and to fit it with a little spunge tyed to it, which shall be put handsomely into the said cleft with the pallet: and it must be put in when the child would sucke, and then taken out againe when he hath done. And this I have practised with good success [45].

The wife of Ashley Bowen, a New England colonist, managed to rear one of her sons to the age of six months, even though he was born without a palate and was unable to suck [112], probably by the method described by Hans Sloane, the physician. In a letter of 1748 to the governors of the Foundling Hospital, he said that the lives of some children with such deformities could be saved by giving

> breast milk with a spoon . . . by which, in some cases, where children had their tongue, lips, or noses obstructed, either by diseases or accidents, before or in the birth, their lives have been saved by receiving the same proper nourishment [of breast milk] though not by suckling [102].

iii) *Prematurity.* Premature or very underweight babies rarely survived for long without the specialised care which has been available only within the last 100 years [71], but for short periods some infants in this category were fed by hand because they were too weak to suck. The man-midwife Percivall Willughby described the delivery of twins in 1667 in which 'the weake-borne childe lived but could not suck. It was fed with boiled milk, thickened with white bread and sweetened with sugar'. This case had a successful outcome: 'I saw the mother Anno 1669. She said that her son lived and was able to go [walk] about the house.' But a baby of only six months gestation, which he delivered in 1669, survived barely 24 hours, despite attempts at spoon feeding; 'The child would suck milk and water mixed together from a spoon, and died . . . the next morning' [118].

iv) *Congenital or acquired infantile syphilis.* Syphilis was a new epidemic disease of 'plague' proportions in Europe at the end of the 15th century, and throughout the 16th century was a serious problem among all social classes and all age groups [42,102]. The risk of infants with congenital syphilis infecting their nurses, and thereby introducing the infection to others in her family, was particularly discussed by surgeons and physicians, as well as receiving the attention of lay administrators [83,106]. In Verona in the 1580s it was relatively common for the wet nurses of foundlings to apply to the hospital governors for treatment for the syphilis which they allegedly contracted from their nurselings. Sometimes they obtained free treatment for their other sucklings also, and for their husbands who had been infected by their wet nursing wives [82].

The opposite circumstance also prevailed: infants infected by syphilitic nurses. In 1575 the French surgeon Ambroise Paré described a relatively common occurrence:

> A certaine very good citizen of this citie of Paris granted to his wife, being a very chaste woman, that she shoulde nurse her owne childe of which she was lately delivered, shee should have a nurse in the house to ease her of some part of the labour: by ill-hap, the nurse they took was troubled with this disease; wherefore she presently infected the childe, the child the mother, the mother her husband, and hee two of his children [aged three and four] who frequently accompanied him at bed and board, being ignorant of that malignity wherewith he was inwardly tainted [83].

The increasing incidence and public fear of syphilis in this period led to women refusing to suckle infants with congenital or acquired syphilis. As a result, a different form of artificial feeding was developed for these particular infants: direct suckling from the udders of animals such as cows, asses, sheep and, most frequently, goats. For example, Jacques Guillemeau said that if a child had already infected one nurse and 'you cannot find a nurse, that will venter to give the childe sucke, instead thereof, you shall cause him to sucke a goat; which I have caused some to do' [45].

¶ Direct suckling of infants by animals is a very ancient and widespread practice, and mythology depicts abandoned infants raised by wolves (most notably Romulus and Remus), goats (Jupiter and Aegysthus), and mares (Pelias). But it was used most frequently for the feeding of foundlings in institutions, in certain countries, and especially in France (plates 11.2–11.5). Faced with the 'new plague' of syphilis, the French keenly recommended the sucking of goats as a better means of preserving infected infants than by hand feeding with pap [45,72,83]. The practice became fairly common in France during the 16th century; as described by an Italian writer in 1581, it was the 'custome of divers women in France', to 'bring up their infants only with the milk of beasts' [44]. This method of feeding syphilitic and abandoned children con-

Plate 11.2. Direct suckling by a goat,
c.1816, from a book by K. Zwierlein.

tinued to be used in France, with goats and asses being kept on some
hospital premises, until the early years of the 20th century [11,88].

Nowadays too, feeding children by animals still takes place, and
this occurs in Paris in the big foundling and childrens hospital
(*Hôpital des enfants assisté*). Children suspected of having infectious
diseases are not fed by wet nurses but are applied to asses' udders.
A special pavilion has been built for this in the garden of the great
institution. There are stalls attached to two sides of the actual ward
where the children are, and in each of these stalls four asses are
kept permanently for this purpose alone [88].

There is not much evidence that animal suckling was ever widely
used in Britain, although the linking of suckling houses (normally used
for rearing young lambs and calves) with inns, in at least two English
parishes, in descriptions of the spread of bubonic plague among

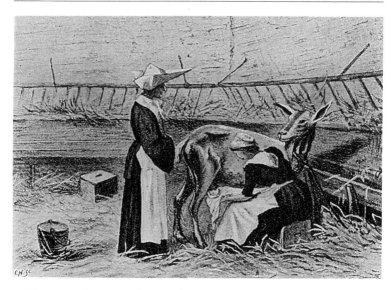

Plate 11.3. Goats were kept on the premises of some foundling hospitals to suckle infants (especially those with infantile syphilis). They were particularly popular from the late 18th C. onwards.

parishioners, implies that there were also several humans on the premises [108]. It is possible that the term 'suckling house' was at that time used not only with reference to young animals but also denoted a house where infants were wet nursed. In the 16th and 17th centuries, a place where young mammals were being suckled was possibly the obvious place to take a child without a nurse.

Following publication of a book by a German, Conrad Zwierlein, in 1816, *The goat as the best and most agreeable wet-nurse*, the suckling of infants by goats became briefly fashionable in other European countries [34,91] but, with the increasing availability of artificial foods, was soon overtaken by dry nursing as a feeding method. Representations of animal nursing, which date from the ancient art of Mesopotamia and of Egypt, continued until the 20th century. A popular theme in European art was the depiction of the infant Jupiter, who was traditionally reared by a goat [14,88,91]. Although suckling by animals in times of need has been recorded very widely, it is employed today only in pre-industrial societies.

Despite this antiquity and universality, direct suckling of human infants by other mammals never gained the widespread approval of

Plate 11.4. Infants being suckled by asses,
which were kept at the *Hospice des enfants
malades*, Paris, until the early 20th C.

physicians, because of the belief that the infant acquired the characteristics of the animal. Sixteenth-century writers believed that infants fed
on animal milk were 'fierce and not like men' [44], and that infants fed
on goat's milk became 'very swift and nimble' [45]. Romulus and Remus
were said to have been so cruel because they were nursed by she-wolves
[76,89], whilst Pelias' brutishness was supposedly as a result of sucking
an 'unhappy mare'. The idea that animal milk passed animal characteristics into the child was still being repeated in the late 18th century [97],
and was the reason why animal feeding was used only in cases of necessity. Its apparently greater use in France than in other lands may have
been because Frenchmen did not share, or disregarded, this belief;
probably they were more realistic in assessing the value to the child of
direct suckling. Proof of the efficacy of the method could be seen in the
French countryside. In 1580 Montaigne wrote 'it is common around
here to see women of the village, when they cannot feed the children at
their breast, call the goats to their rescue': and in 1755 Brouzet observed 'I have known in the country . . . some peasants who have no
other nurses but ewes, and these peasants were as strong and vigorous
as others' [7]. In Paris in 1780, a report to the Queen by the lieutenant
governor of police stated 'one sees in society numerous strong and well
constituted men who have been fed by goats or nourished by the milk of
other animals; one sees many who have never been suckled' [30].

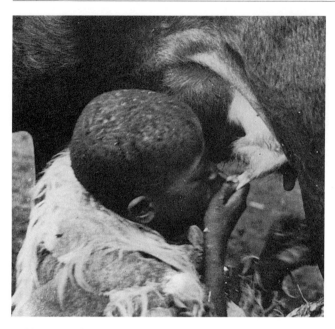

Plate 11.5. An eight-year-old Basuto boy
drinking ass's milk.

The following account of conditions in late 19th-century Kansas
shows why, in pre-industrial societies, direct suckling was a safer
method of artificial feeding than conventional dry nursing. It reduced
the number of opportunities when contamination could occur.

> If you could . . . see our cows, or barn, the milk pail and cans, and
> our lack of facilities for keeping milk cold, you would doubtless
> have been convinced that no baby could survive such insanitary
> milk. It is my belief I could have survived being fed on milk
> contaminated with stable filth. It was the cloth strainer which a
> baby could not compete with his defence mechanisms. We rinsed
> the strainer after pouring the morning's milk through it, and hung
> it up to dry. In summer more than fifty flies would alight on it
> within a minute and feed upon the milk residues, speckling it with
> fly specks. In the evening, the fresh milk was poured through this
> fly-excrement-laden cloth. A baby could scarcely ever fail, when
> fed such contaminated milk, to suffer from diarrhoeal infection
> and die' [54].

The suckling of young mammals by lactating women was also well-
known in all levels of society. In pre-industrial Europe, rich women used

puppies, mainly to relieve distension or 'knots' in their breasts shortly before, and in the early stages of, breastfeeding; in other cultures motherless baby animals of many species were, and occasionally still are, reared by lactating women. Records exist of North American Indians suckling bears [91], dogs and deer; piglets were favoured in the New Guinea highlands, puppies in ancient Hawaii, and deer in Guyana [54]. Other reasons for this practice include promotion and continuation of lactation, to prevent conception, and for development of good nipples in the latter stages of pregnancy. In the art of many lands women are represented suckling animals. Medieval carvings in English churches depict mermaids suckling a lion [1]; an 18th-century Japanese *Ainu* drawing shows a woman of the lowest class suckling a young bear [88]. An English political cartoon of 1784 shows Charles Fox as a fox being nursed at the breast of his sponsor, the breastfeeding Duchess of Devonshire [88,119]. There is an 18th-century painting by A. Utrillo of a woman suckling a dog at each breast (plate 4.2).

¶ Two social institutions employed dry nursing, either wholly or partly, in pre-industrial Europe: foundling hospitals, including general hospitals which also received foundlings; and (in England) the parish, which was responsible for the nurture of poor orphans and bastards born or abandoned within its boundaries.

Foundling hospitals. The exposure of infants, particularly bastards and females, was common in many ancient societies, and provision for rearing these unwanted infants was made by various cities and states in Ancient Greece and Rome [3]. The first English foundling hospital was not founded until the mid-18th century, but in many (predominantly catholic) European countries and their colonies such institutions were well-established long before this date [34,90]. The first is said to have been founded in 787 AD in Milan, and many more were opened, particularly in Italy, between the 11th and 15th centuries, the majority supported by the church [90]. In the 16th and 17th centuries provision was made for receiving foundlings in Lisbon, Amsterdam and Paris [64].

The most usual method of feeding such abandoned infants was by the employment of wet nurses. The wet nurses either lived within the hospital or hospice and breastfed the children in one large room, or the infants were assigned to outside wet nurses who took them into their own homes for varying lengths of time. Some children returned to the hospital when they were weaned, others (for example in Venice where the hospitals were run by the state) remained with their nurses until the age of 12 years [82]. However there are several reasons for believing that this ideal method of nutrition was not always fully carried out. The wet nurses were often poor women, and the pay was not very good, so that shortages frequently occurred. For example, in Verona in 1581 there were only two wet nurses to feed 18–20 infants, and in 1584 the general paucity of wet nurses forced the authorities to raise the pay to attract more women. Twenty years earlier, in nearby Brescia, the records show that children were dying for lack of wet nurses [82].

If no wet nurses could be found, or were insufficient to feed the large numbers of foundlings, some form of dry nursing was used to supplement or replace breast milk. An example of this practice comes from Treviso where, in 1581, the hospital board, because they were so short of wet nurses, decided to pay a goat keeper 7 soldi a month for the hire of goats to feed the foundlings [82]. In 1531 feeding bottles or horns were said to be in use in the Hôtel Dieu in Paris [14]; feeding horns (cornets) were part of the equipment which accompanied each foundling from Paris (in 1702) and from Rheims (in 1780) to the home of a wet nurse [14]. Although these may have been intended for weaning the child, they provided a ready means for dry nursing if the nurse did not wish to breastfeed or had insufficient breastmilk. In 1634, when the problem of feeding Paris foundlings was aired, it was decided that goats should be brought into the hospice, since their milk was adjudged superior to that of cows; in 1680 the committee for foundlings at the Hôtel Dieu debated whether the infants could be brought up by hand, as they had heard was done in England and Germany (an early reference to the use of artificial feeding in England). Partly this was related to fear of syphilitic infection among the infants, but in July 1680 the practice of raising some foundlings by hand, on pap made from wheat and water, was established [14].

In France, throughout the 17th and 18th centuries, different methods of raising foundlings were discussed by the various city hospitals and foundling homes. Increasing experimentation led to some institutions using pap, or a similar substance, to dry nurse their infants while others preferred direct suckling by goats. The latter became well established after 1775. In that year the administrators of the foundling hospital at Aix applied to the medical faculty in Paris for assistance in saving their infants who were dying in large numbers. Dr Alphonse Leroy was sent to conduct an investigation and concluded that the deaths were due to the 'vital principle' in milk being lost as soon as milk (whether human or animal) came into contact with air. He decided that this was why 'it is impossible to rear infants with animal milk or with milk which has been expressed from the woman's breast'. His recommendation to the Aix hospital board was

> the nourishment of these infants at the udder of the goat . . . since that time the cribs are arranged in a large room in 2 ranks. Each goat which comes to feed enters bleating and goes to hunt the infant which has been given to it, pushes back the covering with its horns and straddles the crib to give suck to the infant. Since that

time they have raised very large numbers in that hospital [29].

It may be that mortality dropped significantly at Aix after Leroy's experiment, but the death rate of foundlings in such institutions was universally high. The worst record was that of the Dublin foundling hospital (founded 1702) where all the children were dry nursed. In 1760 Lady Arabella Derry presented the nursery there with a clock which bore the inscription:

> For the benefit of infants protected by this hospital, Lady Arabella Derry presents this clock, to mark that as children reared by the spoon must have a small quantity of food at a time, it must be offered frequently; for which purpose this clock strikes every twenty minutes at which notice, all the infants which are not asleep, must be discreetly fed [117].

By the end of the 18th century the 99.6% mortality of Dublin foundlings was being attributed to the use of artificial feeding, but no improvement in feeding methods took place, and the institution was closed down in 1829 because it was judged incapable of raising any of its infants to maturity [39, 120].

Some indication of the mortality in European foundling homes, and the relationship between the principal method of feeding and the level of mortality, can be gained from table 11.1; but the method of feeding was not the only factor involved in the high mortality rate. The state of health and nutrition of the infant when he was abandoned was particularly relevant, since a baby who was reasonably healthy was more likely to survive the rigours of a foundling institution than one who was already half-starved or very weak. Children who remained in an institution (often containing hundreds of infants) were much more vulnerable to infectious diseases, such as measles, smallpox and dysentery, and to cross-infection from bedding, nursing personnel and feeding equipment. This is demonstrated by the Moscow foundling home, where all infants were kept within the building. The year in which the highest mortality was recorded (1767) was also the year in which a smallpox epidemic raged in the town, and 98% of the 1089 children died [95]. Similarly, children sent out to wet nurses fared in direct relationship to the quality of care each woman offered. For instance, the mortality of foundlings from Paris who were put out to rural wet nurses in the years 1771–73 varied according to the province which received the babies [38]. In many areas of France the quality of care given by wet nurses was very low [38, 100] and it is probable that even when infants were fostered out to wet nurses, they were at least partially dry nursed [100]. In several regions of France in these years the mortality of infants breastfed by wet nurses was double that of infants breastfed by their own mothers (many of whom were equally poor) [38, 100]. There were, therefore, two unknown factors when children were put out to nurse: the exact method of

Table 11.1. The mortality in some European foundling homes/ hospitals in the eighteenth century related, where possible, to the principal method of infant feeding.

Date	Hospital	Percentage mortality	No. of deaths	Principal feeding method	Source
1741 (1st year)	London	48.5	66	dry nursing	Found. Hosp. 1749
1741–59	London	56	7,833	country wet nursing	Jones 1978
1771–73	Paris (Hôtel Dieu)	62.5 to 75		out to wet nurse	Flandrin 1979
1773–77	Paris (all foundlings)	80	25,476	out to wet nurse	Chamoux 1973
1775–96	Dublin	99.6	10,227	dry nursed within hospital	Forsyth 1911
1779–	Rheims	45	360	out to wet nurse	Chamoux 1974
1797–1801	Dept of Eure	80	560+	dry nursed (died for lack of wet nurses)	Shorter 1977
Late 18th c.	Moscow	80 to 90	1,600–1,800	(probably) dry nursed within hospice	Ransel 1976
Late 18th c.	St Petersburg	80 to 90	1,200–1,400	(probably) dry nursed within hospice	Ransel 1976
Late 18th c.	Rouen	90		out to nurses	Flandrin 1979
No date. ?late 18th/ early 19th c.	Lyons	33.7		out to wet nurses	Wickes 1953
No date. ?late 18th/ early 19th c.	Paris	50.3		wet nursed within hospice	Wickes 1953
No date. ?late 18th/ early 19th c.	Rheims	63.9		out to dry nurse	Wickes 1953

Plate 11.6. Sucklings' ward in the Paris
Foundling Hospital, late 18th/early
19th C. With large numbers of infants
in such close contact, an epidemic
could spread rapidly.

feeding employed while the foundling was 'wet nursed', and the quality
of general infant care given by the wet nurse. In contrast, the care and
feeding provided within the hospital or home, whether by wet or dry
nursing, was supervised,and presumably standardised, by a board or
committee in each institution [14,82] (plate 11.6).

These factors may explain some of the apparent discrepancies between the method of feeding and foundling mortality. In most cases
where artificial feeding is known to have been used, such as Dublin and
Moscow, the mortality was very high, but it is comparable to areas such
as Rouen and Paris (1773–77) where infants were put out to country
wet nurses. Although many circumstances need to be considered when
looking at foundling mortality, there is no doubt that foundlings as a
group were often dry nursed, and where this was undertaken inside an
institution the mortality rate was higher than when breastfeeding by wet
nurses was employed; the exception to this being those institutions
which utilised direct suckling by animals rather than conventional dry
nursing [29,117].

The first English foundling hospital, the *London Foundling Hospital*,
achieved a lower mortality rate than most of the European institutions
discussed above (plate 11.7). This was probably related to the fact that

Plate 11.7. A perspective view of the
London Foundling Hospital, 1751.

it was established at a later date (1739) than those in other countries,
and was therefore able to draw upon both the good and bad experiences
of the latter in feeding their infants. The governors took particular note
of the information obtained from foundling homes in Paris, Amsterdam,
Lisbon and Venice, although they found none of their methods exactly
suited to the London situation [40]. A second factor was that the
London hospital planned a smaller, closely-supervised intake of foundlings, rather than using the cradle or 'tour' which was a common feature
of European hospitals. This was a device that allowed an unwanted baby
to be placed in a special box or cradle outside the hospital, which, when
revolved 180°, deposited the child inside the hospital, allowing whoever
had abandoned the infant to depart unseen [90]. It is still used in some
countries today, as, for example, Bolivia. A third factor (after an initial
period of experimentation) was the careful selection and supervision, by
an inspectorate, of suitable country women to act as wet nurses to the
foundlings, until they were old enough to return to the main hospital
[40,55,64]. As a result, the quality of care given by country wet nurses

was closely monitored and was more standardised than that given by rural wet nurses in France (particularly those who suckled foundlings from Paris and Rouen [38,100].

The early years of the London Foundling Hospital are of particular interest in the history of artificial feeding because, initially, the governors decided to experiment in bringing up all or most of the foundlings by hand, due to the difficulty they foresaw in finding sufficient numbers of healthy and suitable wet nurses [9,40]. Dr Hans Sloane was particularly against this, and wrote at length to the Governors in 1748, setting out the relative mortality of the foundlings reared by dry and wet nursing during 1741 [102]. Initially the hospital employed only two wet nurses, and in the first three months 90 foundlings were taken in at a rate of 30 a month. These were assigned to dry or wet nurses, with over two-thirds being fed by hand. The relative mortality – 19% in the case of wet nursed, and 53% of those dry nursed – derived from Sloane's letter and the hospital records, is shown below:

Table 11.2. Method of feeding the first three intakes of London foundlings, March–May 1741.

Date of intake	No. of children	Wet nursed	Died	Dry nursed	Died	Total deaths
25 March 1741	30	2	0	28	15	15
17 April 1741	30	7	1	23	11	12
8 May 1741	30	17	4	13	8	12
Total	90	26	5	64	34	39

The mortality for the whole of the first year was 48.5% (66 out of a total intake of 136 infants) and the governors attributed this 'to the endeavouring to bring them up by hand, which they had been advised to make tryal of'. They also noted that, whatever the type of feeding, far fewer died when they were nursed in the country: of 80 children sent to the country 29 died within the year (36% mortality); of 56 children kept in London 45 died within the year (80% mortality), 'which was not owing to any want of care, but probably from the air of London being less pure, and especially in a place where numbers of nurses and children were kept in so small a compass' [40]. Despite the misgivings of some well-known and well-respected figures who continued to condemn the wet nurse and favoured the continuance of dry nursing, the governors declared at the end of the first year that:

> Experience shewed [wet nurses] to be the only safe method of nursing children [and resolved to send all the foundlings to the country until they were three years old] and all such as would suck,

should be nursed by wet nurses only. These facts are mentioned to caution persons against bringing up children by hand; and rather to have them nursed in the country than the town [40]

A small number of foundlings continued to be dry nursed, either because of a temporary shortage of wet nurses or because infants could not or would not suck. The figures for 1756–57 show that of 1487 deaths only 163 (11%) were dry nursed, although this was a large proportion of the comparatively small number who were hand fed:

Table 11.3. The mortality of London foundlings
1756–57 and their method of feeding [64].

Method of feeding	No. of children	No. of deaths	% mortality
Total no. of children boarded out	3,300	1,487	45
No. of children sent to wet nurses	2,904	1,324	46
No. of children sent to dry nurses	396	163	41

The mortality rates of the English foundlings remained consistently lower than those of European institutions, but they varied from year to year, reflecting local patterns of nutrition and disease, the varying numbers admitted, and the health of the abandoned infants. Following an Act of Parliament of 1756, instituting the general reception of all infants, mortality rose. Between March 1756 and September 1760 the mortality of the intake of infants ranged from 43% to 81%, although children nursed in the country were still more likely to survive than those nursed, perforce, within the hospital [55,64]. For the period 1756–60 parishes in a 60-mile radius around London record in the burial registers lists of foundlings who had been sent from 'the Hospital' to be nursed [37]. However, once the scheme for admitting unlimited numbers of foundlings from all over the country had been shown to be unworkable, and the hospital began again to have a limited intake, the mortality of foundling infants compared favourably both with other foundling institutions and with the reported death rates of infants within parish workhouses in the capital; and with those reported in the Bills of Mortality and by contemporary medical writers [55,64]. None of these can be compared directly because each used the term 'infant mortality' to cover different time spans: 2 years in the Bills of Mortality and some medical works; 3 years in Jonas Hanway's figures for London workhouses; 1 year by some institutions and by present-day demographers. Restrictions and inaccuracies occurred, particularly in the Bills of Mortality, but consensus of 18th-century opinion was that half to two-thirds of all infants baptised did not survive to their second birthday. The relative success of the London Foundling Hospital in rearing abandoned infants must have been related to careful selection and supervision of wet nurses (for example, if a hospital wet nurse lost two children at the breast she was no longer employed [55,64]); to the realisation that rearing infants as individuals within country families was more likely to succeed than feeding many babies within one building in a town [40]; and to the near abandonment of dry nursing as a method of nourishing infants after a preliminary trial had demonstrated that it compared unfavourably with breastfeeding [63,64].

The parish. In England, the parish was responsible for administering poor relief, and this included the care of any infants born or abandoned within the parish boundaries who had no relatives living or able to rear them. Boarding-out such infants with families living in the parish was first mentioned in the Poor Law Act of 1536 and, from the mid-16th century, was the usual means of rearing them [87]. The quality of care given to infants varied from parish to parish and between town and country [70,87]. In some parishes (such as Westbury-on-Trym during the 17th century) the infant mortality of the parish poor was no greater than that expected within the parish as a whole [70]; in others the death-rate was higher than for other infants because the pay of parish nurses was inadequate or was not regularly paid, as a result of which the children suffered [87]. In towns, even where there was a parish workhouse, infants were frequently boarded out in the same way rather than reared within the workhouse [70,87]. The women who undertook to nurse these babies were usually poor; with a high incidence of widows [32,37], often themselves receiving parish relief, who took in several infants at a time as a means of earning a living [70]. It is unlikely that most parish nurses were wet nurses. Although it is physiologically possible for women to provide sufficient breastmilk to feed three or four infants at a time, it requires a nourishing and high-calorie diet and a good amount of rest and sleep [54]. It also consumes a great deal of time. Poor women who needed to take in infants for a livelihood were unlikely to have had a sufficiently high-calorie intake over the long periods of time in which they were supposedly lactating [31]. They frequently had young children of their own [70], and if the mother was lactating then at least one of these was an infant. In addition, whatever her poverty, she had to run her home, including such time-consuming chores as cooking, laundering and spinning. It is therefore unrealistic to believe that such women spent most, or even a significant amount, of their time breastfeeding. Parish infants boarded out in these circumstances must have been partially or totally raised by hand.

From the late 16th century there were abuses by parish officials and by nurses. Quarter sessions records show that some women had to go to court to extract their promised wages from the parish [87], and others show women being prosecuted for starving and/or murdering children entrusted to their care. The Middlesex Sessions book of April 1694 records an

> order concerning the putting out to nurse of parish children. This matter is brought into notice owing to one Mary Compton having starved and murdered several infants placed into her care by public officers [46].

The average wage of the parish nurse (about 1/6d a week) was quite good by 17th-century standards, but in many parishes this wage remained stable until late in the 18th century, by which time the cost of living had risen steeply. In the second half of the 18th century it was often insufficient to keep an infant (wages were particularly low for taking-in children under two years of age), with the result that many died, usually from starvation [70,87]. Examples of payments to parish nurses (per infant) are shown facing. Conditions in London were much worse than in other parts of England, especially in the 18th century. In the capital (where many parishes had a workhouse) infants were either reared within the workhouse by female inhabitants who were designated as nurses [87] or were boarded out to poor women within the parish. Whichever method was used, nearly all the infants left to the care of London parishes died within a few months [70,87]. In her tract against men-midwives (1760), the midwife Elizabeth Nihell was particularly concerned about hand feeding among the very poor:

> There will be found not one but many, even of the most populous parishes where for fourteen, twenty, or more years, not one poor babe of the thousands taken in have escaped the general destruction . . . this is so rigidly true of some parishes, that if I am not misinformed, the verification not long ago made, as to one of them before a court of justice, of not a single infant having been brought up in the term of fourteen years. And I could name another in which, in the course of above twenty years, all the newborn children that fall under the administration of the parish charity, perished, except one boy, of whom it is recorded as a prodigy, that he lived till he was five years of age, when he filled up the numbers, and died like the rest [79].

Following the researches and petitions of the philanthropist Jonas Hanway (1712–86), who was particularly concerned about the vast infant mortality in the London parish workhouses, there were many reforms of the system during the 18th century [12,87,96]. Samples of the infant mortality described by Hanway are shown in tables 11.5, 6 and 7. The absolute accuracy of his figures may be in doubt, due to his enthusi-

Table 11.4. Some examples of payments made to parish nurses (per infant). For ease of comparison these are all given as weekly payments, although some parishes paid quarterly or monthly.

Year	Parish	Pay	Source
1557	Boxford, Suffolk	5d	Northeast 1982
1577	Ipswich, St Helen's	10d	Webb 1966
1577	Ipswich, St Margaret's	1s	Webb 1966
1578	Ipswich, Christ's Hospital	10d	Webb 1966
1611	Nantwich, Cheshire	2s	Pinchbeck & Hewitt 1969
1630	Aldenham, Herts	1s/6d	Newall 1983
1660	Aldenham, Herts	2s/3d	Newall 1983
1689	Cheshunt, Herts	1s/6d	Cheshunt 1689
1689	Cheshunt, Herts	2s	Cheshunt 1689
17th c.	Westbury on Trym, Gloucestershire	1s/6d	Marshall 1926
1701	Aldenham, Herts	1s/6d	Newall 1983
1708	Totteridge, Herts	1s/9d	Totteridge 1703–53
1713	Hitchin, Herts	1s/8d	Hitchin 1686–1713
1724	Chipping Barnet, Herts	1s/6d	Chipping Barnet 1725–44
1736	Elstree, Herts	1s	Elstree 1685–1722
1750	Cheshunt, Herts	2s	Cheshunt 1734–56
1750	Cheshunt, Herts	1s	Cheshunt 1734–56
1760s	St Clement Dane	2s	Pinchbeck & Hewitt 1969
1764	St Mary's, Whitechapel	2s/6d	Pinchbeck & Hewitt 1969
1768	Said to be generally allowed	1s/6d	John Fielding (cited in Pinchbeck & Hewitt 1969)

asm for reform, but the fact that the mortality of parish infants in some London parishes was as high as 100% was recounted by other writers, who linked it directly to the use of artificial feeding [79, 102].

In his *Earnest appeal for mercy to the children of the poor* (1766), Hanway showed why the care and feeding of infants within the workhouses of the mid-18th century was unsuccessful. It was not simply that they were handfed but (as was recognised by the foundling hospitals) it was the *conditions* in which they were fed, and the general lack of care, which killed them:

> To attempt to nourish an infant in a workhouse, where a number of adults are assembled in one room, and consequently the air becomes putrid, be these nurses ever such proper persons, I will pronounce, from the most intimate knowledge of the subject, is but small remove from slaughter, for the child must die; [and] these children were put into the hands of indigent, filthy or decrepit women, three or four to one woman, and sometimes sleeping with

Table 11.5. Infant mortality in four London workhouses 1757–63 [87].

Parish	No. of infants born or received	No. removed from workhouse soon after birth	No. remaining	Of the children remaining:		Percentage mortality
				No. of infants dying under 3 years	No. of infants surviving	
St Luke's, Middlesex	53	0	53	53	0	100
St Giles	415	228	187	169	18	90
St Martin's-in-the-field	312	147	165	158	7	96
St George's, Hanover Square (one of the best houses)	288	115	173	137	36	79

Table 11.6. Infant mortality at St George's, Middlesex, in the year 1765–66 [87].

No. admitted	No. taken out of workhouse	No. remaining	Of the 16 remaining:			Percentage mortality
			Dead within 50 days	Dead within 9 months	No. surviving	
19	3	16	12	4	0	100

284

Table 11.7. St Giles' workhouse records 1765, showing the
disposal of infants. The overseers of this workhouse preferred to
raise infants within the workhouse rather than boarding them out
with nurses [87].

No. of infants born or received	133
No. of infants out of workhouse to mother after c.1 month	54
No. of infants received at end of year, . . not included	67
No. of infants remaining	67
Of the 67 remaining:	
Died after c.1 month	53
No. surviving	14
percentage mortality	79

them. The allowance of these women being scanty, they are tempted to take part of the bread and milk intended for the poor infants.
The child cries for *food*, and the nurse beats it *because* it cries. Thus
with blows, starving and putrid air, with the addition of lice, itch,
filthiness he soon receives his quietus [87].

Although Hanway preferred the system of boarding-out parish infants, many of these fared no better. The parish of St Clement Dane
entrusted one nurse, Mary Poole, with 23 children for whom she was
paid 2/- per week each. The fate of these children was:

18 died after a month or so; 2 were discharged; 3 were still alive at
the end of the year [87].

Hanway was not the only man to suggest that there was a deliberate
policy of killing unwanted parish infants either by starvation or the
administration of opiates [47,79]:

Would not any man in his senses conclude, after the death of three
of four children in one woman's hands, that the nurse was very
unfortunate; and after five or six, that she was very ignorant or very
wicked? But when in so short a period, the mortality of seven or
eight had happened, would it not create a suspicion that she
starved them, or gave them sleeping potions? And would not the
same commonsense and candour lead one to think that upon
seeing the eighteenth child brought within this parish nurse's den,
that those who sent them preferred that they should die? And what
is preferring that a child should die but something too shocking to
mention or think of? But it has been said and continues, in many
parishes, to be so common a practice, that this violence on human-
ity . . . is become as familiar in these renowned cities, as the use of
the bowstring in Morocco for those who offend the Emperor [12].

The use of dry nurses from the poorest part of urban society was
undoubtedly a major contributory factor to infant deaths. In 1748 the

physician Hans Sloane described the use of dry nurses in London parishes:

Infants, which by the management of parish nurses, in giving them . . . opiates to quiet them when fretting with diseases occasioned by their poor nourishment . . . and the want of the breast by wett nurses, scarce ever live to two years old . . . as may be seen at St Giles parish, there being no wett nurses provided, but being bred up by hand, that out of foundling or other children sent thither, scarce one in seven lived. . . . At the Temple and at Chelsea, I am assured there dyes above one half of the foundling children [102].

In confirming the use of dry nursing for parish infants, Elizabeth Nihell suggested that artificial feeding

. . . is almost as entirely as yet confined to the very poor, that is to say, to newborn babes thrown upon the public charity for their sustenance. . . . As proper wet nurses, from the difficulty in procuring them, might be dearer than dry ones; the cheapest method is preferred, and forms a kind of passive interest or saving economy.

She said that death by starvation was the usual result and made the additional important point that artificial feeding was less likely to engender affection for the child:

In the very act of lactation there is, by nature, generated such an endearment of the suckled child to the nurse, as that she began it perhaps only for hire, finds herself engaged by a growing affection to supply in some measure the place of the mother to the orphan or deserted babe. The rearing by the spoon is so far from inspiring any such dearness, that the innocent babe is considered only as an imbarassment, of which the quicker the riddance, in the death of the brat, so much the better [79].

This observation (which, bearing in mind 18th-century methods, is confirmed by modern research [54]) may be connected with the relative success in rearing infants of the London Foundling Hospital. Although the fact that infants were nursed in the country rather than in the capital was an important factor, the careful selection and supervision of the foundling hospital nurses did ensure that they were *wet* nurses in fact and not only in name [55,63,64]. In contrast some European wet nurses were known to dry nurse their charges rather than breastfeed them [100]. Inefficient artificial feeding methods may have been the principal reason for the death of so many dry nursed infants, but the lack of any affection for an unknown child taken in only for gain must also have been a significant factor, particularly in those parishes where women took in large numbers of parish children each year.

Boarding out to a parish nurse, however, could be successful. In the year 1764–65 Mrs Howes of St Mary's, Whitechapel, took in 18 infants at 2/6d a week each (a comparatively good wage) and only two of these died. But in London and its environs she was an exception. In 1763 an experiment by the parish of St James, Westminster, demonstrated that parish infants could be successfully reared, provided the conditions were controlled and the nurses were rewarded for keeping babies alive. The pauper children were sent to cottagers on Wimbledon Common who were paid 3/- a week for each of the 5 or 6 children they took in. A local surgeon or apothecary was overseer of the children's health, and the nurses were paid a bonus for good care, for successful nursing through certain infectious diseases, and if the child survived its first birthday [87]. If women were taking in 5 or 6 children at a time it is highly unlikely that they were being breastfed although, if the children were of varying ages, occasional wet nursing may have occurred. Thus partial or complete raising by hand could apparently be successfully performed by the poor in the mid-18th century if the conditions and incentives were right. In 1767, Hanway's petitions resulted in an Act of Parliament that enforced upon all London parishes a similar system of country nursing, good pay, and a bonus for the survival of parish infants. This was estimated by contemporaries to have reduced their mortality by 1500 lives a year [87]. The drop in mortality may have been due to an increased number being breastfed rather than dry nursed, and to the healthier country environment, but by the end of the 18th century a significant number of the parish poor were still being fed by artificial means [84].

Christ's Hospital, founded in 1552, took in illegitimate and destitute children to be fed, clothed and educated at the expense of the City of London. In the first few decades it accepted hundreds of infant foundlings, but it was intended to be primarily an educational establishment and increasingly fewer sucking-infants were accepted. By 1640 it accepted only children above 4 years of age [85]. A study by Cunningham [22] of the mortality for the years 1563 to 1583 shows that the death rate was particularly high among infants who were put out to nurse in their first year of life (she estimates probably over 500 per 1000). Many babies were not nursed in the country but boarded out with women living in the city of London, who were paid 8d to 1/- a week [85]. Like the later parish nurses of the 17th and 18th centuries, women took in 2 or 3 infants at the same time [70,87] and Cunningham suggests that the high mortality was a reflection of the poor standard of care, and of the likelihood that the wet nurses may have had insufficient milk to feed several infants simultaneously, resulting in malnutrition [22]. There are many parallels with parish nursing in 18th-century London, where dry nursing was definitely employed; in particular the fact that some women were allowed to take in infant after infant (ranging from a few days to several weeks of age) over a period of years, very few of whom survived [22]. It is therefore likely that these babies were not wet nursed but were partially or totally dry nursed.

¶ *Fashions in artificial feeding.* In England during the last quarter of the 17th century there was a radical change in ideas and practice of infant feeding among some of the wealthier classes. Families who previously would have employed wet nurses began to reject both wet nurses and the idea of maternal breastfeeding in favour of bringing up their children by hand from birth. This experiment continued into the 18th century where its progress, development and effects among the aristocracy has been extensively documented by Trumbach [111]. However, the origins of this change in practice clearly lie in the 17th century. The earliest known instance of a wealthy father refusing to have his newborn child suckled by a wet nurse is recorded by the man-midwife Percivall Willughby. In 1658 Sir Tenebs Evanks of Middlesex said:

> ... that he scorned that his child should suck any pocky nurse in, or about London. Hee well knew many unworthy women in that, and other places.

As a result of his attitude the child died after 10 days [118].

The first significant references to parents rearing infants by hand appear about the year 1680, although there may well have been a trend for some time before this date. Throughout the 1680s mention was made of dry nursing both by physicians and by families [8,73,107]. The best-documented and the most significant was the decision of King James II in 1688 to raise his son and heir by hand, rather than by a high-born wet nurse, which was the usual method of feeding royal infants [41,51,81]. This decision was made because several of the king's previous children had suffered convulsions and died whilst being wet nursed. The prince was fed from birth with various combinations of bread and water, including boiled bread, water gruel composed of barley-flour, water and sugar, to which a few currants were sometimes added, and a species of paste made of oatmeal, barley and water [51]. Initially he appeared to thrive, as one of his attendants, the Duchess of Powys, described in a letter to the Duchess of Beaufort dated 25 June 1688, when he was two weeks old:

> I can assure you that the prince is very well . . . a likely thriving child. . . . we dare not give it a drop of food, but by the Doctor's orders, and what it has had hitherto, has been only plain water-gruel, without any bread or spice: and his drink, water boyled and poured upon a plain wheaten toast, and so let stand till it be cold; and twice a day we give him the same kind of water poured upon a very small proportion of aniseeds. One day I had to give him a water pap, with a spoon of sack in a whole porringer of pap, but the day following that was forbid. We shall see what liberty they will allow him this day [81].

By early August, however, he was dying from 'colic dysentery and similar disorders' and, after being totally dry nursed for 7 weeks, the Prince of Wales came so close to death that the King over-ruled his medical advisers and sent to the nearest village for a wet nurse, upon whose milk the royal infant thrived and survived to maturity [51].

From the accounts of contemporaries [41,51,81] (some of whom were very unhappy about this method of feeding) several important facts emerge. First, artificial feeding was a procedure recommended and instigated by the royal physicians, who had a free hand in decreeing the child's diet from day to day. The physicians recommended dry nursing because they thought it was preferable to a bad wet nurse, and apparently had not found it difficult to persuade the royal parents to rear the most precious infant in the kingdom by artificial means rather than on breast milk. Rearing a child by hand was not regarded as sufficiently uncommon in England in 1688 for it to have aroused widespread comment or censure, but from the comments of foreign diplomats at the English court, a similar practice had not been adopted elsewhere in Europe (although this disagrees with the findings given earlier in this chapter). The French diplomat, M. Barillon, had reported, soon after the prince was born that:

> There will be no wet nurse and he will be reared by hand, as are many infants in this country; at first they are giving nothing but boiled milk and crumbs of bread, and soon after, more solid food. One can but hope that a thing so unheard of among all other nations will prove successful [51].

Although it preceded by several years the first specific mention (by James McMath in 1694) of artificial feeding in the English medical literature [69], by the late 1680s the concept of raising infants by hand must have been relatively well established among important and/or influential physicians and some of the aristocracy; although it is difficult to know how far it was approved by physicians in general, and to what extent it was practised by other social groups. Trumbach confines his discussion to the aristocracy [111], but well-to-do families in Yorkshire and Essex were also raising their infants by hand [73,107]. By the early 18th century the practice was being satirised by Richard Steele in *The Tatler* (1709) [104,105], and recommended to the gentry by Daniel Defoe in his *Compleat Country Gentleman* of 1728 [24]. It is reasonable to expect that some families would follow the royal example of James II and bring up their own infants by hand; and if there were an increase in the number of infants reared by hand at this time, this may well be related to the observed increase in infant mortality in the last decades of the 17th century, which was particularly noticeable in the 1680s [36].

The change in preferred feeding methods from wet nursing to artificial feeding is said to have been due to the aristocracy's dissatisfaction with wet nurses [111], and there was certainly increased criticism of wet nurses by medical authors in the late 17th century. There are other possible reasons for fathers preferring to experiment with dry nursing rather than employ a wet nurse (remembering that in this period husbands rarely contemplated or allowed their own wives to breastfeed) [52,116,118]. Royalist families who had lived in continental Europe for several years before the Restoration had had the opportunity to observe infants being successfully reared by hand in some areas of northern Europe, and could have brought the custom back to England. Similarly, travellers may have visited those areas where it was customary not to breastfeed children and, later, experimented with their own infants.

At a time of scientific experimentation, the views of the Belgian chemist Johann Van Helmont may have had some influence in Britain. Van Helmont (1579–1644) performed many experiments on the physiology of digestion, and had revolutionary ideas on the feeding of infants; these were translated into English and appeared in his *Oriatrike, or Physick Refined* in 1662 [114]. He condemned the use of milk, particularly breast milk, because it easily soured, transmitted diseases and the vices of the nurse to the infant, because nurses did not stop suckling when they became pregnant, and because they usually had to supplement their milk. All nurses, he thought, were exposed to passions, violence, terrors and melancholy which affected the quality and quantity of their milk. Van Helmont's alternative was to feed all babies by hand with a panada of 'bread, slightly boiled in smallbeer and sweetened with clarified honey or sugar'. This could be further diluted with smallbeer for the child to drink. Although no reference has been found in English medical works to Van Helmont's (1662) theories, prior to Brouzets's translated discussion of 1755, this (at that period) completely alien ideal of infant feeding, originally proposed in the early 17th century, could have been influential.

The preference of the aristocracy and gentry for artificial feeding continued until the mid-18th century, although it was a matter for controversy in some families where women wanted to employ a wet nurse (or sometimes to breastfeed themselves) but were over-ruled by their husbands [52,111]. In 1710 the infant son of the Duke of Buckingham died of starvation after his father insisted on his being reared by hand, refusing to employ a wet nurse 'from the apprehention he had that there was no sound woman to be met with'. When the infant was dying attempts failed to find a wet nurse as a last resort. When a post-mortem was performed 'they could see nothing else but that it was starv'd' [116].

From the mid-18th century, some upper-class mothers were beginning to breastfeed their own children in preference both to wet nurses and to handfeeding. This change coincided with the increasing number of books written by physicians in which handfeeding was frequently stated to be better than a wet nurse if the mother were unable to breast-

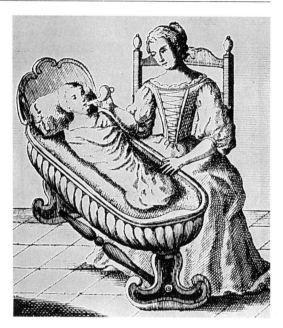

Plate 11.8. How to use the newly invented
feeding bottle of F. Baldini, 1784
(illus. in chapter 13, appendix plate 40).

feed [36,111]. By the 1780s, artificial feeding was established as the
method of choice if the mother could not feed her own children [113];
in 1789, one wealthy woman wrote:

> I ever had a great objection to a wet nurse and, had I not been able
> to persevere in nursing my girls myself, I would have brought them
> up by hand [48].

As a result of the experimentation by wealthy fathers in the late 17th and
early 18th centuries, artificial feeding rapidly gained social acceptance.
The diversity of feeding vessels which became available from this
period (plate 11.8) and the development and medical discussion of
more suitable substitute foods were a direct consequence of this change
in fashion, due to consumer demand by a wealthy and influential section
of the population.

¶ Although there was very little discussion of artificial feeding in the
medical literature for most of the period 1500–1800, evidence from
other sources shows that it was practised for various reasons in most
countries in Europe and their colonies. Major reasons for raising infants

by hand included local custom, particularly in Northern Europe; necessity, such as prematurity, lack of breastmilk, congenital defect or infantile syphilis; fashion or experimentation by the wealthier groups in society, associated with a growing dislike of wet nursing; and it was essential for feeding abandoned infants in foundling institutions and in English parishes especially when there was a shortage of wet nurses. Direct suckling from animals was employed as a form of artificial feeding, particularly for syphilitic infants and some foundlings, but this was more popular in France than in other European countries and there is little evidence of its use in Britain. The mortality of dry-nursed infants generally was much higher than that of breastfed infants, related to unsuitable foods and feeding vessels and lack of a clean water supply, but a contributory factor among some foundlings was their initially poor state of health. Parish infants and sucklings taken in by Christ's Hospital were supposedly wet nursed but in fact many of these children were probably dry nursed or only partially breastfed and this was a contributory factor to the high mortality of these infants, particularly in towns. Aristocratic and other wealthy families in the late 17th and early 18th century experimented with artificial feeding which resulted in its becoming the socially accepted alternative to maternal breastfeeding by the second half of the 18th century. Direct consequences of this (due to consumer demand) were the diversification of feeding vessels, the development of more suitable substitute foods and increased medical discussion of handfeeding.

REFERENCES

1. Anderson, M. D. (1971) *History and imagery in British churches*, London.
2. Appleby, A. B. (1973) Disease or famine? Mortality in Cumberland and Westmorland 1580-1640, *Econ. Hist. Rev.* *26*, 403-32.
3. Beckmann, J. (1846) *A history of inventions, discoveries, and origins*, trans. Johnson, W., 4th ed. *2*, 434-54.
4. Boemus, J. (1555) *The fardle of facions*, London.
5. Bokay, J. (1922) *Die geschichte der kinderheilkunde*, Berlin.
6. Bracken, F. J. (1956) The history of artificial feeding of infants, *Maryland St. Med. J.* *5*, 40-54.
7. Brouzet, N. (1755) *An essay on the medicinal education of children; and the treatment of their diseases*, trans. anon., London.
8. Browne, T. (1681) in Bryant, A. (1936) *Postman's horn. An anthology of the letters of later seventeenth century England*, London.
9. Brownlow, J. (1847) *Memoranda; or chronicles of the Foundling Hospital, including memoirs of Captain Coram*, London.

10. Bruning, H. (1908) *Geschichte der methodik der kunstlichen sauglingsernahrung*, Stuttgart.
11. Budin, P. C. (1907) *The nurseling. The feeding and hygiene of premature and full-term infants*, trans. Moroney, W., London.
12. Caulfield, E. (1931) *The infant welfare movement in the eighteenth century*, New York.
13. Caulfield, E., Infant feeding in colonial America. *J. Pediat. 41*, 673-87.
14. Chamoux, A. (1973) L'allaitement artificiel, *Annales de demographie historique*, Paris, 410-18.
15. Chamoux, A. (1974) Town and child in eighteenth century Rheims, *Loc. Popul. Stud. 13*, 45-6.
16. *Cheshunt parish overseers' accounts, Cheshunt Street ward* (1689), HRO D/P 29 12/3.
17. *Cheshunt parish overseers' accounts, Cheshunt Street ward* (1729), HRO D/P 29 12/5.
18. *Cheshunt parish overseers' accounts, Waltham Cross ward* (1734), HRO D/P 29 12/1.
19. *Chipping Barnet parish overseers' accounts* (1720-44), HRO D/P 15 12/1.
20. Cone, T. E. (1976) *200 years of feeding infants in America*, Columbus, Ohio.
21. Cone, T. E. (1981) History of infant and child feeding: From the earliest years through the development of scientific concepts, in Bond, J. T., Filer, L. J., Levielle, G. A., Thomson, A. M. & Weil, W. B. (eds), *Infant and child feeding*, New York, 3-34.
22. Cunningham, C. (1977) Christ's Hospital: infant and child mortality in the sixteenth century, *Loc. Popul. Stud. 18*, 37-40.
23. Dee, J. (1842) *The private diary of Doctor John Dee*, Halliwell, J. O. (ed.), London.
24. Defoe, D. (1728-29) *The compleat English gentleman*, Bulbring, K. D. (ed.), London, 1890.
25. Delasselle, D. (1978) Abandoned children in eighteenth-century Paris, in Forster, R. & Ranum, O. (eds), *Deviants and the abandoned in French society*, Baltimore.
26. De Mause, L. (ed.) (1976) *The history of childhood*, London.
27. Deruisseau, L. G., Infant hygiene in the older medical literature, *Ciba symposia 2*, 530-60.
28. Donnison, J. (1977) *Midwives and medical men. A history of interprofessional rivalries and women's rights*, London.
29. Drake, T. G. H. (1930) Infant feeding in England and in France 1750 to 1800, *Am. J. Dis. Child. 34*, 1049-61.
30. Drake, T. G. H. (1937) Infant nutrition in Paris in the year 1780, *Can. Med. Ass. J. 37*, 595-7.
31. Drummond, J. C. & Wilbraham, A. (1957) *The Englishman's food. A history of five centuries of British diet*, revised ed., London.

32. Dulley, F. (1982) Nurse-children: a forgotten cottage industry, *Hertfordshire Countryside 37*, 14-15.
33. *Elstree parish overseers' accounts* (1685-1762) HRO D/P 36 12/1 and 2.
34. Feldman, W. M. (1927) *The principles of ante-natal and post-natal child hygiene*, London.
35. Fildes, V. (1981) The early history of the infant feeding bottle, *Nurs. Times 77*, 128-9 and 168-70.
36. Fildes, V. (1982) Changes in infant feeding practices and ideas from 1600 to 1800 with particular reference to those affecting infant mortality and maternal-infant bonding in Eckart, W. & Geyer-Kordesch, J. (eds), *Heilberufe und kranke im 17. und 18. jahrhundert die quellen-und forschungssituation*, Munstersche Beitrage zur geschichte und theorie der medizin nr.18, Munster, 174-200.
37. Fildes, V. A. (1984) The English wet nurse and her role in infant care 1538-1800. In press, *Med. Hist.*, 1986.
38. Flandrin, J-L. (1979) *Families in former times*, trans. Southern, R., Cambridge.
39. Forsyth, D. (1911) The history of infant feeding from Elizabethan times, *Proc. Soc. Med. 4*, 110-41.
40. Foundling Hospital (1749) *An account of the hospital for the maintenance and education of exposed and deserted young children*, London.
41. Foxcroft, H. C. (ed.) (1902) *A supplement to Burnet's History of my own time*, Oxford.
42. Garrison, F. H. (1929) *An introduction to the history of medicine*, Philadelphia and London.
43. Goff, C. W. (1968) A still-working survival from the past: the Foundling Hospital of Florence, Italy, *Clin. Pediat. 7*, 632-5.
44. Guazzo, M. S. (1581 and 1586) *The civile conversation*, trans. Pettie, C. & Young, B., in *The Tudor translations*, 2nd series *8*, London.
45. Guillemeau, J. (1612) *Childbirth or The happie deliverie of women. . . . to which is added a Treatise of the diseases of children: with the cure of them*, trans. anon., London.
46. Hardy, W. G. (1905) *Middlesex county records. Calender of the sessions books 1689 to 1709*, London.
47. Harris, W. (1689) *A treatise of the acute diseases of infants*, trans. Martyn, J., London, 1742.
48. Heber (1936) *Dear Miss Heber. An eighteenth-century correspondence*, Bamford, F. (ed.), London.
49. *Hitchin parish churchwardens' accounts* (1686-1713) HRO D/P 53 5/1.
50. Hollingsworth, T. H. (1957) A demographic study of the British ducal families, in *Population in history. Essays in historical demography*, Glass, D. V. & Eversley, D. E. C. (eds), London.

51. Hopkirk, M. (1953) *Queen over the water. Mary Beatrice of Modena, Queen of James II*, London.
52. Hughes, H. S. (1940) *The gentle Hertford. Her life and letters*, New York.
53. Hutchings, N. W. (1958) 4000 years of infant feeding, *Chemist Drugg. 169*, 714-18.
54. Jelliffe, D. B. & Jelliffe, E. F. P. (1978) *Human milk in the modern world*. Oxford.
55. Jones, A. (1978) *The Foundling Hospital and its arrangements for country nursing 1756-67 illustrated by examples from Hertfordshire*, Unpublished dissertation for Extension Diploma in History, University of London.
56. Knodel, J. & van der Waale, E. (1967) Breastfeeding, fertility and infant mortality: an analysis of some early German data, *Popul. Stud. 21*, 109-31.
57. Knodel, J. (1977) Infant mortality and fertility in three Bavarian villages: an analysis of family histories from the 19th century, *Popul. Stud. 22*, 297-318.
58. Knodel, J. (1977) Breastfeeding and population growth, *Science 198*, 1111-15.
59. Knodel, J. (1980) Paper presented at a meeting of the Population Studies society, London School of Hygiene and Tropical Medicine, 13 January 1980.
60. Knodel, J., Personal communication.
61. Lacaille, A. D. (1950) Infant feeding bottles in prehistoric times, *Proc. R. Soc. Med. 43*, 565-8.
62. Lithell, U-B. (1981) Breastfeeding habits and their relation to infant mortality and marital fertility, *J. Fam. Hist. 6*, 182-94.
63. Lloyd Hart, V. E., *John Wilkes and the Foundling Hospital at Aylesbury 1759-1768*, Aylesbury.
64. McClure, R. K. (1981) *Coram's children. The London Foundling Hospital in the eighteenth century*, New Haven and London.
65. McLaren, D. (1978) Fertility, infant mortality and breastfeeding in the seventeenth century, *Med. Hist. 22*, 378-96.
66. McLaren, D. (1979) Nature's contraceptive. Wet nursing and prolonged lactation: the case of Chesham, Buckinghamshire 1578-1601, *Med. Hist. 23*, 426-41.
67. McLaughlin, M. M. (1976) Survivors and surrogates: children and parents from the ninth to the thirteenth centuries in De Mause, L. (ed.), *The history of childhood*, 101-81.
69. McMath, J. (1694) *The expert midwife: a treatise of the diseases of women with child, and in childbed . . . with fit remedies for the various maladies of new born babes*, Edinburgh.
70. Marshall, D. (1926) *The English poor in the eighteenth century. A study in social and administrative history*, reprinted 1969, New York.
71. Marx, F. F. (1968) *Die entwicklung der sauglings – inkubatoren. Eine medizin-technische chronik*, Bonn.

72. Mauriceau, F. (1673) *The accomplisht midwife, treating of women with child, and in childbed . . . with fit remedies for the several indispositions of newborn babes*, trans. Chamberlen, H., London.
73. Meade, S. (1686) Letter to her mother, Margaret Fox (nee Fell) 7 April 1686, *Abraham MSS No.30* Friends House Library, London.
74. Mettler, C. C. (1947) *History of medicine*, Philadelphia.
75. Metlinger, B. (1473) *Ein regimen der jungen kinder*, Augsburg; also trans. in full in Ruhrah, J. (1925) *Pediatrics of the past*, New York, 71-98.
76. Muffet (Moffet), T. (1584) *Health's improvement: or rules comprising the nature, method, and manner of preparing all sorts of food used in this nation. Corrected and enlarged by Christopher Bennet*, London, 1655.
77. Newall, F., Personal communication.
78. Newall, F. (1983) *Some consequences of nurse children in 17th century Aldenham*. Seminar paper read at Cambridge Group for the history of population and social structure, 28 November 1983.
79. Nihell, E. (1760) *A treatise on the art of midwifery*, London.
80. Northeast, P. (ed.) (1982) *Boxford Churchwardens Accounts 1530-1561*, Woodbridge, Suffolk.
81. Orrery, Countess of Cork and, (ed.) (1903) *The Orrery papers*, London, vol.1.
82. Palmer, R., Personal communication.
83. Paré, A. (1575) *The workes of that famous chirurgion Ambrose Parey*, trans. Johnston, T., London, 1634.
84. *Parish nurse, The* (c.1796), Anon. pamphlet, London.
85. Pearce, E. H. (1908) *Annals of Christ's Hospital*, London.
86. Peiper, A. (1966) *Chronik der kinderheilkunde*, 4th ed., Leipzig.
87. Pinchbeck, I. & Hewitt, M. (1969) *Children in English society. Vol. 1. From Tudor times to the eighteenth century*, London.
88. Ploss, H. H., Bartels, M. & Bartels, P. (1935) *Woman*, Dingwall, E. J. (ed.), London, vol.3.
89. Quillet, C. (1655) *Callipaediae or, An art how to have handsome children*, trans. anon.
90. Radbill, S. X. (1955) A history of children's hospitals, *Am. J. Dis. Child. 90*, 411-16.
91. Radbill, S. X. (1976) The role of animals in infant feeding, in Hand, W. D. (ed.), *American folk medicine A symposium*, Berkeley.
92. Radbill, S. X. (1976) Reared in adversity: institutional care of children in the 18th century, *Am. J. Dis. Child. 130*, 751-61.
93. Radbill, S. X. (1981) Infant feeding through the ages, *Clin. Pediat. 20* (10), 613-21.
94. Raulin (1769) *De la conservation des enfants*, cited in Bracken, F. J. (1956) The history of artificial feeding of infants, *Maryland St. Med. J. 5*, 40-54.

95. Ransel, D. (1976) Abandoned children of imperial Russia: village fosterage, *Bull. Hist. Med. 50*, 501-10.
96. Rodgers, B. (1949) *Cloak of charity. Studies in eighteenth century philanthropy*, London.
97. Rosenstein, N. R. von (1776) *The diseases of children and their remedies*, trans. Sparrman, A., London.
98. Rosenthal, R. (1936) A short pictorial review of the evolution of infant feeding vessels up to the beginning of the 19th century, *Bull. Med. Libr. Ass. 25*, 89-94.
99. Ruhrah, J. (1925) *Pediatrics of the past*, New York.
100. Shorter, E. (1977) *The making of the modern family*, Glasgow.
101. Shorter, E. (1978) *The great transformation of mother-infant relations, eighteenth to twentieth centuries*, Unpublished paper.
101a Singer, C. & Underwood, E. A. (1962) *A short history of medicine*, Oxford.
102. Sloane, H. (1748) *Letter to John Milner, vice-president of the Hospital for the maintenance and education of exposed and deserted young children*, 28 October 1748. Quoted in full in Brownlow, J. (1847) *Memoranda; or Chronicles of the Foundling Hospital, including memoirs of Captain Coram*, London.
103. *Soranus' Gynecology* (1956) trans. Temkin, O. *et al.*, Baltimore.
104. Steele, R. (1709) On the birth of an heir, in *The Tatler*, no.15, Thursday, 12 May.
105. Steele, R. (1709) Account of the life of Isaac Bickerstaff, in *The Tatler*, no.89, Tuesday, 1 November.
106. Still, G. F. (1931) *The history of paediatrics*, Oxford.
107. Stukeley, W. (1882) *The family memoirs of the Rev. William Stukeley MD*, Durham.
108. Tate, J. S. (1862) *The history of parish registers in England*, Wakefield, reprint of the 2nd ed., 1976.
109. *Totteridge parish vestry minutes* (1703-1753) HRO D/P 46 B/8/1.
110. Trexler, R. C. (1973) Infanticide in Florence: new sources and first results, *Hist. Childh. Quart. 1*, 98-116.
111. Trumbach, R. (1978) *The rise of the egalitarian family*, New York.
112. Ullrich, L. T. (1982) *Good wives. Image and reality in the lives of women in Northern New England 1650-1750*, New York.
113. Underwood, M. (1784) *A treatise on the diseases of children. With directions for the management of infants from birth: especially such as are brought up by hand*, London.
114. Van Helmont, J. B. (1662) *Oriatrike or, Physick refined*, trans. J.C., London.
115. Webb, J. (ed.) (1966) *Poor relief in Elizabethan Ipswich*, Ipswich.
116. Wentworth, T. (1883) *The Wentworth papers 1705-1739*, Cartwright, J. (ed.), London.
117. Wickes, I. G. (1953) A history of infant feeding, *Archs Dis. Childh. 28*, 151-8, 232-40, 332-40, 416-22, 495-502.

118. Willughby, P. (1630-69) *Observations in midwifery. As also the country midwife's opusculum or vade mecum*, Blenkinsop, H. (ed.), Warwick, 1863.

119. Witkowski, G-J. (1903) *Les seins dans l'histoire*, Paris.

120. Wodsworth, W. D. (1876) *A brief history of the ancient Foundling Hospital of Dublin from the year of 1702*, Dublin.

121. Wurtz (Wuertz), F. (1563) *The children's book*, Bound with *An experimental treatise of surgerie in four parts*, trans. and corrected Lennerton-Fox, A, London, 1656.

122. Zglinicki, F. von (1979) *Die wiege: volkskundlich-kultur-geschichtlich-kunstwisssenschaftlich-medizinhistorisch*, Regensburg.

CHAPTER TWELVE

Artificial Feeding:
Medical Ideas and Opinions about
Artificial Feeding

> " They who on meare curiositie (where no urgent necessitie
> requireth) try whether their children may not as birds be
> nourished without sucking, offend contrary to this dutie of
> breast feeding and reflect that meanes which God hath
> ordained as best; and so oppose their shallow wits to his
> unsearchable wisdom."
>
> William Gouge, *Of domestical duties,* 1622

ALTHOUGH dry nursing was practised by various groups in Britain,
North America and continental Europe, it was not discussed in the
British medical literature until the 18th century. John Jones (1579)
and the Puritan William Gouge (1622) referred to it very briefly as an
unsuitable means of rearing children. Johann van Helmont's suggestion,
that infants should be nourished on his version of panada rather than wet
nursed, was translated into English in 1662. This panada was made of
   ... bread boyled so long in thin ale, with clarified honey, if not, with
   sugar, until they shall come together in the likeness of a mucilage,
   or glew, or jelly: then as much thin ale is mingled with and washed
   on this jelly, as is sufficient for it to serve instead of drink [38].
In 1694 the surgeon James McMath gave the first direct reference to
finger-fed infants but he, and those who in the following half-century
referred to the use of dry nursing, did so only to the extent of recommending it, condemning it, or describing the consequences of giving
unsuitable foods. Full discussion of artificial feeding, giving methods,
foods, feeding vessels, and opinions for and against its use, did not
begin until 1755, when Brouzet's *Essay on the medicinal education of
children* was translated into English. Only four medical writers subsequently devoted a significant amount of space to the topic; George
Armstrong and Hugh Smith in the 1770s, and William Moss and
Michael Underwood in the 1780s (plate 12.1).
   This fact, taken in conjunction with the evidence described in chapter
11, illustrates the importance of looking at written sources *other* than
those of medical authors since, in this aspect of infant feeding, written
medical opinion appears to have followed experimentation and practice

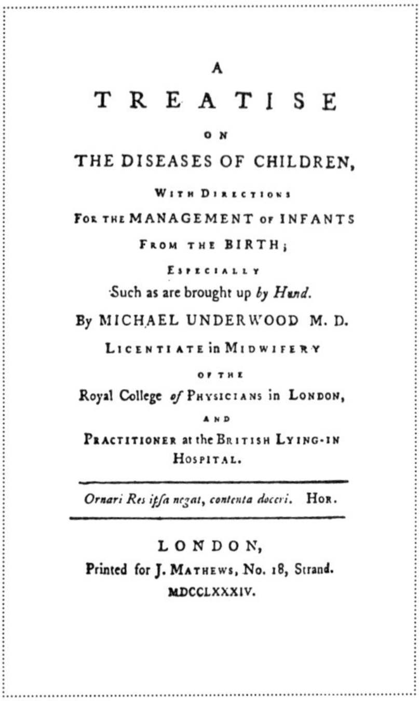

A

T R E A T I S E

O N

THE DISEASES OF CHILDREN,

WITH DIRECTIONS

FOR THE MANAGEMENT OF INFANTS

FROM THE BIRTH;

ESPECIALLY

Such as are brought up *by Hand*.

By MICHAEL UNDERWOOD M. D.

LICENTIATE in MIDWIFERY

OF THE

Royal College *of* PHYSICIANS in LONDON,

AND

PRACTITIONER at the BRITISH LYING-IN
HOSPITAL.

Ornari Res ipsa negat, contenta doceri. HOR.

L O N D O N,

Printed for J. MATHEWS, No. 18, Strand.

MDCCLXXXIV.

Plate 12.1. Underwood, *A Treatise on the
Diseases of Children*, 1784. It contains
a section on hand-feeding.

among physicians and populace alike. A probable reason for the publication of detailed instruction and advice on handfeeding in the late 18th century was to satisfy the need or demand for expert knowledge by the patients and colleagues of these early paediatric writers. It may be significant that two of the authors attended the wealthy and fashionable in the capital [34,37], and two were particularly concerned with treating the urban poor [2,29], the two groups in society which were most likely to employ handfeeding.

There was some overlap of advice on artificial feeding as, for example, some authors advised handfeeding in some circumstances and not in others [2,29], or gave both good and bad consequences from the practice [29] (table 12.1). Those who advised or recommended it did so only for certain reasons, or in specific situations. Artificial feeding was mentioned by 13 medical writers in the 18th century, most of whom advised against it if maternal breastmilk were available, and gave warning of the

300

possible consequence if dry nursing were undertaken. Reasons given for handfeeding included lack of breastmilk, a bad wet nurse, the child's inability to suck, and dire necessity. Two writers recommended it as an experiment (table 12.2). Out of 13 who strongly advised against it, 3 condemned it outright, and 3 warned of dangerous ill-effects (table 12.3). The dire consequences said to result from dry nursing included several specific conditions, among them griping, convulsions, and rickets; but almost all said that death was the common outcome. Four authors said that some handfed infants thrived very well, but since these writers favoured artificial feeding in certain circumstances, this may have been mentioned to support their recommendations [5,25,29,33]. Most emphasised the dangers of dry nursing. Infants were said to be prey to illnesses in general, but the most frequent outcome was death due to gastro-enteric complaints or starvation (table 12.4). Three authors gave an estimate based upon their own observations and experience of the number of dry nursed infants who died. The anonymous *Ladies physical directory* (1739) stated that 5 out of 6 (83%) died, whilst Cadogan (1748) and Hans Sloane (1748) gave a mortality of 2 out of 3 (67%); for dry nursed parish infants this rose to more than 6 out of 7 (86%). This is a figure close to those quoted for bottle-fed infants in some Third-World countries today, where 'the baby in a rural area of a developing country who has no access to breast milk has virtually no chance of survival' [11].

Medical opinions about the foods used to feed infants by hand in the 18th century show a clear preference for milk and milk-mixtures, with an equal bias against bread-and-water pap (table 12.5). Before that date no information was given in the medical literature about feeding young children by hand from birth.

Thus medical opinion on artificial feeding was divided. Although some physicians recommended it, most did so only in cases of necessity or as an alternative to a bad wet nurse. It is clear that even those who favoured this method thought it was a dangerous and often fatal undertaking, and gave copious instructions on its management [5,29,34]. Undoubtedly the frequent references to illness and death were related to lack of knowledge about i) suitable foods; ii) sterilisation of both food and utensils; iii) the unsuitability of some feeding vessels (see chapters 13 and 14). This is demonstrated by the stated relationship (well known today in Third-World countries) [8,20] between dry nursing and gastro-intestinal complaints and starvation. The latter was frequent among both rich [39] and poor [32], and was probably due to infants being fed on water pap, or on similar foods which contained little or no milk.

Regardless of medical preference, it is clear (table 12.5) that bread-and-water pap was the most common food given to handfed infants: the fact that it was strongly condemned indicates that it was frequently used (as it was for feeding the dry-nursed Prince of Wales in 1688). Babies fed on milk, or milk mixtures such as bread and milk or panada, may have fared better nutritionally, but were possibly more liable to gastro-intestinal upsets, especially if the milk was not boiled. In 1781 William Moss said of newborn infants:

> It is of the utmost importance to have this subject properly under-stood and attended to, as the number of children who suffer in their health and lose their lives by the gripes with looseness, at this critical juncture, is very considerable: and as there is no complaint which, at this tender age, they suffer so frequently and so much from, and which is to be more dreaded, especially with those who are dry nursed, and are of course confined to it for a longer time: for although a child who is wet nursed may suffer a good deal by improper food, yet it is but for a short time, and as he gets the breast in two or three days, the cause is removed, and he generally, sooner or later, overcomes the effect of a short irregularity: yet puny, weak children may, and often do, lose their lives from it in that short space of time. But when children are dry nursed,and confined to such like food, no wonder so few should thrive and do well: those, who live, are most commonly teazed with a frequent griping and looseness, which keeps them always weak, puny, and spiritless, and gives them a pallid, sickly look; and daily experience but too fully convinces us that numbers are carried off by it.

In an attempt to overcome this problem, George Armstrong advised:

> ... the victuals should be made fresh twice a day, that is, morning and evening in winter; and three times in summer, especially in hot weather, and the milk must never be boiled with the pap, but by itself, and added to the pap every time the child is fed, otherwise it will curdle and grow sour on the child's stomach.

The recommendation of milk, milk and water, or milk mixtures in the later 18th century reflected the greater scientific understanding of the value of milk [36,41]; and some writers were beginning to recommend diluting cow's milk to make it more like human milk [29,30,34]. Hugh Smith said in 1772 that despite the fact that many people disagreed with him, he 'preferred cow's milk to every other kind of nourishment, in the early months when it is necessary to bring up a child by hand'. And Armstrong said (see plate 12.2):

> If the infant is to be bred up by hand from the birth it ought to have new cow's milk mixed with its victuals as often as possible, and now and then some of it alone to drink. Asses milk will be still better when it can be conveniently had, and the parents can afford it.

The most common foods given to handfed children were apparently bread-and-water pap, milk, or milk mixture. No evidence has been found to show that the meat broths and diluted milk recommended by

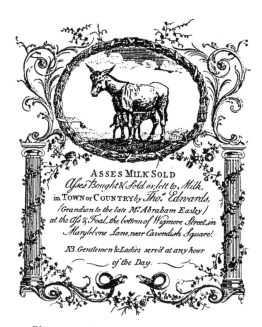

Plate 12.2. An 18th C. tradesman's card
advertising asses' milk.

physicians after c.1750 were ever given to children. Although diluted milk was evidently given to some dry nursed infants [40], it is probable that most mothers and nurses prepared the same foods for artificial feeding as they did for mixed or supplementary feeding. As to the times of feeding, Armstrong recommended that the child that was hand reared from birth should take most of his food during the day so that his sleep was not disturbed during the night; but Underwood said that 'no man can lay down any certain rules on the occasion and therefore ought not to attempt it'.

Although mothers and nurses were said to give large quantities of paps, milk and other foods to their infants, Hugh Smith gave a stricter regimen: one pint of milk in 24 hours at first, but never more than half a pint at a time; in 10–14 days increase this by a quarter of a pint a day, and by the end of the first month allow 1½ pints in 24 hours; this should be increased by another half pint by the time the child was three months of age; for a voracious child this could be increased to 3 pints a day. When the child was older then he was to be fed the same supplementary foods as the breastfed child, so that by the time the latter was weaned, both hand-reared and breastfed infants received the same diet.

303

¶ Artificial feeding was discussed by a small minority of medical writers in the second half of the 18th century. It was seen as a dangerous and frequently fatal undertaking and was recommended only in necessity, although increasingly regarded as the method of choice after maternal breastfeeding. Recommended substitute foods contained milk and/or meat broths but those most commonly fed to infants were bread-and-water pap and (in the later 18th century) milk. It is probable that the foods used by mothers/nurses for dry nursing were not substantially different from those used for mixed feeding. The observed association between gastro-intestinal conditions, starvation, and artificial feeding was related to lack of knowledge about foods, utensils, and sterilisation, and has parallels in some Third-World countries today.

REFERENCES

1. Aitken, J. (1786) *The principles of midwifery*, London, 3rd ed.
2. Armstrong, G. (1771) *An essay on the diseases most fatal to infants. To which are added rules to be observed in the nursing of children: with a particular view to those who are brought up by hand*, London, 2nd ed.
3. Baudelocque, J-L. (1790) *A system of midwifery*, trans. Heath, J., 3 vols, London.
4. Baynard, E. (1706) *The history of cold bathing: both ancient and modern, Part 2*, London, 2nd ed.
5. Brouzet, N. (1755) *An essay on the medicinal education of children: and the treatment of their diseases*, trans. anon., London.
6. Buchan, W. (1769) *Domestic medicine; or the family physician*, Edinburgh.
7. Cadogan, W. (1748) *An essay upon nursing and the management of children, from their birth to three years of age*, London.
8. Chetley, A. (1979) *The baby killer scandal*, London.
9. Clarke, W. (1790) Observations on the properties commonly attributed by medical writers to human milk, on the changes it undergoes on digestion and the diseases supposed to originate from this source in infancy, *London Med. J. 11*, 71-91.
10. Ebrahim, G. J. (1978) *Breastfeeding the biological option*, London.
11. Ebrahim, G. J. (1979) *Care of the newborn in developing countries*, London.
12. Exton, B. (1751) *A new and general system of midwifery*, London.
13. Fildes, V. A. (1981) The early history of the infant feeding bottle, *Nursing Times 77*, 128-9, 168-70.
14. Fildes, V. A. (1982) *The history of infant feeding 1500-1800*, Unpublished PhD thesis, University of Surrey, Dept Human Biology and Health.

15. *Gentleman's Magazine, The* (1765) Anonymous article *On some of the causes that occasion the mortality of children under two years of age. In answer to queries in the public papers, concerning the cause of the great mortality of infants in this metropolis under that age,* December 1765, London.

16. Gouge, W. (1622) *Of domestical duties. Eight treatises,* London.

17. Hamilton, A. (1792) *A treatise on the management of female complaints and of children in early infancy,* Edinburgh.

18. Hoffmann, F. (c.1740) *A system of the practice of medicine vol.2,* trans. Lewis, W., London, 1783.

19. James, R. (1746) *The modern practice of physic. As improv'd by ... H. Boerhaave, and F. Hoffmann. ... Being a translation of the aphorisms of the former with the commentaries of Dr van Swieten,* 2 vols, London.

20. Jelliffe, D. B. & Jelliffe, E. F. P. (1978) *Human milk in the modern world. Psychosocial, Nutritional and economic significance,* Oxford.

21. Jones, J. (1579) *The arte and science of preserving bodie and soule in healthe, wisedome, and catholicke religion: physically, philosophically and divinely devised,* London.

22. *Ladies physical directory: by a physician. 7th edition, with large additions, alterations, and amendments* (1739), London.

23. Lara, B. (1791) *An essay on the injurious custom of mothers not suckling their own children; with some directions for chusing a nurse, and weaning of children, etc.,* London.

24. Mackenzie, C. (1770) *Lectures in midwifery,* Library of the Wellcome Institute for the History of Medicine, London, MS 3392.

25. McMath, J. (1694) *The expert midwife: a treatise of the diseases of women with child, and in childbed ... with fit remedies for the various maladies of newborn babes,* Edinburgh.

26. Mantell, T. (1787) *Short directions for the management of infants,* London.

27. Maubray, J. (1730) *The female physician containing all the diseases incident to that sex ... together with the diet and regimen of both the mother and child,* London.

28. Memis, J. (1765) *The midwife's pocket companion,* London.

29. Moss, W. (1781) *An essay on the management and nursing of children in the earlier periods of infancy,* London.

30. Nelson, J. (1753) *An essay on the government of children. Under three general heads: viz health, manners and education,* London.

31. Rosenstein, N. R. von (1776). *The diseases of children and their remedies,* trans. Sparrman, A., London.

32. Sloane, H. (1748) *Letter to John Milner, vice-president of the Hospital for the maintenance and education of exposed and deserted young children,* 28 October 1748. Quoted in full in Brownlow, J. (1847) *Memoranda; or Chronicles of the Foundling Hospital,* London.

33. Smellie, W. (1752) *Treatise on the theory and practice of midwifery*, London, vols 1 and 3.
34. Smith, H. (1774) *Letters to married women on nursing and the management of children. The 3rd edition, revised and considerably enlarged*, London.
35. Spence, D. (1784) *A system of midwifery*, Edinburgh.
36. Still, G. F. (1931) *The history of paediatrics*, London.
37. Underwood, M. (1784) *A treatise on the diseases of children. With directions for the management of infants from the birth: especially such as are brought up by hand*, London.
38. Van Helmont, J. B. (1662) *Oriatrike or Physick refined*, trans. J.C., London.
39. Wentworth, T. (1883) *The Wentworth papers 1705-1739*, Cartwright, J. (ed.), London.
40. Willughby, P. (1630-69) *Observations in midwifery. As also the country midwife's opusculum or vade mecum*, Blenkinsop, H. (ed.), Warwick, 1863.
41. Young, T. (1761) *De lacte,* Edinburgh. Cited in Still, G. F. (1931) *History of paediatrics*, London.
42. Young, T. (late 18th century) *Young's midwifery*, Library of the Wellcome Institute for the History of Medicine, MSS 5106 and 5107.

CHAPTER THIRTEEN

Artificial Feeding:
Feeding Vessels: the Evidence from
Artefacts and Art

"March 6, 1700. This morning, the child received almost a
miraculous deliverance from choking, by a pin, which he
suck'd out of the silver nipple of his bottel, tho' wee knew
not how it came there."
Cotton Mather, *Diary*

FEEDING vessels have survived from the neolithic period in northern Africa [1,36] and from the Late Bronze and Early Iron Ages in
Europe [36]. A description that began only in 1500 would therefore give
a false impression of infant feeding bottles, since the period from 1500
to 1800 represents only a brief phase in their development. This chapter
will therefore attempt to describe the evolution of different types of
feeding vessels from the earliest recorded examples until the early 19th
century. Examples from many parts of the known world are included, to
show that the development of specific shapes was not localised or
confined to particular countries, although minor modifications of basic
design occurred in different regions; as, for instance, in upright sucking
bottles. Throughout, function defines form, and there are extraordinary
continuities across millennia. In addition, feeding bottles were imported
and exported, and their designs were often adopted by the importing
country. For instance, England imported sucking bottles from Germany
and Italy in the 16th century [53], while vessels from England and
Holland were exported to the American colonies in the 17th century [8].

In this chapter the pictorial record is dominant (see appendix, pp.
328–42). As much care as possible has been taken to show shapes and
designs which were representative rather than exceptional, and in most
cases other vessels of similar design in the same period have been
identified. Where they are known, the measurements of vessels are
given. The plates that follow show some examples, in European painting
and sculpture from the 14th to the 18th century.

Feeding vessels were made from the following materials: i) naturally
occurring structures, as, for example, animal horns; ii) artefacts. Their
materials include *pottery*, from the Neolithic period onward; *glass*, from

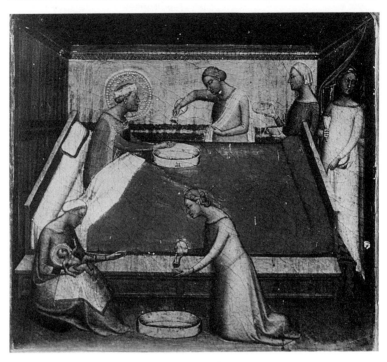

Plate 13.1. Bernardo Daddi, *The Birth of
the Virgin*, first half 14th C. The woman
in white, *right*, holds a feeding horn.

Roman times; *wood*, from the 15th century at least; *pressed leather*, from
the 16th century at least; *metals* (e.g. pewter, tin, silver) from the 16th
century; *porcelain*, from the 18th century; and *bone* and *horn* [5,46,53].

Animal *horns* were probably the oldest form of feeding vessel, both
for infants and adults, since they were widely available both to hunter-
gatherers and to livestock farmers. A horn in terracotta, from ancient
Egypt (plate 13.App.1), is among the earliest-known manufactured
infant feeding vessels. By its nature, the horn allowed little variety of
shape, and as such is distinct from other feeding bottles, although both
upright and boat-shaped bottles probably evolved from it (plates 13.1,2).

Manufactured vessels. Two distinct forms of man-made feeding vessels
have existed since prehistoric times: round *jugs*, and *boat-shaped bottles*.
A third, the upright feeding bottle, developed much later (plates 13.3,4).

The round *jug-shape* with a sucking spout and, usually, a handle
either above, at right angles, or opposite the spout was in use from the
Late Bronze and Early Iron Age in northern Europe, and from the

Plate 13.2. Breugel, *The poor kitchen*,
1563 (detail). Feeding a child with
a cow's horn.

neolithic Sudan [36], until the 19th century, and evolved into the feeding can or 'Bubby-pot', invented by Hugh Smith in 1772 [60]. It still survives today as the spouted cups which are used by mothers for weaning from the bottle or breast.

The *boat-shaped* bottle had a sucking spout or hole at one end and, usually, a second larger hole for filling. This design was also in use from the Early Iron Age in northern Europe until the 18th century, when it evolved into two different types of feeder: i) the pap-boat, which first appeared about 1680–1710 [5] and which survived until the late 19th century; ii) the boat-shaped feeding bottle which was still in use in England in the 1950s [12].

Upright feeding vessels with a screw top, which incorporated an artificial nipple or teat, first appeared in illustrations of the late Medieval period. Due principally to national differences in design, there was considerable variety in the outline of these bottles during the next 500 years, but they were the precursors of the upright feeding vessel in general use throughout the world today.

The feeding vessels in use in different periods are summarised in figure 13.1. The fact that examples of certain types of vessel have not been found in some periods does not necessarily mean that they were not in use. It is probable that animal horns were utilised throughout, since they were easily available and not costly. Particular designs of manufactured vessels may have gone temporarily out of fashion. For example, there are no examples of boat-shaped bottles from the 16th and 17th centuries. This may mean no more than that none have yet been found.

Period	Horns	Jug-shaped	Boat shaped	Upright bottles
Prehistoric				
Ancient Egyptian				
Greek				
Roman				
9th century				
10th century				
12th-13th century				
13th-14th century				
15th century				
16th century				
17th century				
18th century				

Figure 13.1. Summary of feeding vessels in use in different periods, from prehistory to the 18th century.

¶ The infant feeding vessels of the Greek and Roman period [64] fall into two distinct sizes independent of design: i) a height of 30–70 mm and a maximum diameter of 60–70 mm; ii) a height of 95–120 mm and a diameter – depending on the design – of 100–150 mm.

The smaller feeders were the type commonly found in infant graves [19,36]. Although cremation was common in the ancient world, infants were buried rather than cremated until they were old enough to have teeth [50]. An explanation for these two different sizes is that the smaller ones were used for feeding neonates before they were put to the breast several days after birth, or for giving extra fluids in the early days of

Plate 13.3. Germany, 1515. Child drinking from a feeding can. Detail from an altarpiece in Lübeck.

breastfeeding. The larger vessels were probably used for giving supplementary foods to older infants, and when weaning the child from the breast.

In the medieval period, and during the era 1500–1800, feeding vessels also varied in size, but it has been possible to examine closely very few of the feeders from this period, so only estimates of the measurements are given (plates 13.3, 4, 5).

Pap-boats of the 18th century have a capacity ranging from about 60 ml up to approximately 300 ml [20, 28], and examination of some of the records of the Wellcome Collection at the Science Museum shows that pap-boats ranged from 105–208 mm in length, and from 41–72 mm in width. The majority were 100–110 mm long and 50–60 mm wide.

Sucking bottles in the Cow & Gate Collection vary from 120–200 ml in capacity [28]. Some of those in the Wellcome Collection have measurements of 90–178 mm in height and from 40–101 mm in width for upright versions. Possibly two sizes of these were manufactured: i) 90–130 mm in height and 40–60 mm in width; ii) 155–175 mm in height and 80–105 mm in width. The boat-shaped sucking bottles measured 174–226 mm in length and from 59–226 mm in width.

Plate 13.4. England, 1593. Portrait of a
15-week-old child holding a wooden,
upright feeding bottle.

¶ There are very few complete *bubby-pots* or feeding cans in the Wellcome Collection, but the measurements found were 86–107 mm in
height (including spout) and 68–99 mm in width (including handle).

Plate 13.5. Jan Steen (1625-79),
detail from *The Baptismal Feast.*
Metal feeding can.

Hugh Smith (1774) gave the capacity as 'little more than a quarter of a pint' [58], that is, 150 ml. The Pennsylvanian feeding cans described by Dittrick (1939) have similar measurements: 100 mm in height and a diameter of 60 mm. The average capacity varies from 150–170 ml, although one larger version has a capacity of 390 ml [14].

Wieuon die künfte der maifter geyt
das des kindes rechte zeit
Zů feügcnd fy zwey jar
wie doch es gar dick fürwar
Entwenet wirt von milche ee
hie nach fo fagent die maifter mc
Das man das kind entwenen fol
noch vnd noch das thůt jm wol
p iuj

Plate 13.6. Upright sucking bottle
illustrated in H. von Louffenberg,
Versehung des leibs, 1491.

From the available material, the size of all designs of feeding vessels
in the 17th and 18th centuries appears to have varied much more than
in the ancient world; the existence of two distinct sizes not being noted
after the Roman period. It is unclear whether this fact has any significance in relation to artificial feeding. Possibly the greater variation in
size reflected greater consumer demand. Both the Cow & Gate Collection and the Wellcome Collection specimens (the main sources used
for this survey) represent the private collections of an individual; N.
Hutchings and H. Wellcome respectively. Thus they may contain a dis-
proportionate number of rare or attractive examples of feeding vessels,
and not necessarily give a representative idea of the sucking bottles and
pap-boats in general use in the 17th and 18th centuries, although specimens in other notable collections, such as the Drake Collection in Toronto and the Eisenberg Collection in New Mexico, show a similar range
and variety. Secondly, in the use of pictorial evidence, there may be representations which are not strictly in keeping with items of the period,
since later artists may have copied the idea or design of an earlier artist
[37,57]. To minimize problems arising from these facts, confirmatory

evidence from literary and medical sources as well as surviving artefacts has been sought before arriving at any firm conclusion.

There has been some controversy over ancient feeding bottles, some authorities claiming that these vessels were used as lamp fillers or for functions other than infant feeding [19,33]. Four factors have been identified to show that many of these controversial items were indeed used for feeding babies: i) remnants of food remaining in some vessels have been shown, on analysis, to contain casein [19,36]; ii) absence of lamp blackening [19,36]; iii) presence of such vessels in infant graves, together with other infantile impedimenta, such as toys, probably intended for any afterlife [1,36]; iv) the small bore of the feeding-spouts which were the right size for the mouth of a small baby, but too small for an older child or adult.

Some doubtful specimens, particularly from the Greek and Roman periods, have not been included in this history because, on examination, the structure was such that if the spout was put into a child's mouth and the vessel tipped up for drinking, some other part of the utensil would have hit the child on the nose or in the eye, or could have obstructed its breathing. It is possible that these, usually very decorative versions, were used as ornamental gifts or votive offerings and not intended for feeding. It has been postulated that some of the sucking bottles of the 17th and 18th centuries were not used for feeding infants, but were used solely for rearing young animals, such as lambs rejected by their mother [8]. However, sufficient pictorial, literary and medical evidence is presented here to show that many, if not all, of these sucking bottles were intended for administering food to young children.

Related artefacts. Although not strictly feeding vessels, two other structures were used in relation to feeding; the pap-warmer and the sucking-bag, sometimes also the warming or soaking container. In the 18th and 19th centuries pap-boats, and other infant or invalid feeders, were placed into a china receptacle and a small flame heater was lit beneath them so keeping the food warm, either during a feed or until the child cried for food, especially during the night [13,15,19]. Sucking-bags were the forerunners of the modern dummy or 'comforter'. They consisted of a piece of gauze or other thin cloth soaked in a mixture of sweet pap or panada, or a solution of sugar or honey in water, squeezed free of excess fluid and given to the child to suck [40,52,60,61]. Small round containers with lids, made of pewter or china, which can be found in some museums, were used for soaking the comforter or for storage when a child did not want it [15,18]. The sucking bag was of ancient origin and is depicted both in sculptures, and in pictures of the virgin and child, at least from the 15th century (see p.211) [24,40].

Spoons adapted for feeding both medicines to adults and thin paps to infants were used in the later 18th and 19th century. Sometimes these were called pap-spoons; they had a hollowed-out handle leading to the bowl of the spoon so that the spoon could be put to the child's mouth and by blowing down the handle the pap could be introduced into it. These were early versions of the Gibson's medicine spoon of the 19th century [18]. Drinking tubes similarly were used for both adult invalids and children. They were made of metal and were designed to be placed in a cup of soup, caudle or other mixture which might contain solid particles; the perforations at the end of the tube allowed only liquid to be sucked up and ingested by the child, leaving unwanted lumps at the bottom of the cup [12,31].

REFERENCES

1. Addison, F. (1949) *The Wellcome excavations in the Sudan*, Oxford, 2 vols.
2. Auvard & Pingat (1889) *Hygiène infantile ancienne et moderne*, Paris.
3. Baldini, F. (1784) *Methodo di allatare amano i bambini*, Naples. Also the French translation published in Paris, 1786.
4. Bartsocas, C. S. (1978) Ancient Greek feeding-bottles, *Trans. Stud. Coll. Phys. Philad. 45*, 297-8.
5. Bennion, E. (1979) *Antique medical instruments*, London.
6. Bidault, P. & Lepart, J. (1972) *Etains médicaux et pharmaceutiques*, Paris.
7. Brüning, H. (1908) *Geschichte der methodik künstlichen saüglingsernährung*, Stuttgart.
8. Caulfield, E. (1952) Infant feeding in colonial America, *J. Pediat. 41*, 673-87.
9. Chamoux, A. (1973) L'allaitement artificiel, *Annales de démographie historique*, Paris, 410-18.
10. Cone, T. E. (1976) *200 years of feeding infants in America*, Columbus, Ohio.
11. Cone, T. E. (1979) *History of American pediatrics*, Boston.
12. *Cow & Gate collection of feeding vessels catalogue*, undated, Trowbridge.
13. Crellin, J. K. (1969) *Medical ceramics. A catalogue of the English and Dutch collections in the Museum of the Wellcome Institute for the History of Medicine*, London.
14. Dittrick, H. (1939) The nursing can. An early American feeding device, *Bull. Hist. Med. 7*, 696-704.
15. Drake, T. G. H. (1932-33) Antiques of pediatric interest, *J. Pediat. 1*, 502-3, 764-5; *2*, 68-9; *3*, 374-5, 639-40, 779-80.
16. Drake, T. G. H. (1938) The child in antiquity, *Health*, Spring.
17. Drake, T. G. H. (1938) Antique English Delft pottery of medical interest, *Can. Med. Ass. J. 39*, 585-8.
18. Drake, T. G. H. (1941) Antique pewter articles of medical interest, *Bull. Hist. Med. 10*, 272-87.

19. Drake, T. G. H. (1956) Infant feeders and feeding in bygone days, *Chemist Drugg. 165*, 614-18.
20. Driscoll, R., of the Wellcome Collection at the Science Museum, London, Personal communication.
21. Feeding vessel retrieved from the river, *Country Life CLX* (2883), 4 May 1951.
22. Fildes, V. A. (1979) It's a wonder babies ever survived. The first food of infants 1500-1800, and the consequences for maternal and child health, *Nursing Mirror 149* (2), supplement viii-xiv; *149* (3) 22-4.
23. Fildes, V. A. (1979) The early history of the infant feeding bottle, *Nursing Times 77*, 128-9; 168-70.
24. Fildes, V. A. (1982) *The history of infant feeding 1500-1800*, Unpublished PhD thesis, University of Surrey, Dept of Human Biology and Health.
25. Forsyth, D. (1911) The history of infant feeding from Elizabethan times, *Proc. Soc. Med. 4*, 110-41.
26. Füngling, D. (1949) *Beitrage zur geschichte der trinkgefasse für sauglinge*, MD dissertation, Marburg.
27. Gervais, T. (1979) Pediatric antiquities. The Eisenberg Collection, *Amer. J. Dis. Child. 133*, 779-81.
28. Gunnel, Mr, of Cow & Gate, Trowbridge, Wiltshire, Personal communication.
29. Haskell, A. & Lewis, M. (1971) *Infantilia, The archaeology of the nursery*, London.
30. Huard, P. & Laplane, R. (1979) *Histoire illustré de la puériculture. Aspects diététiques, socio-culturel et ethnologiques*, Paris.
31. Hutchings, N. W. (1958) 4000 years of infant feeding, *Chemist Drugg. 169*, 714-18.
32. Jackson, W. A. (1981) *The Victorian chemist and druggist*, Princes Risborough, Aylesbury, Bucks.
33. Jonckheere, F. (1955) Un chapitre de pédiatrie Egyptienne l'allaitement, *Aesculape 37*, 203-23.
34. Kern, J. H. C. (1957) An Attic feeding bottle of the 4th century BC in Leyden, *Mnemosyne 10*, 16-21.
35. Klebe, D. & Schadewalt, H. (1955) *Gefasse zur kinderernährung im wandel der zeit*, Frankfurt am Main.
36. Lacaille, A. D. (1950) Infant feeding bottles in prehistoric times, *Proc. Roy. Soc. Med. 43*, 565-8.
37. Langmuir, E., University of Sussex, Personal communication.
38. Leca, A-P. (1971) *La médecine Egyptienne au temps des pharaons*, Paris.
39. Leibowitz, J. O. (1976) Oriental feeding cups (Iranian 10th century) at L. A. Mayer Institute for Islamic Art, Jerusalem, *Bull. Cleveland Med. Libr. 22*, 64-5.
40. Levin, S. (1971) Dummies, *S. Afr. Med. J. 45*, 237-40.

41. MacGregor, Mr, of the Ashmolean Museum, Oxford, Personal communication.
42. Mahler, B. (1966) *Beitrage zur geschichte des schnullers*, MD dissertation, Dusseldorf.
43. Marshall, R. (1976) *Childhood in seventeenth century Scotland*, Edinburgh.
44. Matthews, L. G. (1971) *Antiques of the pharmacy*, London.
45. Metlinger, B. (1473) *Ein regimen der jungen kinder*, Augsburg. Also translated in full in Ruhrah, J. (1925) *Pediatrics of the past*, New York.
46. Moss, W. (1781) *An essay on the management and nursing of children in the earlier periods of infancy*, London.
47. Mössmer, A. (1983) Sauglingsflaschen aus holz, in Schadewalt, H., Μετανοειτε. *Wandelt euch durch nevesdenken. Festschrift fur H. Schadewalt*, Gopfert, W. & Otten, H-H. (eds), Dusseldorf.
48. *Description of the Museum of the History of Medicine, Academy of Medicine, Toronto, Canada* (contains the T. G. H. Drake collection of infant feeding bottles).
49. Peiper, A. (1966) *Chronik der kinderheilkunde*, Leipzig, 4th ed.
50. Pliny (1st century AD) *Historie of the world. Commonly called the naturall historie of Plinius Secundus*, trans. Holland, P., London, 1601.
51. Radbill, S. X. (1981) Infant feeding through the ages, *Clin. Pediat. 20* (10), 613-21.
52. Rich, I. (1957) Narresutten i historisk perspektiv, *Medicinsk Forum 3*, 90-6.
53. Rosenthal, R. (1936) A short pictorial review of the evolution of infant feeding vessels up to the beginning of the 19th century, *Bull. Med. Libr. Ass. 25*, 89-94.
54. Ruhrah, J. (1925) *Pediatrics of the past*, New York.
55. Sadler, S. H. (1895) *Infant feeding by artificial means: a scientific and practical treatise on the dietetics of infancy*, London.
56. Sadler, S. H. (1896) *Infant feeding by artificial means*, London, 2nd ed., preface.
57. Sears, E., formerly of the Warburg Institute, London, Personal communication.
58. Smith, H. (1774) *Letters to married women on nursing and the management of children. The 3rd edition, revised and considerably enlarged*, London.
59. Snelling, E. D. (1955) Infant feeding in the past: 2. Artificial feeding, *Nursing Mirror*, June 10.
60. Still, G. F. (1931) *The history of paediatrics*, London.
61. Struve, C. A. (1800) *A familiar treatise on the physical education of children during the early period of their lives*, trans. Willich, A. F. M., London.
62. Tubbs, F. (1947) Infant feeding bottles with particular reference to Romano-British and British medieval vessels,

Br. Med. Bull. 5, 255-6.

63. Vallambert, S. de (1565) *Cinq livres, de la manière de nourir et gouverner les enfants des leur naissance,* Poictiers.

64. *Wellcome collection at the Science Museum, London,* Excerpts from the unpublished and uncompleted catalogue.

65. White, J. C. (1976) 'Damascan glass nursing bottle' in the Howard Dittrick Museum, *Bull. Cleveland Med. Libr. 22* (1), 11-17.

66. Wickes, I. G. (1953) A history of infant feeding, *Archs Dis. Childh. 28*, 151-8, 232-40, 332-40, 416-22, 495-502.

67. Zglinicki, F. von (1979) *Die Wiege: volkskundlich-kutur-geschichtlich-kunstwisssenschaftlich-medizin-historisch,* Regensburg.

Table 13.1 (pp.320-7). The development of infant feeding vessels c.3000 BC to c.1800 AD. (Where known, the country of origin of vessels, illustrations and comments is given in italics. Only one statement or description of each definable shape and type in each period is given. Some artefacts and illustrations of vessels survive in relatively large numbers, others occur infrequently; the latter are indicated by (rare) at the end of the description. Unless otherwise stated the vessels are of earthenware or terracotta.)

Artefacts	Paintings, illustrations, sculptures, carvings	Discussed in medical literature	Mentioned in non-medical literature
c.3000–c.2000 BC Round vessel with spout; no lid (rare) *Egypt* Anthropomorphic vases for milk *Egypt*			
c.2000–c.1000 BC Round cup-shaped vessel with spout; with or without handle; no lid *Cyprus, France, Egypt* Earthenware horn *Egypt* Anthropomorphic vases for milk *Egypt*			
c.1000–c.500 BC Round, jug-shaped vessel with spout; with or without handle *Phoenicia, Greece, Cyprus* Round, cup-shaped vessel with spout; no lid *Sudan, Cyprus* Ovoid or boat-shaped vessel with round neck for filling; spout at one end; imperforate projection at opposite end; with or without claw feet *Hesse, Savoy, Lower Austria, Bohemia, Germany* Round, jug-shaped vessel with vertical elongated spout; handle *Cyprus*	Woman using a rod and bottle to feed infant *Babylon*		
c.500 BC–c.1 AD Round vessel with spout; with or			Feeding vessel referred to in

Phoenicia, S. Italy, Germany
Round vessel with spout; strainer in lid; with or without handle; *Greece*

Boat-shaped vessel with spout at one end; strainer in lid; handle *Greece, S. Italy*

Animal-shaped with spout *Greece, Cyprus, Phoenicia, Egypt*

. . . .

c.1–c.500 AD
Round vessel with spout; with or without handle; earthenware or glass *Roman, England, Italy, France, Hungary*

Jug-shaped vessel with spout; with or without handle; sometimes ridged round centre *Roman, Italy, France, England*

Round cup-shaped vessel with spout; strainer in lid; handle (rare) *Roman*

Flattened spherical vessel with spout; filling hole at top (rare) *Roman, France*

Round glass vessel with elongated spout *Roman*

Boat-shaped vessel with spout at one end; filling hole at opposite end; handle *Roman*

Boat-shaped vessel with lid and lip for pouring *Roman*

Vessel shaped as negro child's head with spout; filling hole; handle (rare) *Roman*

. . . .

Soranus referred to artificial nipples for giving fluids *Greece, Rome*

Moschion described a glass feeding vessel

Samian-ware feeding vessels made in *France* imported or carried by Roman families into *Britain*

Artefacts	Paintings, illustrations, sculptures, carvings	Discussed in medical literature	Mentioned in non-medical literature
c. 500–c. 1000 AD Rounded jug-shaped vessel with very short spout; handle; no lid *Germany* Round, cup-shaped glass vessel with long, curving spout (rare) *Iran*			Cow's horn *Germany*
c. 1000–c. 1400 AD Horn *France* Rounded jug-shaped vessel with spout; with or without handle *England, Germany* Spherical vessel with spout and handle *France* Cylindrical vessel with ?lip for pouring; handle (rare) *France*	Horn *France, Spain, Italy*		Cow's horn *France, Germany, Iceland*
c. 1400–c. 1500 AD Cylindrical wooden vessel with short spout at right-angles; lid (rare) *France or Germany* Animal-shaped vessel with spout (rare) *Germany* Rounded jug-shaped vessel with spout; with or without handle *England*	Upright wooden sucking bottle with rounded sides; lid with teat *Germany* Upright cylindrical sucking bottle; lid with teat *Germany* Upright wooden sucking bottle; waisted with bulbous base; lid with teat *Germany* Boat-shaped sucking bottle with teat at one end (rare) *Germany*	Reference to nippled nursing flask *Germany* Reference to horn *Germany*	
c. 1500–c. 1600 AD Round jug-shaped vessel with	Horn *Netherlands* Feeding can with rounded sides	Cow's horn recommended *France*	Horns used to feed foundlings at the Hôtel-Dieu, Paris *France*

Upright wooden sucking bottle with rounded sides; lid with teat *Germany*

c.1600–c.1700 AD

Feeding cup with small spout and handle; half-covered top *France, England*

Upright pewter sucking bottle with concave sides; screw cap with a short spout *Bavaria*

Upright pewter sucking bottle with bulbous base; screw cap with short teat *France, England*

Upright, conical glass sucking bottle; pewter screw cap with short, or longer narrow-bore, spout *Bavaria*

Upright glass sucking bottle; round base; waisted near top for attachment of cord / chain to glass stopper (rare) *Holland*

Silver ? pap-boat (rare) *England*

Round pewter container for soaking or storing sucking bags *Germany*

Upright wooden sucking bottle with rounded sides; lid with teat *Germany, Austria, Switzerland, Netherlands*

Upright wooden sucking bottle; wooden lid with teat *England*

Upright glass sucking bottle with rounded sides; wooden lid with teat *Germany*

Spherical sucking bottle with elongated spout (rare) *Germany*

Sucking bags (rare) *Austrian Tyrol, Germany*

Metal feeding can with side spout and handle; lid *Holland*

Upright wooden sucking bottle with bulbous base; lid with short spout *France, Holland*

Upright, conical glass sucking bottle; metal lid with teat *Germany*

Upright sucking bottle with rounded sides; lid with teat *France*

Infant fed with spoon *Holland, England*

References to infant's drinking bottles *Switzerland*

Reference to sucking bottle *France*

Pewter baby's bottle listed in inventory *England*

Upright sucking bottles of wood or pressed leather imported into England *Germany, Italy*

Pewter sucking bottles listed in inventories *America*

Pewter sucking bottles imported into Boston, *America Holland, England*

Pewter sucking bottles manufactured by at least two pewterers *Boston, America*

Reference to sucking bottle *England*

Reference to spoon feeding *England*

Artefacts	Paintings, illustrations, sculptures, carvings	Discussed in medical literature	Mentioned in non-medical literature
c.1700–c.1800 AD Horn with or without simple mouthpiece for sucking *Switzerland, England* Horn either attached by sucking-horn holder to cradle, or separate *Sweden, Finland* Feeding cup or can with small spout and handle; half-covered top *France, England* Feeding cans of pewter, tin, silver or earthenware. Early versions of bubby-pot; upright can with straight sides; long, bent or straight spout from base; usually no lid; sometimes with half-covered top *England, Holland, German immigrants in America* Pewter upright sucking bottle with bulbous base; pewter screw top with short spout; some in three parts which unscrew for cleaning *France, England, Europe* Pewter upright sucking bottle with bulbous base; screw top with extended and bent narrow-bore spout *Europe* Pewter upright flask-shaped sucking bottle with screw cap with teat *England*		References to horn in use *England* Horn recommended only for thin fluids *England* Horn said to be used in *Russia Scotland* Machine of horn or tin said to be common *England* Reference to sucking bottle *Germany* Reference to *Icelandic* and *Russian* infants being fed with modification of sucking bottle *France* Reference to biberon (sucking bottle) used in Easter Bothnia *Sweden* Horn sucking bottle with cow's teat recommended *Sweden* Reference to a sucking vessel	Horns (cornets) issued to wet nurses taking home foundlings from the Rheims and Paris Foundling Hospitals *France* Reference to sucking bottle and pewter sucking bottle *England* Sucking bottles advertised and sold *Boston, America* Pewter sucking bottles listed in inventories *America*

Glass, upright screw sucking bottle with pewter or silver screw cap with narrow-bore spout *Germany, Europe*

Pewter upright conical sucking bottle; screw cap with teat *Bavaria*

Earthenware upright sucking bottle with straight sides *England*

Straight-sided upright pewter sucking bottle with claw feet; screw cap with short spout *Tyrol, Switzerland*

Bell-shaped pewter sucking bottle; screw cap with teat (rare) *England*

Upright glass sucking bottle with opening for sucking at top and central filling hole on one side *England*

Boat-shaped glass sucking bottle with one opening at end for sucking *Venice, Italy*

Pap-boats; gravy-boat-shaped; of pewter, silver, gold, glass, porcelain, creamware or glazed earthenware. All have extended lip for pouring; sometimes with handle; sometimes with half-cover over front; sometimes shaped like a bird *England France, Spain, Portugal, China Holland*

Pap-warmers; porcelain or plain or printed earthenware containers for inserting a full pap-boat for warming *England*

Pap-boats *England*

Pap-boats made to match tea-services *England*

References to the boat *England*

The boat recommended as the best feeding vessel *England*

bottle *America*

Suggestion that sucking bottle be invented because the spoon is frustrating *England*

Artefacts	Paintings, illustrations, sculptures, carvings	Discussed in medical literature	Mentioned in non-medical literature
c.1700–c.1800 AD —*contd*			
Pewter or silver pap-spoons either open-bowled or with lidded bowl and hollow handle for blowing contents into child's mouth *France, England*		Spoon recommended *England, Scotland*	References to spoon *England*
Round pewter container with lid for soaking / storing sucking bags *Germany*		Reference to sucking bags *Germany*	
Metal drinking tubes *England*			
c.1770–c.1800 AD			
Boat-shaped sucking bottles of silver, glass, porcelain, transfer-printed earthenware or cream-ware. Opening at one end for sucking; central filling hole; sometimes with glass teat *England, France*		Newly invented glass feeding bottle with spherical base and extended neck; screw top with sponge for sucking *Italy*	
Bubby-pots. Upright cans or pots in pewter, silver, porcelain or creamware; sometimes with rounded sides; long, curved spout from base with rounded tip with several perforations for sucking; lid attached or separate *England*		Newly invented bubby-pot described *England* Bubby-pot recommended *England*	
Tin feeding cans; base wider than top; straight sides with short			

the can and has a rounded tip, perforated for sucking; with handle and overlapping lid (individual cans are slight variants on this basic design) *German* immigrants to *Pennsylvania, America*

Pewter feeding can with straight sides and rounded top; straight spout at 45° angle; with attached lid and handle   *European* immigrants to *America*

Appendix

Horn

13.App.1. Ancient Egyptian terracotta feeding horn, and anthropomorphic vase for infant foods.

13.App.2. Finland, c.1815. Cradle with sucking horn and holder.

Cup-shaped

13.App.3. England, 1984. Spouted feeding cups for weaning.

13.App.4. Neolithic feeders from a) France, b) Sudan.

13.App.5. Cyprus, c.10th C. BC. Feeding vessel.

13.App.6. Greece, 5th C. BC. Example of a common form of Greek feeder.

13.App.7. S. Italy, 4thC. BC. Feeder with non-spill design: the diagram shows the section.

13.App.8. Roman, c.1st C. AD. Glass feeding vessel.

13.App.9. Silchester, England, 2nd C. AD. Roman pottery feeding vessel.

13.App.10. Colchester, England, 1st/2nd C. AD. Roman Samian ware feeding vessel.

13.App.11. London, England, 2nd C. AD. Roman pottery feeding vessel.

13.App.12. Roman, 2nd C. AD. Black terracotta feeding vessel in the shape of a human (? African) head.

13.App.13. Roman, 2nd C. AD. Rough buff-ware feeding vessel.

Cans and bubby pots

13.App.14. England, 18th C. Pewter feeding can.

13.App.15. Pennsylvania, USA, 18th C. Feeding can used by German immigrants: the diagram shows the section.

13.App.16. Holland or England, 18th C. Pewter feeding can.

13.App.17. England, 18th C. Pewter 'bubby pot' after the design of Dr Hugh Smith, 1775.

13.App.18. England, 18th C. Smith's 'bubby pot' in silver, 1783.

13.App.19. England, 18th C. Smith's 'bubby pot' in cream-ware, 'in order that the poor may be accommodated', c.1780.

Boat-shaped

13.App.20. England, 1940-50. Boat-shaped glass feeding vessels.

13.App.21. Late Bronze Age Europe. Boat-shaped feeders from a) Germany, b)Austria.

13.App.22. Greek colonial. Pottery boat-shaped feeder, probably originating in S. Italy. Inscribed MAMO (= breast).

13.App.23. Cyprus, c.3000 BC. Animal variant of boat-shaped feeder.

13.App.24. Roman, 1st/2nd C. AD. Boat-shaped clay feeder.

13.App.25. England, 18th C. Silver pap boat.

13.App.26. England, 18th/19th C.
Boat-shaped sucking bottle.

13.App.27. England, 18th/19th C.
Boat-shaped feeding bottles and
pap boats in porcelain from Spode,
Davenport and Wedgwood.

Upright

13.App.28. England, 1980s. Upright
polycarbonate feeding bottle.

13.App.29. Europe. Lathe-turned
wooden sucking bottle of a pattern
originating in the 15th C.

13.App.30. Holland, 17th C. Glass
feeding bottle, designed not to fall
over easily.

13.App.31. England, mid 18th C.
Pewter sucking bottle.

13.App.32. England, mid 18th C.
Pewter sucking bottle. This model
sometimes unscrewed in the
middle, and had a detachable lid
for easier cleaning.

13.App.33. England, mid 18th C.
Pewter sucking bottle with the
narrow sucking tube extending
inside to the bottom of the bottle.

13.App.34. England, 18th C. Flask-
shaped pewter sucking bottle.

13.App.35. England, mid 18th C.
Flask-shaped pewter sucking
bottle. The narrow spout made
this model hard to clean.

13.App.36. Germany, mid 18th C.
A design common in Germany
and Scandinavia.

13.App.37. ?Germany, 18th C.
Glass conical-shaped sucking
bottle with pewter mouthpiece.
The glass showed when it was

empty and/or needed cleaning.

13.App.38. Europe, 18th C. Engraved glass sucking bottle.
The mouthpiece – which was often
of silver – is not original.

13.App.39. Europe, 17th/19th C.
Fluted glass sucking bottle with
metal mouthpiece.

13.App.40. Italy. Illustration of the
feeding bottle invented in 1784 by
Filippo Baldini (*Methodo di allatare
a mano i bambini*).

13.App.41. Europe, late 18th C.
An example of a 'Baldini' bottle.

Miscellaneous

13.App.42. England, c.1785.
Chelsea porcelain pap-warmer.
This example has a candlestick lid.

13.App.43. England, mid 18th C.
A utilitarian version of no.42.
Examples of this type have been
found, in pottery and metal, in
N. America.

13.App.44. 'Gibson spoon', 1827, for
administering unpleasant medicines. The child put the spoon end
in its mouth and when the mother
took her thumb off the hollow
handle the medicine ran into the
child's mouth.

13.App.45. England. Silver drinking tube, called a 'sick syphon'.

13.App.46. Germany, c.1800.
Pewter vessel for soaking an
infant's sucking-bag.

13.App.47. Europe. Limewood
sucking barrel with filter and
spout. Probably 19th C., but the
model was in use from the 15th C.

13.App.1

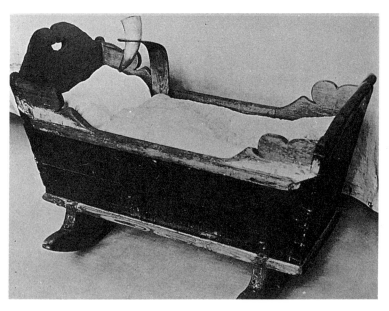

13.App.2

13.App.3

13.App.4

13.App.5

13.App.6

13.App.7

13.App.7

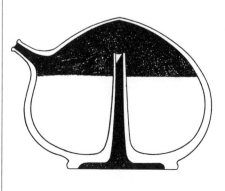

13.App.8

13.App.9

13.App.10

13.App.11

13.App.12

13.App.13

13.App.14

13.App.16

13.App.15

13.App.15

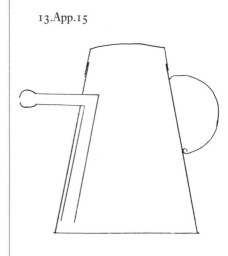

13.App.17

13.App.18

13.App.19

13.App.20

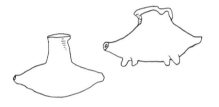

13.App.21

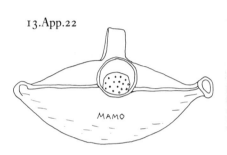

13.App.22

MAMO

13.App.23

13.App.24

13.App.25

13.App.26

13.App.27

13.App.28

13.App.29

13.App.30

13.App.31

13.App.32

13.App.33

13.App.34

13.App.35

13.App.36

13.App.37

13.App.38

13.App.39

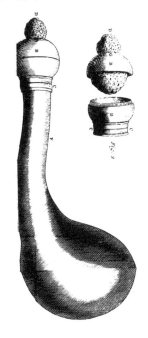

13.App.40

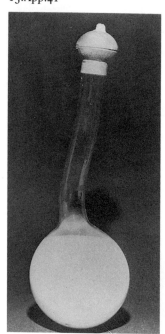

13.App.41

13.App.42

13.App.43

13.App.44

13.App.45

13.App.46

13.App.47

CHAPTER FOURTEEN

Artificial Feeding:
Medical Discussion of Feeding Vessels

"When the infant is very thirsty after the meal one should
give it water or a little watery wine through artificial nipples."
Soranus of Ephesus, AD 98–138

THE METHOD of administering foods to handfed infants was not
discussed in British medical literature until the late 18th century. Nine
authors recommended feeding vessels, or described those in common
use between 1755 and the end of the 18th century. Five types of vessel
were discussed: the horn [1,15]; the (pap) boat [1]; the spoon [5,7,11];
the bubby-pot [10,13]; other vessels, including sucking bottles [2,7,9].
These will be considered in sequence.

The horn. Three authors described the horn as a common feeding
vessel [1,10,15]:

> The horn made use of for suckling, is a small polished cow's horn
> which will hold about a gill and a half [225 ml]. The small end of
> it is perforated, and has a notch round it to which are fastened two
> small bits of parchment, shaped like the tip of the finger of a glove,
> and sewed together in such a manner, as that the food poured into
> the horn can be sucked through between the stitches [plate 14.1].
> This appears to be a very simple and ingenious contrivance, and is
> admired by some, who look upon it as a kind of artificial nipple [1].

The disadvantage of the horn was that only thin fluids could pass
between the stitches, so that larger quantities had to be given:

> . . . and hence [the child's] stomach and bowels are too much
> relaxed, whereby it is in danger of falling into the watery gripes, as
> was the case with two of mine, which were fed for some time in that
> way [1].

Armstrong (1771), who fed three of his children by hand, discovered by
trial and error that, when he used the horn, his daughters had constant
gripes and tummy upsets. When he used the boat instead, his children
thrived. Although he makes no mention of it, this must have been
because the boat was much easier to clean and, being made of materials
such as pewter or glazed porcelain, was less likely to harbour pathogenic

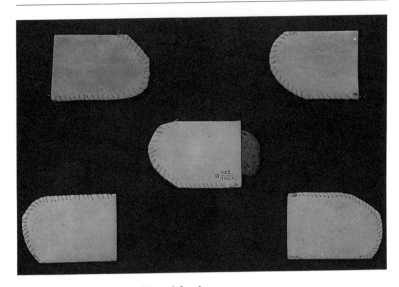

Plate 14.1. Examples of 'teats' for the
spouts of sucking vessels or horns.
They were made by stitching parchment
into a convenient shape and inserting
a small sponge. Rubber teats did not
come into general use until the mid-
nineteenth century.

organisms than the very narrow tip of a cow's horn, covered by absorbent materials such as parchment or cloth [4]. Smith (1774), in search of
a suitable artificial nipple, also said he had seen sucking 'inventions of
this kind, by means of parchment or leather sewed to the pointed end of
an horn'. And Thomas Young said that in many countries, including
Russia, cow's milk was given to infants by 'putting the teat to a horn with
a hole and lett the child suck' [15].

The boat. As noted above, the pap-boat was preferred to the horn by
George Armstrong (plate 14.2). In addition to his view about the gripes,
he noted that: i) one daughter fed with the horn seemed constantly hungry because only thin food could be given, whilst those fed with the boat
were more satisfied and content; ii) thicker and more nourishing foods
could be given with the boat and this was more satisfying for the child.

Hugh Smith, however, disapproved of the boat, because large quantities of food were given very quickly. He believed infants should have
to work for their food by sucking, as they did when sucking at the breast.

Surely it is wrong to put a large boat full of pap into their little
mouths, suffering them to swallow the whole of it in the space of a

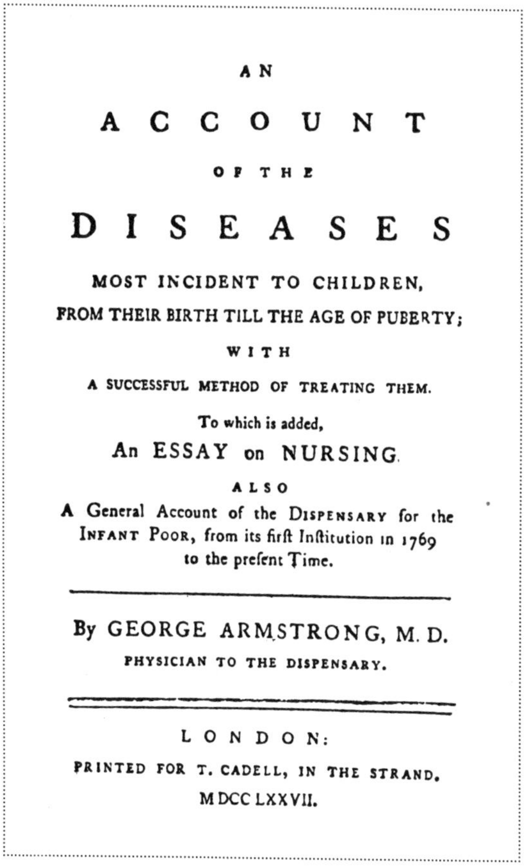

A N

A C C O U N T

OF THE

D I S E A S E S

MOST INCIDENT TO CHILDREN,

FROM THEIR BIRTH TILL THE AGE OF PUBERTY;

WITH

A SUCCESSFUL METHOD OF TREATING THEM.

To which is added,

An ESSAY on NURSING.

ALSO

A General Account of the DISPENSARY for the
INFANT POOR, from its firft Inftitution in 1769
to the prefent Time.

By GEORGE ARMSTRONG, M. D.

PHYSICIAN TO THE DISPENSARY.

L O N D O N:

PRINTED FOR T. CADELL, IN THE STRAND.

MDCCLXXVII.

Plate 14.2. The third edition of George
Armstrong's book, 1777 (first published
in 1769), in which he described the use
of the horn and pap-boat in the artificial feeding of his own children.

minute; and then perhaps from their cries, to ply them with a second, which is no sooner down than thrown up again.

Underwood (1784) gave a similar reason against using the pap-boat:
The child is tempted to take too much at a time; whilst the nurse in order to quiet it, often forces down a second or third boat full, to put a stop to the cries, which indigestion from the first or second may have occasioned.

The spoon. Rearing by the spoon was an early term for artificial feeding, used by both medical and non-medical writers [5,6,8,12] and, because it was an everyday piece of cutlery in most households, it was possibly used for feeding infants more frequently than other more specialised and less versatile means. In her advice-book published in 1767, Sarah Pennington said:

> ... nothing is more unnatural and tormenting, than feeding them with a spoon that must be taken every minute from their mouths to be replenished,

but it was recommended as the best method by Moss (1781) and Mantell (1787). Underwood (1784) thought there was as much danger of overfeeding with a spoon as with a pap-boat.

The Bubby-pot, a sophisticated version of the feeding can, was invented by Dr Hugh Smith and first described in the 3rd edition (1774) of his popular advice book *Letters to married women*:

> Since this book made its first appearance [1772] I have contrived a milk pot for my own nursery ... it appears to my family, and to many of my patients, preferable to those now in use and may probably be still further improved. ... This pot is somewhat in form like an urn; it contains a little more than a quarter of a pint; its handle, and neck or spout, are not unlike those of a coffee pot, except that the neck of this arises from the very bottom of the pot, and is very small; in short, it is upon the same principle as those gravy-pots which separate the gravy from the oily fat. The end of the spout is a little raised, and forms a roundish knob, somewhat in appearance like a small heart; this is perforated by three or four small holes: a piece of fine rag is tied loosely over it, which serves the child to play with instead of the nipple, and through which, by the infants sucking, the milk is constantly strained. The child is equally satisfied as it would be with the breast; it never wets him in the least; he is obliged to labour for every drop he receives in the manner as when at the breast; and greatly in recommendation of this contrivance, the nurses confess it is more convenient than a boat, and that it saves a great deal of trouble in the feeding of an infant; which is the greatest security to parents, that their servants will use it, when they themselves are not present. The model of this milk pot is left with Mr Morrison, at the Three Kings, in Cheapside, for the benefit of the public. The milk-pots are now also made in the Queens-ware, in order that the poor may be accommodated; any person, therefore, at a very trifling expense, may be convinced of their utility by making the experiment. [See plate 13.App.19.]

This postscript confirms the view that, by the 1770s, sufficient numbers of the poor were hand-feeding their infants, or weaning them very early, to make worthwhile the mass-production of feeding vessels such as the bubby-pot.

Ten years later, Underwood strongly advocated the use of Smith's Bubby-pot in preference to all other methods of artificial feeding:

> The boat, the spoon, and the horn, are in no way comparable to the pot, which is so contrived, not only as to please the child by its resemblance to the nipple, and the milk coming slowly into its mouth, but also to afford the infant some little degree of labour and fatigue, in order to acquire the quantity it needs: which the horn does not do.

This, he thought, avoided the problem of over-feeding:

> ... as they are [apt] to be overfed by the boat or the spoon, the food of which ... requiring only the trouble, or rather the pleasure of swallowing, the child is tempted to take too much at a time.

Rather than Smith's suggestion of placing a piece of fine rag over the spout, Underwood suggested: 'a piece of vellum or parchment, ... is nearly as acceptable to many children as the breast, as I have often been a witness'.

Other vessels/sucking bottles. The Swiss surgeon, Feliz Wurtz (1563) referred to drinking bottles, and Guillemeau (1612) mentioned that sucking bottles were used for feeding infants with a cleft palate. The devices used in Russia and Iceland, which were described by Brouzet in 1755, were possibly sucking bottles: 'the infant sucks the milk through a tube, fixed to a small spunge, or a bit of linen loosely rolled together!' and, 'a vessel ... in which is put a tube, the upper extremity of which the infant knows how to find, and putting his mouth to it, sucks. ..'.

Apart from a fleeting reference by Mantell (1787), and despite the large number of surviving artefacts of English manufacture, no British medical writer has been found who discussed sucking bottles, apart from one possible allusion by William Moss, in 1781. He described 'a machine made of horn, or tin, in use with many for feeding children; it is so contrived that the child sucks his food from it as from a breast'. Although he preferred the spoon, Moss said 'some children will not, without difficulty take their food with a spoon or boat who will take it more readily with this machine'. This may be a reference to a sucking bottle, but could equally refer to a feeding can or bubby pot, especially since surviving sucking bottles are made from pewter, glass, silver or porcelain.

Hugh Smith (1774) described a Dutch feeding vessel which was probably a sucking bottle:

> The Hollanders when they travel, have a small pewter vessel, somewhat in the form of a cone, which is filled with milk, and a piece of sponge covered with a linnen cloth is tied over the smaller end. This serves the children very well as an artificial nipple: for it is observed that a Dutch woman seldom or never gives suck to her child before strangers.

Rosenstein (1776) recommended a *biberon* or sucking bottle, which he said was in universal use in the Easter-Bothnia region of Sweden. It sounds very much like an adapted cow's horn, rather than a manufactured sucking bottle:

> It is to be made of horn, the smaller end of which may be fastened to a tanned skin of a cow's teat, or if that is not to be procured, we may use any other thin skin pierced with many small holes.

(Cf. the description of the horn given by Armstrong (1771) and Smith (1774).)

The discrepancy between the number of surviving sucking bottles (which must be only a fraction of those produced in the 17th, and particularly the 18th centuries) and their absence from the English medical literature is difficult to explain. Were sucking bottles disapproved of by the medical establishment, or were they not used by the wealthy patients of the medical authors? The latter seems unlikely, since only the rich could have purchased vessels made in silver or cut-glass. Another explanation is that sucking bottles were so common as to be considered unworthy of comment. The existence of these bottles in many different materials, from the most expensive silver to the cheapest pottery, indicates that they must have been used by all sections of the population, whether or not they were medically recommended.

The first mention of cleanliness of feeding vessels as a factor in artificial feeding was made by Rosenstein in 1776, when he insisted that the sucking bottle he described ought always to be kept clean. In 1784, Underwood said that the bubby-pot must be carefully cleansed and scalded, at least once every day, and the spout be thoroughly rinsed, lest any sour curds should stick about it. Thomas Mantell (1787) preferred the spoon for administering food, because:

> ... the invention of horns, sucking bottles, and many other contrivances for artificial nipples, are too lame and imperfect imitations of nature to be useful ... as these machines cannot be kept perfectly clean, the victuals that hangs about them will be liable to become, in a few hours, very unfit for a nice taste to swallow, or a delicate stomach to digest.

These are the only specific references to cleanliness of feeding vessels which have been found in the period 1500 to 1800. None of the three gave prognostic reasons for keeping feeding vessels clean, and it is not clear whether the comments are personal opinions, reflected contemporary medical opinion on general cleanliness, or whether experience with the increased practice of dry nursing was beginning to show a link between unclean feeding vessels and the illness or death of handfed infants. Therefore no conclusions can be drawn from the comments of these writers, especially since it is not known how representative their opinions were of other medical practitioners of the period, or how they related to general practices in infant feeding.

Modern knowledge of the factors which favour the growth of most micro-organisms (i.e. warmth, moisture, food and absorbent materials) [4] suggests that the spoon and pap-boat were safer utensils than the horn, bubby-pot or sucking bottle. The last three all had spouts, or similar structures of narrow bore, frequently covered with absorbent materials such as linen, sponge, parchment or cow's teats, which are difficult to clean and which tend to retain moisture. The hard, open, and thus easily accessible and visible surfaces of spoons and most types of pap-boat would mean that any attempt at washing or cleaning, however primitive or perfunctory, was more likely to be effective than the same procedure performed on vessels with convoluted and hidden interiors, such as the bubby-pot. Although washing with contaminated water could have had minimal effect, Underwood's reference to 'scalding' is important, since it implies that boiling water was to be used; an instruction which, if followed, would have been a much more effective method of cleaning.

REFERENCES

1. Armstrong, G. (1771) *An essay on the diseases most fatal to infants*, London, 2nd ed.
2. Brouzet, N. (1755) *An essay on the medicinal education of chidren; and the treatment of their diseases*, trans. anon., London.
3. Guillemeau, J. (1612) *Childbirth or The happie deliverie of women. . . . To which is added a treatise of the diseases of infants and young children*, trans. anon., London.
4. Hawker, L. E. *et al.* (1967) *An introduction to the biology of micro-organisms*, London.
5. Mantell, T. (1787) *Short directions for the management of infants*, London.
6. Meade, S., Letter to her mother, Margaret Fox (nee Fell), 7 April 1686, *Abraham MSS*, Friends House Library, London.
7. Moss, W. (1781) *An essay on the management and nursing of children in the earlier periods of infancy*, London.
8. Pennington, S. (1767) *Letters on different subjects*, London, vols 3 and 4.
9. Rosenstein, N. R. von (1776) *The diseases of children and their remedies*, trans. Sparrman, A., London, 1765.
10. Smith, H. (1774) *Letters to married women on nursing and the management of children*, London, 3rd ed.
11. Spence, D. (1784) *A system of midwifery*, Edinburgh.
12. Stukeley, W. (1882) *The family memoirs of the Rev. William Stukeley MD*, Durham.
13. Underwood, M. (1784) *A treatise on the diseases of children*, London.

14. Wurtz, F. (1563) *The children's book,* Bound with *An experimental treatise of surgerie in four parts,* trans. and corrected Lennerton-Fox, A., London, 1656.

15. Young, T. (late 18th century) *Young's midwifery,* Library of the Wellcome Institute for the History of Medicine, MSS 5106 and 5107.

Weaning Practices

WEANING the child from the breast was a subject of great importance from Biblical times until the end of the 18th century, and frequent references were made to it in diaries, journals and plays, many of which were written by men. In medical texts weaning was normally considered in a section or chapter quite separate from the discussion of other aspects of infant nutrition, such as mixed feeding. These points demonstrate that weaning was a subject which concerned fathers as much as mothers and nurses, and was a time of considerable anxiety for everybody involved. To contemporaries, weaning was arguably the most dangerous period of infancy, associated as it was with specific 'diseases' and a high mortality. It was a period of change, not only of diet but in station; a suckling was an infant with all that that implied, but once the breast was left for good he was regarded as a child and, as such, became a true member of the family. The upper-class child left his wet nurse and returned home to his biological family while, among the poorer classes, he was no longer fed at a different time but ate with the rest of the family.

In the following chapters, the various aspects of weaning will be considered in the order of importance assigned to them by contemporaries (as signified by the amount of space each was allotted, and the frequency with which it was discussed). The definition of weaning throughout is the relatively short period during which the child was weaned completely from the breast.

CHAPTER FIFTEEN

Weaning Practices:
The Age of Weaning

"The proper age for weaning a child is to be gathered from
the particular circumstances attending it."
Underwood, *A treatise on the diseases of children*, 1784

THE AGE at which children were weaned was mentioned by nearly
all the medical authors who discussed weaning, but not all gave a
specific age or considered only one factor. Since many medical writers
did recommend a specific age, and some indicated a time at which
infants were usually or commonly weaned, this chapter will show, first,
to what extent these medical opinions were in line with what happened
to a sample of named children. Three types of weaning age were
considered:
    i) The age recommended by physicians and surgeons (*recommended
age*). This was frequently based upon the recommendations of the
ancient authorities, particularly Aetios [1], Paul of Aegina [73], and
Avicenna [4]. As late as the 1740s, medical authors were still basing
their advice on the length of suckling advised by authorities such as
Soranus [92], Galen [28] and Avicenna [4]. The median ranged from 24
to 21 months in the 16th and 17th centuries, to 10 months in the 18th
century (*Statistical Appendix*, tables 15.6, 15.7).
    ii) The age said to be common (*common age*). This was the age at
which most children were said to be weaned, in fact rather than ideally,
and was obtained from statements such as 'some are weaned in the
tenth month, and some in the twelfth' [75], and 'the ordinary term of
nine months' [12]. This varied very little over three centuries; the
median ranged from 11–12 months in the 16th and 17th centuries, to
10.5 months in the 18th century (tables 15.6 and 15.7).
    iii) The age at which particular children were weaned (*actual age*).
This was obtained by examining letters, diaries, and case histories given
in medical textbooks. To avoid misleading results (such as the common
error of supposing that a child left the wet nurse immediately it was
weaned) [16], children were only included where weaning was specifically stated to be the reason for leaving the nurse, and where the precise

date and age of weaning could be reliably ascertained. The statements of other writers about weaning ages were only accepted when they were the biographers of the children concerned [78,106]. The median age was 14.5, 13.75 and 8 months in the 16th, 17th and 18th centuries respectively (tables 15.6 and 15.7, in *Statistical Appendix*).

The data relevant to these considerations is set out in the following tables (and in *Stat. App.* tables 15.1 to 15.4).

The age of weaning children from the breast recommended by medical authors 1500–1800 (*Stat. App.*, table 15.1).

Author	Date	Age (months)	Source (where different from author)
E. Roesslin	1540	24	
A. Paré	1575	24	Paré 1634
Gordonius	pre 1579	36	Jones 1579
S. Ste Marthe	1584	24	Ste Marthe 1710
J. Guillemeau	1612	24	
D. Sennert	1657	21 (18-24)	Still 1931
J. Sharp	1671	12	
N. Culpeper	1675	12	
N. Culpeper	1676	21 (18-24)	
J. Pechey	1697	21 (18-24)	
M. Ettmueller	1699	12	
Nurses Guide	1729	19 (18-20)	
J. Maubray	1730	21 (18-24)	
J. Astruc	1746	21 (18-24)	
W. Cadogan	1748	12	
H. Sloane	1748	8	
J. Nelson	1753	9	
H. Smith	1774	12	
W. Hunter	1775	8.5 (8-9)	
W. Osborne & T. Denman	1776	9.5 (9-10)	
W. Moss	1781	7 (6-8)	
Practice of Midwifery	1783	8.5 (7-10)	
M. Underwood	1784	12	
T. Mantell	1787	12	
H. Downman	1788	9	
W. Cullen	1788	<9	
B. Lara	1791	8.5 (8-9)	
A. Hamilton	1792	10.5 (9-12)	
T. Young	late 18th	10.5 (9-12)	

The age of weaning in the ancient world.
(*Stat. App.*, table 15.2)

People: Author/work or region	Age (months)	Recommended, common or actual age	Source
Ancient Egyptian:			
Pharaonic Egypt	36	Common	Jonkheere 1955
Babylonians:			
Babylon	36	Common	Brim 1936
Hebrews:			
The Bible	36	Common	Maccabees 7:27
The Bible: Isaac	24	Actual	Rashi Gen. 21:8
The Bible: Samuel	36	Actual	1 Samuel 1:23
The Talmud	24	Recommended	Margalith 1968
Greeks:			
Greece	6	Actual (wet-nursing contract)	Garrison 1923
Romans:			
Roman Egypt 1	6-36	Common	Lindsay 1963
Roman Egypt 2	16	Actual (wet-nursing contract)	Lindsay 1963
Greeks in Rome:			
Soranus, 1st/2nd c. AD	18-24	Recommended	Soranus 1956
Galen, 2nd c.	36	Recommended	Galen 1951
Byzantine:			
Aetios of Amida, 6th c.	20	Recommended	Paulus Aeginata 1844
Paul of Aegina, 7th c.	24	Recommended	Paulus Aeginata 1844
Islamic:			
The Koran	24	Recommended	Pickthall 1948
Avicenna, 10/11th c.	24	Recommended	Avicenna 1966
Hebrews:			
Maimonides, 12th c.	24	Common	Maimonides 1971-72

The age of weaning children from the breast said by medical writers to be common, 1500–1800 (*Stat. App.*, table 15.3).

Author	Date	Age (months)	Source (where different from author)
E. Roesslin	1540	12	
A. Paré	1575	19 (18-20)	Paré 1634
Mokerus	pre 1579	12	Jones 1579
J. Jones	1579	12	
J. Pechey	1697	11 (10-12)	
H. Sloane	1748	12	
J. Nelson	1753	3.5 (3-4)	
N. Brouzet	1755	15.5 (15-16)	
T. Denman	1777-78	12	Denman & Osborne 1777-78
W. Moss	1781	9 (8-10)	
W. Cullen	1788	9	
H. Tytler	1797	6	
T. Young	late 18th	13.5 (12-15)	

The age at weaning from the breast of a sample of named children, 1500–1800. (*Stat. App.*, table 15.4).

Name	Date weaned	Season	Age (months)	Source
a) *16th and 17th centuries*				
Mary Tudor	1517	Winter	12	Waldman 1972
Elizabeth Tudor	1534	Autumn	12+	Tucker 1976
Jane Grey	1538	—	18	Pearson 1957
Charity Johnson	1545	Autumn	36	Winchester 1955
John Jones	pre 1550	—	36	Jones 1579
Arthur Dee	1580	Summer	13.5	Dee 1842
Katherine Dee	1582	Summer	14.5	Dee 1842
Theodore Dee	1589	Summer	18	Dee 1842
Madinia Dee	1591	Summer	15.5	Dee 1842
Francis Dee	1593	Winter	13.5	Dee 1842
Margaret Dee	1596	Spring	7.5	Dee 1842
John Evelyn	1622	Winter	14.5	Evelyn 1908
Mary Josselin	1643	Spring	12	Josselin 1976
Robert Sibbald	1643	Summer	26	Sibbald 1932
Thomas Josselin	1645	Winter	13	Josselin 1976
Mary Green	1646	Autumn	6	Greene 1929
Jane Josselin	1647	Spring	18	Josselin 1976
John Josselin	1653	Spring	19	Josselin 1976
Anne Josselin	1655	Autumn	16	Josselin 1976
Elizabeth Josselin	1665	Summer	12	Josselin 1976
Robert Thornton	1665	Autumn	36	Thornton 1875
— Josselin	1674	Winter	12.5	Macfarlane 1970
Robert Walpole	1677	—	18	Plumb 1975
— Josselin	1679	Summer	9	Macfarlane 1970
William Stukeley	1687	Winter	0.25	Stukeley 1882
b) *18th century*				
Jack Lovatt	1708		12	Verney 1930
— Marklew	1709		18	McHenry & MacKeith 1966
Samuel Johnson	1709		2.5	McHenry & MacKeith 1966
Case history 1	1733-42		10	Hurlock 1742
Case history 2	1733-42		24	Hurlock 1742
Case history 3	1733-42		6	Hurlock 1742
Lord Warkworth	1743		6	Hughes 1940
N. Brouzet	pre 1750		18	Brouzet 1755
George, Prince of Wales	1763		9	Hedley 1975
Prince Frederick	1764		8	Hedley 1975
Princess Royal	1767		6.5	Hedley 1975
William, Duke of Clarence	1767		4	Hedley 1975
— Armstrong	pre 1771		1	Armstrong 1771
— Armstrong	pre 1771		1	Armstrong 1771
— Armstrong	pre 1771		1.5	Armstrong 1771
Princess Sophia	1771		8	Hedley 1975
Case history 1	c.1781		37	Moss 1781
Case history 2	c.1781		21	Moss 1781

Most of the above children were from the upper strata of society, as shown below (*Stat. App.*, table 15.5).

The social composition of the sample of named children, 1500–1800 (*Stat. App.*, table 15.5).

Century	Royalty	Aristocracy	Gentry	Educated classes*	Merchants/shopkeepers	Others	Total
16th	3	0	0	7	1	0	11
17th	0	0	3	11	0	0	14
18th	5	1	1	3	1	6	17
Total	8	1	4	21	2	6	42

* Includes physicians, lawyers, clergymen, etc.

Eight were royal, one of aristocratic parentage, and four from the gentry; twenty-one were the offspring of physicians, lawyers, clergymen and other educated classes; two were the children of merchants, and a further six included a child of a wet nurse and the children of 'a countrywoman near Liverpool'. The areas in which they lived included London (1), Leicestershire (1), Essex (7), Surrey (7), Buckinghamshire (1), Yorkshire (2), Norfolk (1), Staffordshire (2), Lancashire (2), Scotland (1) and Wales (1). The three case histories of Hurlock and the children of George Armstrong were probably reared in, or near, London as both were working in that locality at the time described [25]. The royal children were atypical. Both Mary and Elizabeth Tudor were moved from place to place during infancy [43,53], and the family of George III lived mainly at Kew, in Surrey [35].

Statistical analysis of the above information showed that, in the 16th century, the *recommended* age of weaning was significantly greater than both the *common* age and the *actual* age. In the 17th century there was no significant difference between the recommended and the actual age; comparison with the common age was not made because only one example of a common age was found. In the 18th century there was no significant difference between the recommended, common, and actual weaning age [24,25].

This appears to indicate that the age at which children were commonly said to be weaned was similar to the age at which a sample of children were actually weaned, and that the age recommended by physicians in the 16th century was unrelated to actual practice; and in the 17th and 18th centuries, when recommendations changed, it became similar to common and actual practice.

However, not all these findings can be taken as evidence of what was happening in Britain. All the recommendations before the second half

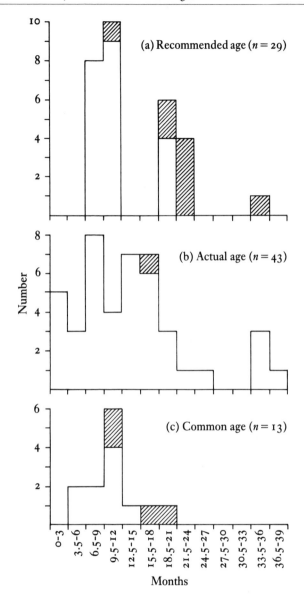

Figure 15.1. Histogram showing a) recommended weaning ages compared with b) actual weaning ages and c) common weaning ages, 1500–1800, and the effect of non-British examples. (Shaded areas represent writers of non-British origin.)

357

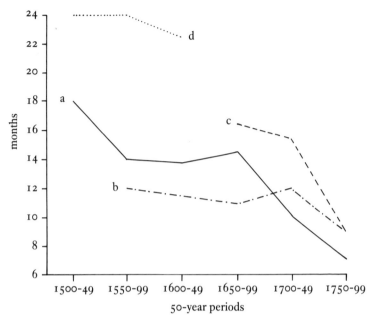

Figure 15.2. The median recommended, common and actual
weaning age in Britain, 1500–1799, with recommendations of
non-British writers 1500–1650 given for comparison.
a) Weaning age of a sample of children ($n = 42$); b) Weaning age
reported to be common ($n = 9$); c) Weaning age recommended
by medical writers ($n = 21$); d) Weaning age recommended by
European medical writers translated into English ($n = 6$).

of the 17th century were derived from non-English writers, as were four
out of the thirteen references to what was common practice. In contrast,
all but one of the sample of children were from Britain (figures 15.1 and
15.2 show how this may bias the results, since the weaning age in France
or Germany may well have been different from that in Britain).

When the European examples were excluded, there was no significant difference between the recommended and the actual age in the
17th and 18th centuries. There was also none between the recommended ages in the 17th and 18th centuries. However, comparison of the
actual age showed that although there was no significant difference
between centuries, the children in the 18th century were weaned significantly earlier than those in the 16th and 17th centuries. When each
50-year period after 1650 was considered separately there was no
significant difference between the recommended, common and actual
ages of weaning. This shows that the main influence of non-British

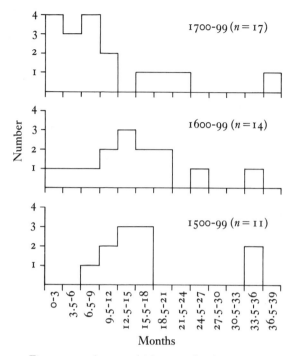

Figure 15.3. Ages at which a sample of 42 British children were weaned from the breast between 1500 and 1800, showing the change over three centuries.

writers was in the 16th century, so that it would be inadvisable to accept a recommendation given by a European writer at that time, as being applicable to Britain. But it is by no means certain that the views of British physicians and surgeons in the 16th century would have been very different from those in continental Europe since, in other aspects of infant feeding and child care, there is similarity between the views of English writers such as Phaire (1545) and Jones (1579) and those of Roesslin (1540) and Paré (1575). All passed on the advice of the Ancients [24,25].

Much doubt has been expressed [11] as to whether, in this context, the comments of physicians can be accepted as having any relation to practice. From the preliminary findings given here it seems (as there was no significant difference in the period 1650–1800 between the recommended, actual and common age of weaning) that the comments of British medical authors may be accepted as representative of the period and country in which they were made. For the preceding 150-

year period this is not the case. Comments of French and German writers may be representative of weaning practices in their own regions but should not be presumed to represent British practice. Until further evidence is found for this period, the range of weaning ages of particular British children is likely to be of more value in assessing the usual length of suckling between 1500 and 1650 [24,25].

¶ As this study resulted in the collection of the largest known sample of actual weaning ages in Britain, it provided an interesting opportunity for further investigation into the feeding and weaning of these children.

The majority were wet nursed, either in their own home – like the 8 royal children – or put out to nurse in a village near to the family home. At least one (Charity Johnston), who lived in London, was nursed at some distance from her home. The method and length of feeding is summarised below (*Stat. App.*, tables 15.8, 15.9).

The method of feeding employed for the sample of 42 children (*Stat. App.*, table 15.8).

Century	Wet nursed	Breastfed by mother	Uncertain
16th	11	0	0
17th	4	8	2
18th	8	7	2
Total	23	15	4

The length of suckling (in months) in infants fed by their mothers and those fed by wet nurses (*Stat. App.*, table 15.9).

Century	Wet nursed			Breastfed by mother		
	Range	Median	No.	Range	Median	No.
16th	7.5-36	14.5	11	—	—	0
17th	6.0-26	16.25	4	0.25-36	14.5	8
18th	2.5-10	7.25	8	1.0-37	18.0	7
Total	2.5-36	12.0	23	0.25-37	16.0	15

Statistical analysis showed no significant difference between the weaning ages of all the infants breastfed by their mothers and those who were wet nursed. No comparison could be made for the 16th century, but no significant difference was found when the comparison was made for the 17th and 18th centuries. Thus, the age at weaning of the children in the sample was not affected by the use or non-use of wet nurses [24].

There may be some bias in the figures for children breastfed by their mother (Mary, Thomas, Jane, John, Anne and Elizabeth Josselin, Robert Thornton, William Stukeley, – Marklew, Hurlock case 2, three daughters of Armstrong (1771), and two case histories of Moss (1781)), since they do include some examples which were regarded as extreme or atypical. For example, William Moss (1781) gave two examples of children whom he considered were suckled for a long period of time, whilst, in 1687, William Stukeley was weaned after only one week because his mother apparently did not enjoy breastfeeding as 'she had that peculiarity that she could not show in the common feminine tenderness, so that she scarce in her life kisst any of her children'. Similarly, there is no way of knowing how typical the wet nursed children were. For instance, both John Jones (1579) and Robert Sibbald (1641–1722) considered they had been nursed for longer than was usual [44,88].

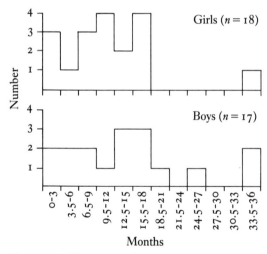

Figure 15.4. Histograms showing the ages at which a sample of 17 boys and 18 girls were weaned, 1500–1800.

The sex of 35 of the children was known (it was uncertain in the case of the two Josselin grandchildren (1674 and 1679) and the five case histories given by Hurlock (1742) and Moss (1781). There were 18 girls and 17 boys. The ages at which they were weaned (figure 15.4) show no significant difference between the boys and the girls, either in the total sample or within each century.

The age at weaning from the breast of children in three different families, fed under different circumstances (*Stat. App.*, table 15.10).

Family	Class/occupation	Manner of feeding	Children	Date of weaning	Age of weaning (months)
John Dee of Mortlake, Surrey	Philosopher at court of Elizabeth I	Out to local wet nurse	Arthur	1580	13.5
			Katherine	1582	14.5
			Theodore	1589	18
			Madinia	1591	15
			Frances	1593	13.5
			Margaret	1596	7.5
				Range = 7.5–18, Median = 14.0	
Ralph Josselin of Earls Colne, Essex	Church of England clergyman	Breastfed by mother	Mary	1643	12
			Thomas	1645	13
			Jane	1647	18
			John	1653	19
			Anne	1655	16
			Elizabeth	1665	12
				Range = 12–19, Median = 14.5	
George III	King of England	Suckled by wet nurses in their own home	George, Prince of Wales	1763	9
			Prince Frederick	1764	8
			Princess Royal	1767	6.5
			William, Duke of Clarence	1767	4
			Princess Sophia	1771	8
				Range = 4–9, Median = 8.0	

The fact that each century included one family of five or six members could have affected the overall result, but as the facing table (*Stat. App.*, table 15.10) shows, there was no significant difference between the weaning ages of each family and the remaining children in each century. Thus, the pattern of weaning within a fairly large family in a particular period may be as representative of that era as a sample of unrelated individuals.

There was no 'set time' for weaning a child within the families studied; it depended upon the circumstances of each nursing couple. Illness of the child at nurse [15]; ill health or tiredness in the mother [2,46]; dissatisfaction with the wet nurse [15]; birth of another child [99]; and the mother's distaste for breastfeeding [96] were some of the reasons for weaning. The decision to wean was often made by both father and mother [15]. In the case of wet-nursed infants, it is not clear how much influence the parents had. The nurse may have made the decision to wean, depending on her own circumstances (her health, the child's health, declining milk supply, etc.) or after consultation with the parents. In the royal family, the physicians and nurses attending the child were involved in the decision [35,39].

The above findings show the sample to be biased towards one particular group in society, that of the educated – or what later was called the middle class. To some extent this is not unexpected, since this was the very group in society which was most likely to record the minutiae of day-to-day living. Further examples from the aristocracy and gentry could probably be found from scrutiny of family records and biographies, whilst evidence of approximate ages of weaning may exist in the records of institutions such as the Foundling Hospital, but it is unlikely that a sample of weaning ages could be collected equally from all levels of society. Geographically, more of the sample derived from the south of England, but London children, who were probably not typical of the country as a whole [26] were in a minority. Most of the infants were born, and spent their early years, in small villages or country towns; such as Lichfield, in the case of Samuel Johnson [48]. The fact that more were wet nursed than suckled by their own mother was atypical of British society as a whole, but not of the particular groups in society to which they belonged. Thus, although this sample is of value in judging the age of weaning in the upper and middle classes of society, it is not necessarily representative of poorer children. The fact that physicians referred to a common age which, throughout this period, was not significantly different from that of these children, might indicate that, in matters such as weaning, there was little difference between different groups in society. There is one indication that the average of weaning among some parish children in the 17th century was about twelve months (cf. Pechey 1697). The amount paid by the parish officials in Norfolk to women who nursed the infant poor in the first year of life was double the amount paid after they attained their first birthday [107]. This suggests that, until the age of one year, infants were presumed to be breastfed, since wet nurses were always paid more than dry nurses [69], and that by the age of twelve months they were expected to be weaned.

The finding that children in the 18th century were weaned significantly earlier than in the 16th and 17th centuries may be related to other changes in infant feeding practices which occurred during the 18th century, especially after 1750: in particular, the trend towards mothers breastfeeding their own children or rearing them by hand rather than employing a wet nurse [25, 101]. Upper- and middle-class women, who in previous centuries would have used wet nurses, may have been unwilling to inconvenience their social life by breastfeeding for as long a period as a woman who was paid for this service. Allied to this, hand-feeding was used and was socially acceptable in the 18th century [34, 101]. With the increasing concentration on the development of more suitable substitute foods and feeding vessels, it could be undertaken after a short period of breastfeeding; a good example of this being the three daughters of Armstrong (1771) who were weaned after 4–6 weeks of breastfeeding by their mother [2]. Whereas children in the 16th and 17th centuries were weaned at an age when they could eat a diet similar to that of the rest of the family, those of the late 18th century could be weaned on to the milk mixtures used for the dry-nursed infant, and later be 'weaned' again on to a more varied diet.

Another factor was the changing social conditions of the 18th century. As a result of land enclosures and the development of manufactories, people were moving away from villages and rural life into rapidly growing towns [36, 100]. This meant that women were moving away from the traditional child-rearing wisdom of family and friends, particularly of the older women of their community; as well as from any influence of wealthy women who may have visited the poor in a particular neighbourhood. In modern pre-industrial societies this process of urbanisation is closely linked to much earlier weaning from the breast [42]. Examples of weaning ages from rural societies and urban societies from different parts of Africa (*Stat. App.*, table 15.11) [62] show – see table opposite – that the urban societies weaned their infants at a significantly earlier age than the rural communities (median 15.6 months for urban and 24.1 months for rural: $p = <0.001$). Other parts of the world where this phenomenon has been observed include Central and South America, the Middle East and Asia [42].

Although these Third-World urban societies also have modern pressures, such as heavy advertising of low-cost weaning foods [10, 42], the factor of early weaning is particularly associated with the loss of the traditional teaching of older women on infant care, when younger women move into towns [42]. It is possible that the situation in 18th-century England, when rapid industrialisation was taking place, had a similar effect on child-rearing practices as that observed in the urbanisation of pre-industrial societies today, where: i) the period of suckling was reduced; ii) this was associated with women working outside the home [42]; iii) this was related to increased use of artificial feeding [10,42]; iv) this was connected with, or resulted in, an increase in diseases related to weaning [23,42]. The last point will be discussed more fully in chapter 17.

The weaning age in 12 rural and 10 urban societies from different parts of Africa (tabulated from information in Mondot-Bernard 1977; *Stat. App.*, table 15.11).

Rural communities	Age (months)	Urban communities	Age (months)
Rural Gambia	21 (18-24)	Abidjan	13.5
Rural Guinea	36	Lagos	12
Rural Ivory Coast	42 (36-48)	Ibadan	14 +
Rural Nigeria	21 (20-22)	Dakar	18.7
Inesis, rural	23.2	Brazzaville	18 (12-24)
Sine, rural	24.3	Leopoldville	18 (12-24)
Burundi (suburb)	24 (18-30)	Kinshasa (I)	16.8
Bambara, rural	30 (24-36)	Kinshasa (II)	19 (11-27)
Highland tribes	27 (18-36)	Baganda, Kampala	14 (12-16)
Kenya Masai	36	Algeria, urban	11.3
Somalia (shepherds)	24		
Algeria, rural	14.4		
Median	24.1	Median	15.6

¶ Despite the number of writers who gave a specific age, many said that age alone was not the only factor to be considered when weaning a child. Twenty-two medical authors discussed factors other than age (*Stat. App.*, table 15.12) [25]. These included the health of the child, number of teeth, season of the year and phase of the moon, health of the nurse/mother, state of the milk, state of the infant's bowels, and its ability to digest other foods. Concern about the health of the child and the number of teeth he possessed was related to two factors:

i) Weaning was a period of change, and change was traditionally associated with danger and death [92], and therefore the child had to be as healthy as possible when change was contemplated.

ii) Teething was associated with disease and death (discussed in chapter 17) and with the ability to chew hard foods, so that possession of teeth meant the child had a) passed some of the dangers of the teething period, and b) was equipped with the apparatus to deal with solid foods.

The reason for the recommendation, from antiquity until the early 18th century, for weaning to take place at 18 months to 2 years was because this was the age by which most children possessed all their teeth [25]. Even some of the more enlightened authors of the late 18th century could not envisage weaning a child from the breast unless he had at least some teeth [82,104]. As late as 1790, the French surgeon Jean-Louis Baudelocque stated that the infant should have cut his first 20 teeth: 'it [weaning] is generally done much sooner but many have been very happy to return to the milk of a nurse at that time, because they were become so weakly during the cutting of their last teeth, that they could digest no other food' [5]. Anxiety about gastro-intestinal conditions, particularly at the time of weaning, explains the specific direction that the state of the infant's bowels should be taken into account before weaning was undertaken [65,104].

The ideal seasons for weaning were spring and autumn, as the extremes of temperature in winter [33,75], and especially the hot weather and associated gastro-intestinal upsets of the summer months [32,65,75], could be avoided. Both the season of the year and the state of the moon were pre-occupations of the 17th century [25]. As can be seen from table 15.4a more children were weaned in the winter and summer than in the 'ideal' seasons given by the physicians. The idea that the child should be weaned when the moon was waxing was probably related to a folk belief that if one wished a treatment to have an increasing effect then this was aided if the moon was waxing, and vice versa [27]. Thus a child weaned when the moon was increasing in size could be expected to increase in size and health, a further aid in the dangerous period of weaning. John Pechey (1697) indicated that this was not just a medically recommended view but a more generally-held belief by nurses: 'some women think, and not without reason, that it is better to wean a child at the increase of the moon, than at the decrease' [75].

The number of factors to be taken into account when weaning increased over three centuries, with many more being considered in the 18th century; a major introduction being concern for the health of the mother or nurse and the state of her milk [25] (table 15.12). Whereas 16th-century writers were concerned only for the child's age, health and number of teeth, by the 18th century 8 different factors were taken into consideration. This may have been due to the greater attention being paid to the problems associated with weaning [23] or because, when weaning was attempted at an earlier age, more factors had to be taken into account to ensure a successful outcome.

¶ Some of the above factors were relevant when early or late weaning was discussed. Late weaning for 'normal' children began to attract the disapproval of medical writers in the late 17th century, but became particularly notable in the last years of the 18th [25], mainly because it was thought to be harmful to the child [12,33] or to the mother [58,65]. Both Culpeper (1675) and Brouzet (1755) said that prolonged breastfeeding was a fault of mothers in particular (although in the sample of children discussed above no significant difference was found between mothers and nurses).

The 9 authors who discussed late or delayed weaning [25] gave two main circumstances in which it was advisable: i) if the child were weak, sickly or diseased; ii) if the child were not eating well from the spoon and/or not eating hard foods. Jones (1579) gave four other reasons for delayed weaning: i) twins should be breastfed for longer than other children; ii) males should be weaned later than females; iii) nobles should be weaned later than other children; iv) if the mother was 'old' at the time of the child's birth he should suck longer than the child of a young and lusty mother. Most of these would still, today, be indications for later weaning, especially in societies where artificial feeding is not a reliable alternative [10,42,64]. The protective function of breastmilk for the weakly, sick or precious child was recognised by parents of the time. Robert Sibbald (1641–1722), the Scottish professor and antiquarian, was the fifth child of his parents, the preceding four children having died before reaching the age of four years. He was born a 'tender child' and:

> . . . by the advice of my uncle . . . Doctor George Sibbald . . . I sucked till I was two years and two months old, and could runn up and down the street, and speake, because my older brothers and sisters had died hectick; which long suckling proved . . . a mean to preserve me alive . . . [88]

Similarly, Robert Thornton was the much-loved 7th child of Alice Thornton, only two daughters having survived early infancy, and was suckled by his mother for three years, until two weeks before the next child was born [99]. The advice that twins and males should be breastfed for a longer period was related to the health and strength of the child. Twins tend to be smaller than singletons, and to be born a week or more before full term [66], and one baby is frequently weaker than the other [66] (Willughby (1863) gives 17th-century examples) and therefore more susceptible to infections than full-term single births. Similarly, boys tend to be harder to rear than girls, more males dying in infancy and childhood than females [94].

Although Jones (1579) was the only physician to make these specific recommendations, they appear logical in the context of his time, and in relation to the more general concern with the health of the infant. His contention was that males and nobles had to survive to run households and governments and that longer suckling would increase this chance. But, from the evidence of the 16th-century children in the sample discussed earlier, boys were not weaned any later than girls and the royal children were not weaned noticeably later (Mary and Elizabeth Tudor, who both became Queens of England, had two of the earliest weaning ages in the 16th century (table 15.4)). Jones himself was weaned late (at 3 years) because, he said, his mother was 'twenty-five and upwards' when he was born. This does not seem a particularly great or dangerous age for women to have borne children (despite the lower life expectancy), and since the average age of marriage in England during this period was the middle to late 20s [50], the majority of children must have been born to women in their late 20s and 30s. The reference to 'marriage' merits the observation that, despite relatively high illegitimacy rates in this period [51], most children were born in wedlock. Possibly Jones cited this reason to account for his own late weaning (from a wet nurse) or he may have been flattering his mother, as he does not give her exact age! An older woman, particularly a primigravida, may have had a prolonged and/or more difficult labour [66] possibly producing a weaker child, which would then need the protection of longer suckling. Although older women (40 + years)are today more likely to have babies which suffer from congenital malformations or specific conditions such as Down's Syndrome [94], this cannot be extrapolated to the 16th century because of possible differences in the age of the menarche, the menopause, the life expectancy and environmental factors [97].

It is notable that, in the 16th and early 17th centuries, prolonged breastfeeding did not attract the disapproval of medical writers; that is probably related to the recommended weaning age of the period. As writers recommended an earlier age of weaning, which was similar to that in actual practice, they became more intolerant of prolonged suckling [12,33,49,58], and it is likely that by the end of the 18th century it was no longer culturally acceptable in Britain for women to breastfeed for as long as had been acceptable in the 16th and 17th centuries. Some evidence of a change in cultural or social mores was given by Osborne and Denman (1777–78) and Hamilton (1792), who said that the age of weaning depended on 'the requirement for suckling' as this was different in different countries [33]. One of the distinctive features about weaning today is that it occurs at different and usually identifiable times in different societies [62,108]. As would be expected from the above, early weaning was not discussed in the 16th century, being principally the concern of physicians in the second half of the 18th [25]. The most noticeable point in the discussion is that concern for the child's health (predominant in all other discussions about weaning) was replaced by concern for the well-being of the mother or nurse or her milk. This tends to confirm the suggestion made earlier that women who previously would have used wet nurses were less prepared to suckle for long periods (since this would be reflected in the writings of those authors who were consulted by the wealthier parts of society). The factors to be considered when a child was weaned early (table 15.13) [25] related to: i) health of mother/nurse; ii) state of the milk; iii) health of the infant – and in that order.

Fright, anxiety, loss of appetite, menstruation, pregnancy, sickness, drunkenness and greediness in the mother or nurse were all indications for early weaning, principally because these would affect the state of the breast milk [25]. The belief that a woman's milk deteriorated during menstruation or strong emotions was very ancient (as was shown in chapter 6), but in the later 18th century it was accompanied by a belief that its composition changed and deteriorated after several months of lactation and was no longer good for the child [33]. Alexander Hamilton (1792) thought that early weaning was harmful and Underwood (1784) gave some indication of common practice when he stated that

> ... when children are weaned much earlier [than 8–10 months] and are fed from birth with that in view, they may be essentially harmed by it [104].

But the opposite view was given by Moss (1781) and Lara (1791) who said that, provided it was healthy, early weaning was easier for the child; an opinion also held by modern authorities [52,68].

Discussion of early weaning by authors such as Armstrong (1771), Moss (1781) and Underwood (1784) confirms the suggestion that the availability and social acceptance of artificial feeding made early weaning from mother or nurse a practical proposition, which it had not been in the 16th century. For instance, a letter of 1793 described an example of early weaning:

> And that day Mr Fane and Lady Elizabeth came, their four daughters with them. Augusta is the name of the youngest: she has had three wet-nurses and none gave satisfaction, so the old lying-in nurse came here with her, and she is fed with pap made of asses milk and it seems to agree with her for she looks extremely healthy and well [34].

Compare this with the Dee family in the 16th century, where early weaning was not considered. Difficulty arose with a wet nurse when Katherine Dee was two months old, so another had to be found, and she was suckled by three different women before being weaned at the safer age of 14.5 months [15].

¶ The median age of weaning in a sample of British children changed over three centuries from 18 months in the early 16th century to 7.25 months in the late 18th; and the period for which a child was breastfed in the 18th century was significantly shorter than during the preceding 200 years. This was probably related to the availability and social acceptability of artificial feeding; the decreased use of wet nurses by the upper and middle classes; and the movement of the population from the countryside into the towns as a result of industrialisation. The median age of weaning said by contemporaries to be common among British children changed relatively little over three centuries and was very similar to the actual weaning age found in a sample of British children. In the period 1650 to 1800 there was no significant difference between the recommended, common and actual age of weaning in Britain. Thus the weaning ages recommended by British medical writers in this period are apparently representative of actual practice. The weaning age recommended by European medical writers translated into English, and widely available in the period 1500 to 1650, was significantly later than both the common age and the actual age, as well as the age recommended by British writers in the following 150-year period. This may indicate that the age of weaning was later in France and Germany, and should be treated with caution when discussing the British case. But in the absence of evidence from Britain in the same period, these medical views could have been similar to those held by British physicians in the 16th and early 17th centuries. The age of weaning was not significantly affected by the person who breastfed the child (mother or wet nurse). There was no significant difference in the weaning age of males and females. The weaning age within families was as varied as, and was not significantly different from, a sample of unrelated individual children in the same period. The reason for weaning was individual to each nursing couple and no evidence was found of parents or nurses following a set or standard age for weaning. Other factors considered when weaning a child included the health of the child, the number of teeth it possessed, the season of the year and the state of the moon (17th century) and the health of the mother (18th century).

Late weaning was used for weakly or 'treasured' children, but from the late 17th century prolonged suckling attracted the disapproval of medical writers. Early weaning was not mentioned in the 16th century but by the 18th century this had become a more viable proposition due to the availability and acceptability of artificial feeding. Factors to be considered when weaning a child early included the health of the nurse or mother, the state of her milk and the health of the infant.

REFERENCES
1. Aetios of Amida (6th century AD) *The gynaecology and obstetrics of the VIth century AD*, trans. and annotated Ricci, J. V., Philadelphia, 1950.
2. Armstrong, G, (1771) *An essay on the diseases most fatal to infants*, London, 2nd ed.
3. Astruc, J. (1746) *A general and complete treatise on all the diseases incident to children from their birth to the age of fifteen*, trans. anon., London.
4. Avicenna (10th century AD), in Shah, M. H., *The general principles of Avicenna's Canon of medicine*, Karachi, 1966.
5. Baudelocque, J-L. (1790) *A system of midwifery*, trans. Heath, J., London.
6. Brim, C. J. (1936) *Medicine in the Bible. The pentateuch. Torah*, New York.
7. Brouzet, N. (1755) *An essay on the medicinal education of children; and the treatment of their diseases*, trans. anon., London.
8. Burton, J. (1751) *An essay towards a complete new system of midwifery*, London.
9. Cadogan, W. (1748) *An essay upon nursing and the management of children, from their birth to three years of age*, London.
10. Chetley, A. (1979) *The baby killer scandal*, London.
11. Crawford, P., of University of Western Australia, Personal communication.
12. Cullen, W. (1788), in Risse, G. B. (1973) William Cullen and childcare: a 1788 letter, *Clio Med. 8*, 65-7.
13. Culpeper, N. (1675) *A directory for midwives*, London.
14. Culpeper, N. (1676) *A directory for midwives or, A guide for women, in their conception, bearing and suckling their children. Corrected from many gross errors*, London.
15. Dee, J. (1842) *The private diary of Dr John Dee*, Halliwell, J. O. (ed.), London.
16. De Mause, L. (ed.) (1976) *The history of childhood. The evolution of parent-child relationships as a factor in history*, London.
17. Denman, T. & Osborne, W. (1777-78) *Notes extracted from several courses of lectures in midwifery given by Dr Denman and Dr Osborne. Taken down by Fran. Kington*, Library of the Wellcome Institute for the History of Medicine, MS 2099.
18. Downman, H. (1788) *Infancy or, The management of children. A didactic poem in six books*, London, 4th ed.
19. *English midwife enlarged . . . containing two new treatises . . . of the diseases of little children, and the conditions necessary to be considered in the choice of their nurses and milk* (1682), London.
20. Ettmueller, M. (1699) *Etmullerus abridg'd: or A compleat system of the theory and practice of physic*, trans. anon., London.

21. Evelyn, J. (1908) *The diary of John Evelyn (1620 to 1706) with an introduction and notes by Austin Dobson*, London.
22. Fildes, V. A. (1980) Weaning the Elizabethan child, *Nurs. Times 76*, 1357-9, 1402-3.
23. Fildes, V. A. (1980) On the bottle again. The diseases of weaning 1600-1800, *Nurs. Mirror. 151*, 18-21.
24. Fildes, V. A. (1982) The age of weaning in Britain 1500-1800, *J. Biosoc. Sci. 14*, 223-40.
25. Fildes, V. A. (1982) *The history of infant feeding 1500-1800*, Unpublished PhD thesis, Dept. Human Biology and Health, University of Surrey.
26. Finlay, R. A. P. (1979) Population and fertility in London 1580-1650, *J. Fam. Hist. 4*, 26-38. Also personal communication.
27. *Funk and Wagnall's standard dictionary of folklore, mythology and legend* (1972) Leach, M. (ed.), London.
28. Galen (2nd century AD) *A translation of Galen's 'Hygiene' (De sanitate tuenda)*, trans. Green, R. M., Springfield, Illinois.
29. Garrison, F. H. (1923) History of pediatrics, in *Pediatrics. By various authors* Abt, I. A. (ed.), Philadelphia.
30. Glisson, F. (1651) *A treatise of the rickets, being a disease common to children*, trans. Armin, P., London.
31. Greene, J. (1928-29) The diary of John Greene (1635-1657), *Eng. Hist. Rev. 43*, 385-94, 598-604; *44*, 106-17.
32. Guillemeau, J. (1612) *Childbirth or The happie deliverie of women. . . . To which is added a treatise of the diseases of infants, and young children: with the cure of them*, trans. anon., London.
33. Hamilton, A. (1792) *A treatise on the management of female complaints and of children in early infancy*, Edinburgh.
34. Heber (1936) *Dear Miss Heber. An eighteenth century correspondence*, Bamford, F. (ed.), London.
35. Hedley, O. (1975) *Queen Charlotte*, London.
36. Hill, C. (1976) *The Pelican economic history of Britain vol.2: 1530-1780 Reformation to industrial revolution*, Harmondsworth.
37. *Holy Bible*, Authorised version of King James, London.
38. Hughes, H. S. (1940) *The gentle Hertford. Her life and letters*, New York.
39. Hunter, W. (1908) An obstetric diary of William Hunter, Stark, J. N. (ed.), *Glasg. Med. J. 70*, 167-77, 241-56, 338-56.
40. Hunter, W. (1775) *Lectures anatomical and chirurgical by William Hunter*, Library of the Wellcome Institute for the History of Medicine, MS 2966. Also dated 1783.
41. Hurlock, J. (1742) *A practical treatise on dentition*, London.
42. Jelliffe, D. B. & Jelliffe, E. F. P. (1978) *Human milk in the modern world. Psychosocial, nutritional and economic significance*, Oxford.
43. Jessopp, A. (1975) Article on *Elizabeth I*, in *Dictionary of*

national biography, Compact edition, Oxford.

44. Jones, J. (1579) *The arte and science of preserving bodie and soule in healthe, wisedome, and catholicke religion: physically, philosophically and divinely devised,* London.
45. Jonckheere, F. (1955) Un chapitre de pédiatrie Egyptienne l'allaitement, *Aesculape 37,* 203-23.
46. Josselin, R. (1976) *The diary of Ralph Josselin 1616-1683,* Macfarlane, A. (ed.), Oxford.
47. *Ladies dispensatory or, Every woman her own physician* (1740), London.
48. Lane, M. (1975) *Samuel Johnson and his world,* London.
49. Lara, B. (1791) *An essay on the injurious custom of mothers not suckling their own children; with some directions for chusing a nurse, and weaning of children, etc.,* London.
50. Laslett, P. (1971) *The world we have lost,* London, 2nd ed.
51. Laslett, P., Oosterveen, K. & Smith, R. M. (1980) *Bastardy and its comparative history,* London.
52. Leach, P. (1974) *Babyhood. Infant development from birth to two,* Harmondsworth.
53. Lee, S. (1975) Article on *Mary I,* in *Dictionary of national biography,* Compact edition, Oxford.
54. Lindsay, J. (1963) *Daily life in Roman Egypt,* London.
55. MacFarlane, A. (1970) *The family life of Ralph Josselin. A seventeenth century clergyman. An essay in historical anthropology,* Cambridge.
56. McHenry, L. C. & MacKeith, R. (1966) Samuel Johnson's childhood illnesses and the King's Evil, *Med. Hist. 10,* 386-99.
57. Maimonides, M. (12th century AD) *The code of Maimonides Book 4: The book of women,* trans. Klein, I., New Haven and London, 1972.
58. Mantell, T. (1787) *Short directions for the management of infants,* London.
59. Margalith, D. (1968) Pediatrics in the Hebrew ancient sources, in *Verhandhungen des XX internationalen kongresses für geschichte der medizin,* Berlin, 22-27 August, Hildersheim, 234-7.
60. Maubray, J. (1730) *The female physician containing all the diseases incident to that sex... together with the diet and regimen of both the mother and child,* London.
61. Mears, M. (1797) *The midwife's candid advice to the fair sex; or The pupil of nature,* London.
62. Mondot-Bernard, J. M. (1977) *Relationships between fertility, child mortality and nutrition in Africa. A tentative analysis,* Paris.
63. Montet, P. (1958) *Everyday life in Egypt in the days of Rameses the Great,* trans. Maxwell-Hyslop, A. R. & Drower, M. S., London.
64. Morley, D. (1973) *Paediatric priorities in the developing world,* London.

65. Moss, W. (1781) *An essay on the management and nursing of children in the earlier periods of infancy*, London.
66. Myles, M. F. (1975) *Textbook for midwives with modern concepts of obstetric and neonatal care*, Edinburgh and London.
67. Nelson, J. (1753) *An essay on the government of children*, London.
68. Newson, J. & Newson, E. (1974) *Patterns of infant care in an urban community*, Harmondsworth.
69. Nihell, E. (1760) *A treatise on the art of midwifery*, London.
70. *Nurses guide: or The right method of bringing up young children. By an eminent physician* (1729), London.
71. Osborne, W. & Denman, T. (1776) *Sketches of the practice of midwifery. From the lectures of Drs Osborne and Denman*, Library of the Wellcome Institute for the History of Medicine, MS 2098.
72. Paré, A. (1575) *The workes of that famous chirurgion Ambrose Parey*, trans. Johnston, T., London, 1634.
73. Paulus Aeginata (7th century AD) *The seven books of Paulus Aeginata. With a commentary*, trans. Adams, F., London, 1844-47, vol.1.
74. Pearson, L. E. (1957) *Elizabethans at home*, California.
75. Pechey (Peachey), J. (1697) *A general treatise of the diseases of infants and children. Collected from the best practical authors*, London.
76. Phaire, T. (1545) *The boke of chyldren*, London, reprinted 1955, Edinburgh.
77. Pickthall, M. M. (1948) *The meaning of the glorious Koran*, London.
78. Plumb, J. H. (1975) The new world of children in eighteenth-century England, *Past & Present* 67, 64-95.
79. Pollock, L. A. (1983) *Forgotten children: parent-child relations from 1500-1900*, Cambridge.
80. *Practice of midwifery, by a pupil of the late Dr W. Hunter* (1783), London.
81. Roesslin the Elder, E. (1540) *The byrth of mankynde*, trans. Jonas, R., London, first published 1512.
82. Rosenstein, N. R. von (1776) *The diseases of children and their remedies*, trans. Sparrman, A., London, 1765.
83. Ryerson, A. (1960) *Medical advice on childrearing 1550-1900*, Unpublished DEd thesis, Harvard.
84. Sainte Marthe, S. de (1584) *Paedotrophiae: or The art of bringing up children*, trans. anon., London, 1710.
85. Sennert, D. (1657) *De mulierum et infantum morbis*, trans. in Johnston, J. (1657) *Idea of practical physick*, London, part trans. in Still, G. F. (1931) *History of paediatrics*, Oxford.
86. Shakespeare, W. (c.1594) *Romeo and Juliet*, Act 1, scene 3, in *The complete works of William Shakespeare*, Alexander, P. (ed.), London and Glasgow, 1960.
87. Sharp, J. (1671) *The midwives book or The whole art of midwifery*

discovered, London.

88. Sibbald, R. (1932) *The memoirs of Sir Robert Sibbald (1641-1722)*, Hett, F. P. (ed.), London.

89. Siegel, S. (1956) *Non-parametric statistics for the behavioural sciences*, Tokyo.

90. Sloane, H. (1748) *Letter to John Milner, vice-president of the hospital for the maintenance and education of exposed and deserted young children*, 28 October. Quoted in full, in Brownlow, J. (1847) *Memoranda or Chronicles of the Foundling Hospital*, London.

91. Smith, H. (1774) *Letters to married women on nursing and the management of children. The 3rd edition, revised and considerably enlarged*, London.

92. Soranus of Ephesus (1st/2nd century AD) *Soranus' Gynecology*, trans. Temkin, O. *et al.*, Baltimore, 1956.

93. Spence, D. (1784) *A system of midwifery*, Edinburgh.

94. Stern, C. (1960) *Principles of human genetics*, San Francisco and London, 2nd ed.

95. Still, G. F. (1931) *The history of paediatrics*, London.

96. Stukeley, W. (1882) *The family memoirs of the Rev. William Stukeley M.D.*, Durham.

97. Tanner, J. M. (1981) *A history of the study of human growth*, Cambridge.

98. Thomson, J. (c.1772-85) *An analysis of midwifery with the diseases incident to pregnancy and those which commonly happen in the month, to child-bed women*, Library of the Wellcome Institute for the History of Medicine, MS 4779.

99. Thornton, A. (1875) *The autobiograhy of Mrs Alice Thornton of East Newton, Co. York*, Jackson, C. (ed.) Durham.

100. Trevelyan, G. M. (1977) *English social history. A survey of six centuries, Chaucer to Queen Victoria*, Harmondsworth.

101. Trumbach, R. (1978) *The rise of the egalitarian family*, New York.

102. Tucker, M. J. (1976) The child as beginning and end: fifteenth and sixteenth-century English childhood, in De Mause, L. (ed.), *History of childhood*, London, 229-57.

103. Tytler, H. (1797) in Sainte Marthe, S. de (1584), *Paedotrophiae*, trans. Tytler, H., London, 1797.

104. Underwood, M. (1784) *A treatise on the diseases of children*, London.

105. Verney, M. M. (1930) *Verney letters of the eighteenth century*, London.

106. Waldman, M. (1972) *The Lady Mary. A biography of Mary Tudor 1516-1558*, London.

107. Wales, T. (1981) *Poverty, poor relief and the life cycle: some seventeenth century Norfolk evidence*. Paper read at SSRC Cambridge Group for History of Population and Social Structure seminar, 27 April 1981.

108. Whiting, J. W. M. & Child, I. L. (1964) *Child training and personality: a cross-cultural study*, New Haven & London.
109. Willughby, P. (1630-69) *Observations in midwifery. As also the country midwife's opusculum or vade mecum*, Blenkinsop, H. (ed.), Warwick, 1863.
110. Winchester, B. (1955) *Tudor family portrait*, London.
111. Young, T. (late 18th century) *Young's midwifery*, Library of the Wellcome Institute for the History of Medicine, MSS 5106 and 5107.

CHAPTER SIXTEEN

Weaning Practices:
The Method of Weaning

"Many errors are daily committed in the method of weaning
children." Alexander Hamilton
Treatise on the management of female complaints, 1792

IN THE period 1500–1800, the method of weaning children was discussed by 30 medical authors; the principal argument was whether sudden or gradual methods should be employed. The emphasis laid upon
gradual methods might suggest that this was the common practice, but
the very vehemence of condemnation of abrupt methods, combined
with statements that the latter were commonly practised by nurses,
tends to confirm that sudden methods of weaning were not unusual and
may well have been the more common practice in the period before
1750 (plate 16.1).

¶ Eleven authors referred to sudden practices which were in use and / or
recommended by them (table 16.1) [16]. These included painting the
nipples with a bitter substance, hiding the nurse, frightening the child
from the breast, and calling the breast nasty names.
    Painting or anointing the nipples is an ancient method of weaning,
still used in some Third World societies today [29,31,50]. Various substances were used including, in order of popularity, aloes, wormwood,
soot and water, mustard, gall, water of colocynth, while honey could be
used if the child disliked sweet things [16]. Some authors cautioned
against using too much, as it could be harmful to the child, but still
recommended its use; only one writer deplored its use as cruel [18]. Its
effect was described in *Romeo and Juliet* (c.1594) [42] when the nurse
tells of the traumatic day of Juliet's weaning, at three years old:
    . . . I remember it well.
    'Tis since the earthquake now eleven years;
    And she was weaned, I never shall forget it,
    Of all the days of the year, upon that day;
    For I had then laid wormwood to my dug . . .
    When it did taste the wormwood on the nipple

Plate 16.1. Germany, 1509. Children of
weaning age with feeding can, bowl and
spoon, and hobby horse. From an altarpiece formerly in the Burgkirche, Lübeck.

Of my dug and felt it bitter, pretty fool!
To see it tetchy, and fall out with the dug. (1.3)
This mention in a popular play must indicate a fairly common procedure in Elizabethan England (common enough for the effects to be
known by a male playwright); one that remained so, in some rural areas,
at least until the early years of the 20th century. For example, Chamberlain (1975) recorded the experiences of an 84-year-old woman living in
a remote fen village:
We didn't have no bottle for our children. Fed them all ourselves.
Everyone. All nine. Till they were three years old, some of them.
You'd be standing there washing, and they'd hang onto you and
want a teat. I didn't know see. I tried to wean them several times,
but then they'd get it again and have another drop. I had no end of
trouble weaning my children. Till somebody give me some bitter

aloes. So I covered my breast with that, and said 'Oh, look, nasty. Don't have that, that's nasty!' And that done the trick [9].

However cruel or undesirable this aversion method may appear today, its main recommendation was that it was obviously effective. Both the above writers were referring to children weaned at up to 3 years of age, when weaning is now believed to be more difficult than in very young infants [23,33]. Perhaps the popularity of weaning by anointing the breasts with bitter substances prevailed more with children who had been breastfed for long periods, since many of the authors who recommended its use before 1750 were also those who recommended that weaning should not be undertaken until 18–24 months (cf. chapter 15). There is also the point that an older child is able to talk and to understand, so that he can be *told* that something tastes nasty. Like the woman quoted above, nurses obviously had difficulty weaning their charges at this age, as Ste Marthe (1584) described:

Some anoint their nipples with ungrateful gall,
Some by vile names the milky fountains call.
A thousand ways will careful nurses try
His relish to disgust, and fright his eye [41].

An alternative abrupt method, probably equally common, was to remove the mother or nurse for a period, or for the woman to hide herself from the child. This was described by some medical authors, although Young (late 18th century) thought this method was upsetting for the child. Again, this is a widely used method in more primitive societies today [50]. A reference to the 'child of a spayner' in the parish register of Greystoke, Cumbria, for 13 April 1592 indicates that some children in the north of England were sent to a special intermediary known as a spayner (spayne = wean in Cumbrian and Yorkshire dialect) to remove them from the breast for a period of time [48].

Evidence from the American Colonies in the 17th and 18th centuries shows that separation of mother/nurse and child was a favoured method [8]. Mothers often went away for a while and left the father to look after the weanling; or the child was abruptly sent away to grandparents or other relatives. One New England diary for 7 June 1733 stated:

Son & daughter minor came & brot their child & left itt hear to wean & went home again & I went with them & lodged there [8].

In England the same procedure was probably adopted in the Josselin family of Essex. Two grandchildren stayed with Ralph Josselin and his wife in 1674 and 1679, the former of whom 'went homewards well weaned' [26].

Possibly this was a slightly less traumatic method than presenting the child on one day with the normal source of comfort and food, and on the next with a foul-tasting, unfamiliar looking-breast. But some modern psychological theories indicate that, if sudden methods *were* used, they may have been preferable for the child, provided he were nursed by his mother. Wet-nursed infants, for whom weaning usually meant leaving for good the familiar foster mother for an unfamiliar home and family, would have fared worse whichever method was adopted.

Erikson (1967) states that:

> Weaning should not mean sudden loss of the breast and loss of the mother's reassuring presence too. A drastic loss of accustomed mother-love without proper substitution at this time can lead to acute infantile depression or to a mild but chronic state of mourning which may give a depressive undertone to the whole remainder of life [14].

If this be so, and if this method of weaning were very extensive, it could be related to the prevalence of melancholia in the late 16th and 17th centuries [6]. To some extent this condition became more fashionable after the publication of books such as Burton's *Anatomy of Melancholy* in 1621 [6], but the upper classes who complained of, or were diagnosed as suffering from, this complaint were the very people most likely to have experienced the trauma of sudden separation from the breast accompanied by loss of the mother figure at weaning; because they came from that part of society which put its children out to wet nurses. There is no doubt that, psychologically, weaning was a traumatic period for the infant and was recognised as being so; all referred to the distress of the 'weaning babe'.

> But how, my pretty infant, wilt thou bear,
> A loss that will thy soul and body tear?
> What floods of tears will deluge from thy eyes,
> What shrieks, what waking groans and sleeping sighs?
> Learn pretty infant, learn to bear these ills;
> Who can avoid what the Creator will? [41]

¶ The majority of medical writers emphasised that gradual weaning was preferable to the above methods. Some said that sudden weaning was dangerous or cruel but did not give their reasons for preferring a gradual process. Ways in which this was to be accomplished (table 16.2) included giving food prior to breastfeeding, increasing or decreasing the relative proportions of these, suckling only at night, and getting the child used to someone other than the nurse.

Writers were vague about how long these procedures were supposed to continue, only Guillemeau (1612) specifying the period of time that weaning should take. He illustrates also the conflict between gradual and sudden methods; the ideal and the practical. The child was to have breastmilk and food for a few days, followed by sucking only at night:

> It will be very fit in the morning, when he is awake and hath been

shifted and dressed, to give him sucke a little, and then to let him stay two or three houres before hee take anything, afterward to give him some dinner, as some pottage, or panada, with a little flesh minced, or cut very small, and then let him stay two houres without giving him anything, at which time you may give him a little sucke, and lay him to sleepe: and when he is wakened and hath been made cleane, then the nurse shall carry him abroad into the aire, if it be faire weather, and give him sucke, and then lay him to sleepe again, with out letting him eate any solide meate, or very little. At his dinner they shall give him to drinke a little boyled water: and this order shall be kept a whole moneth, and when hee shall bee accustomed to eate solide meate then the teate shall be quite taken from him. It happens often times that the child will not forsake the breasts, but still cryeth and is very eager after it, and you must make him loathe it, anointing the nurses breast with mustard, or else rubbing the top of the nipple with a little aloes, and likewise make him ashamed of it [17].

(In this description he is referring to a child of about 2 years of age.) He was writing, however, in a period when times for breastfeeding were not fixed and rigidly adhered to (cf. chapter 3). The regime he described was intended to phase out sucking whenever the child wanted it, and was designed to get it used to solid food, and to leaving a certain length of time between meals. These patterns of demand feeding and weaning are similar to those in many cultures today [50], where aversion methods are used as a last resort after more gradual methods have failed. The period of one month is similar to that recommended today for weaning from the breast [47].

Very little has been discovered about how long women actually took to wean their children. In 1645, the wife of Ralph Josselin took 11 days to wean her son Thomas, and in 1655 spent at least 2 weeks in weaning her daughter Anne [21,26]. Katherine Dee was weaned very suddenly on one day in 1582. Her parents visited her at nurse and removed her immediately because she was sickly, 'and weaned her at home'. But John Dee recorded of Michael, in 1586, and Margaret, in 1596, that they 'begonne to be weaned' thus implying that it would take a certain amount of time [11].

In the late 18th century any distress of the newly-weaned child was eased by the administration of laxatives [18,30], opiates [18,27,30,52], or alcohol [19,52]. William Hunter appeared to favour alcohol:

> You should not do it [weaning] gradually but all slowly let ye child suck in at night for ye last time. . . . In one 24 hours generally the child is weaned, ye first night after a little sack whey with barley water is ye best thing in ye world. This makes them a little drunk, they all like it and afterwards go to sleep very comfortable [19].

The 18th-century Quaker, Hannah Rathbone, in an attempt to ease any
distress her son might suffer from weaning 'gave him 6 drops of laud-
anum and do. antiminial wine' [37].

However it was carried out, by the end of the 18th century weaning
was recognised by physicians as an event whose management required
some 'care and judgement' [44], and was important 'because the mode
of living and future health may depend upon its proper conduct [18].

¶ Sudden or abrupt methods of weaning were apparently common and
were sometimes recommended by medical writers, the most usual being
to paint the nipples with bitter substances or to remove the mother or
nurse for a period. These methods were probably traumatic for the
child and could have been related to the prevalence of melancholia in
the late 16th and 17th centuries. The majority of medical writers
recommended gradual methods of weaning by giving foods beforehand;
increasing these, and decreasing the quantity of breast milk. Any distress which accompanied weaning was soothed by administering laxatives, alcohol and opiates.

REFERENCES

1. Aitken, J. (1786) *Principles of midwifery*, London, 3rd ed.
2. Armstrong, G. (1771) *An essay on the diseases most fatal to infants*, London, 2nd ed.
3. Brouzet, N. (1755) *An essay on the medicinal education of children*, trans. anon., London.
4. Buchan, W. (1769) *Domestic medicine; or The family physician*, Edinburgh.
5. Burton, J. (1751) *An essay towards a complete new system of midwifery*, London.
6. Burton, R. (1621) *The anatomy of melancholy*, Oxford.
7. Cadogan, W. (1748) *An essay upon nursing and the management of children, from their birth to three years of age*, London.
8. Caulfield, E. (1952) Infant feeding in Colonial America, *J. Pediat. 41*, 673-87.
9. Chamberlain, M. (1975) *Fenwomen. A portrait of women in an English village*, London.
10. Culpeper, N. (1676) *A directory for midwives; or, A guide for women in their conception, bearing and suckling their children. Corrected from many gross errors*, London.
11. Dee, J. (1842) *The private diary of Dr John Dee*, Halliwell, J. O. (ed.), London.
12. Denman, T. & Osborne, W. (1777-78) *Notes abstracted from several courses of lectures in midwifery given by Dr Denman and Dr Osborn. Taken down by Fran. Kingston*, Library of the Wellcome Institute for the History of Medicine, MS 2099.

13. Downman, H. (1788) *Infancy or, The management of children. A didactic poem in six books*, London, 4th ed.
14. Erikson, E. H. (1967) Growth and crises of the healthy personality, in Lazarus, R. S. & Opton, E. M. (eds), *Personality. Selected readings*, Harmondsworth.
15. Fildes, V. A. (1980) Weaning the Elizabeth child, part 1, *Nurs. Times 76*, 1357-9.
16. Fildes, V. A. (1982) *The history of infant feeding 1500-1800*, unpublished PhD thesis, Dept. Human Biology and Health, University of Surrey.
17. Guillemeau, J. (1612) *Childbirth or The happie deliverie of women. . . . To which is added a treatise of the diseases of infants, and young children: with the cure of them*, trans. anon., London.
18. Hamilton, A. (1792) *A treatise on the management of female complaints and of children in early infancy*, Edinburgh.
19. Hunter, W. (1775) *Lectures anatomical and chirurgical by William Hunter*, Library of the Wellcome Institute for the History of Medicine, MS 2966. Also dated 1783.
20. Jones, J. (1579) *The arte and science of preserving bodie and soule in healthe, wisedome, and catholicke religion: physically, philosophically and divinely devised*, London.
21. Josselin, R. (1976) *The diary of Ralph Josselin 1616-1683*, Macfarlane, A. (ed.), Oxford.
22. Lara, B. (1791) *An essay on the injurious custom of mothers not suckling their own children; with some directions for chusing a nurse, and weaning of children, etc.*, London.
23. Leach, P. (1974) *Babyhood. Infant development from birth to two years*, Harmondsworth.
24. MacDonald, M., of University of Wisconsin, Personal communication.
25. MacDonald, M. (1981) *Mystical bedlam. Madness, anxiety and healing in 17th century England*, Cambridge.
26. MacFarlane, A. (1970) *The family life of Ralph Josselin. A seventeenth century clergyman. An essay in historical anthropology*, Cambridge.
27. Mantell, T. (1787) *Short directions for the management of infants*, London.
28. Maubray, J. (1730) *The female physician containing all the diseases incident to that sex . . . together with the diet and regime of both the mother and child*, London.
29. Mead, M. (1935) *Sex and temperament in three primitive societies*, New York, 3rd ed., 1963.
30. Mears, M. (1797) *The midwife's candid advice to the fair sex; or The pupil of nature*, London.
31. Mondot-Bernard, J. M. (1977) *Relationships between fertility, child mortality and nutrition in Africa. A tentative analysis*, Paris.
32. Moss, W. (1781) *An essay on the management and nursing of children in the earlier periods of infancy*, London.

33. Newson, J. & Newson, E. (1974) *Patterns of infant care in an urban community,* Harmondsworth.
34. *Nurses guide: or The right method of bringing up young children. By an eminent physician* (1729), London.
35. Paré, A. (1575) *The workes of that famous chirurgion Ambrose Parey,* trans. Johnston, T., London, 1634.
36. Pechey, J. (1697) *A general treatise of the diseases of infants and children. Collected from the best practical authors,* London.
37. Pollock, L. A. (1983) *Forgotten children: parent-child relations from 1500-1900,* Cambridge.
38. Roesslin the Elder, E. (1540) *The byrth of mankynde,* trans. Jonas, R., London, first published 1512.
39. Rosenstein, N. R. von (1776) *The diseases of children and their remedies,* trans. Sparrman, A., London.
40. Ryerson, A. (1960) *Medical advice on childrearing 1500-1900,* Unpublished D Ed thesis, Harvard.
41. Sainte Marthe, S. de (1584) *Paedotrophiae: or The art of bringing up children,* trans. anon., London, 1710.
42. Shakespeare, W. (c.1594) *Romeo and Juliet,* Act 1, scene 3, in *The complete works of William Shakespeare,* Alexander, P. (ed.), London and Glasgow.
43. Sharp, J. (1671) *The midwives book or The whole art of midwifery discovered,* London.
44. Smith, H. (1774) *Letters to married women on nursing and the management of children. The 3rd edition, revised and considerably enlarged,* London.
45. Soranus of Ephesus (1st/2nd century A D) *Soranus' Gynecology,* trans. Temkin, O. *et al.,* Baltimore.
46. Spence, D. (1784) *A system of midwifery,* Edinburgh.
47. Spock, B. (1973) *Baby and childcare,* revised English edition, London.
48. Thiselton-Dyer (1898) *Old English social life as told by the parish registers,* London.
49. Underwood, M. (1784) *A treatise on the diseases of children,* London.
50. Whiting, J. W. M. & Child, I. L. (1964) *Child training and personality: a cross-cultural study,* New Haven and London.
51. Young, G. (1780) *A treatise on opium,* London.
52. Young, T. (late 18th century) *Young's midwifery,* Library of the Wellcome Institute for the History of Medicine, M S S 5106 and 5107.

CHAPTER SEVENTEEN

Weaning Practices:
The Weaning Diet and Diseases
Connected with Weaning

"Make for it lyttel pylles of breade and sugre to eate,
accustome it so tyll it be able to eate all manner of meate."
Eucharias Roesslin, *The byrth of mankynde*, 1540

FOODS to be given before or during weaning from the breast were discussed by 19 medical writers. Weaning foods usually differed from those suggested for mixed feeding, with fewer milk foods and increased use of meat broths and other meat dishes, which were not usually advised for children until they had teeth with which to chew them. Specific foods recommended by 17 authors [20] (table 17.1) included chicken broth, pre-chewed meat, meat broths, bread and butter, pap and panada, and porridge.

Some authors more generally recommended solid or 'hard' foods [27,41,48,49], or a variety of foods [41,57]. Downman (1788) made the interesting recommendation for his time of letting the child decide what food suited it, and how much. Allowing the child rather than the mother to decide was unusual in the 18th century; and even today, when experiments have shown this to be sound advice [11], it remains unusual [37,65]. Only 3 writers forbade particular foods at this stage. Brouzet (1755) disapproved of milk, because he believed it was dangerous to mix it with other foods, and Buchan (1769) and Smith (1774) thought meat should not be given until the child was older.

Some mention was made of the child's diet after he was weaned from the breast (table 17.2), although this received much less attention than the foods given in preparation for weaning. Two authors said that beer, boiled with bread and butter, was commonly used [41,60]; presumably, a more substantial form of pap. Seven writers recommended specific foods to be given after weaning, including beef tea, pre-chewed meat, rusks, milk puddings, cereals in water, pulses and fruit. Nine writers stated that some foods were forbidden to newly-weaned children, and these included meat, pastry, sugar, spice, porridge, stone fruits, fish, fats, and root vegetables in excess [20] (table 17.3).

After weaning, the child's meals were to be orderly and routine, fitting in with those of the rest of the family [20]. Although most did not concern themselves with the management of the child after weaning, 5 physicians stated the number of meals a day it was to receive. Brouzet (1755) and Smith (1774) said 4 meals a day to begin with; Cadogan (1748) and Buchan (1769) thought 3 were sufficient; Downman (1788) believed the newly-weaned child needed only one meal a day. Hugh Smith (1774) was exceptional in stating the exact dietary regime from weaning until 2 years of age:

Breakfast	6 – 7 am	Half a pint of milk with about two ounces of bread in it.
Second meal	10 – 11 am	Half a pint of good broth with the same quantity of bread.
Third meal	2 – 3 pm	Broth as above.
Supper	about 6 pm	New milk and bread as for breakfast.

Plain and simple meat-jellies could be substituted for broth, and barley water and milk could be given if the child was thirsty between meals [63].

That advice about the pre- and post-weaning diet was confined mainly to the 18th century, and, especially after 1750, must relate to the earlier age of weaning in that century. Before then, children were assumed by medical authors to be at least a year old, probably well into their second year of life, and in possession of several teeth, before weaning was considered; and were expected to continue until then on the paps and panadas used for mixed feeding. This implies that, by the time it was ready to be weaned, a child was able to sit up at table, had some ability to feed itself, had teeth with which to chew a variety of hard foods, including meat, and generally looked more like a child than an infant. It was visibly ready for whatever was the normal diet of his particular family.

Since such writers were directing their views mainly towards the wealthy or better educated, they tended to recommend a variety of meats and their products and, to a lesser extent, bread, because these were the main foods eaten by these groups in British society [14,71]. Therefore the few writers who thought the weaning diet worthy of mention in this period all recommended a diet which was familiar to their readers. The description given by John Jones (1579) of the food given after weaning to the children of the French king was probably very similar to that in wealthy English households in the same period [14,21].

Bread of fine wheate floure, of fine starch, also of almonds, of barley, or bigge, of wheat, which we call furmentie, of rye, of pease and suchlike, or soft bread steeped in the broath of fleshe of kiddes, tuppes, calves, hennes, etc. And sometimes a capon's wing minced in small pieces, or the breast of a pheasant rosted, cut in pieces [35].

Milk foods, and milk as a drink, were not a normal part of the adult diet of the wealthier sections of society, especially in the 16th and early 17th centuries. Milk was held to be a food for infants (i.e. children who were not weaned), the very old and the sick [14,17,45,71], which explains its absence in the suggested weaning diets of this era.

If such a diet were given to richer children regularly, over a long period, then diseases such as scurvy, rickets, bladder-stone and some degree of night blindness, accompanied by a lowered resistance to infection, would have been common among young children after weaning because, in a mainly meat and cereal diet which excludes dairy foods, vitamins A, D and C are absent, and the amount of calcium may be insufficient for a growing child [39]. With the exception of rickets, these diseases were all common among the adult population during this period [14].

Poorer families, however, had a different type of diet, consisting mainly of bread, cheese, salt meat (predominantly pork) and pulses; thus the poorer child may well have fared better in nutritional terms (provided he received a sufficient quantity) than the richer one. In the 16th century white meats or dairy foods, including eggs, were eaten by the poor [14] and, as many cottagers kept a cow, milk was more likely to be drunk by these families than by the wealthy, although milk-drinking was rare in towns because of poor supplies; a situation not remedied until the late 18th and early 19th centuries [5,14,68,71]. Until at least the late 18th century there were regional differences in milk-drinking habits; the north of England using milk as a drink more than was usual in the southern countries [14]. The child weaned on to this type of diet, which in summer and autumn probably included hedgerow fruits such as blackberries, may have suffered some degree of scurvy during the winter (as did the adult population [14]) but otherwise would have received all the nutrients necessary for healthy growth [39,54].

The condemnation (by Pemell, 1653) of fish and fats, possible sources of vitamins A and D, was because they were thought to cause worms [51]. This may explain the absence of these items from the recommended diets of physicians, although both rich and poor *did* eat fish, especially those living near the sea [14,21].

By the 18th century the situation had changed. Infants were considered ready for weaning before they could sit up at a table (independent sitting in modern societies is achieved by most children at about 8 months [37,46], although, because of nutritional and environmental factors, this was not necessarily so in the 18th century). They had few or no teeth [37], little ability to feed themselves [37], and were more vulnerable to diseases, especially of the gastro-intestinal tract, than children of one to two years [34]. Therefore much more consideration of diet was necessary, and this explains the recommendations for milk-containing foods during and after weaning. Many physicians still be-lieved teeth were necessary before meat could be given, and for this reason some forbade meat to children until they were older and had most of their teeth [20]. There was apparently some prejudice among the patients of these physicians. Hugh Smith (1774) described the reactions to his suggestions of meat juices and gravies:

> ... parents generally imagine it to be unwholesome for children; and often times when I have recommended it, some good old lady has stoutly opposed me, alledging that it fills the child with humours; whereas on the contrary, this is the only part of the flesh that produces good nourishment [63].

Despite the diversity of weaning foods recommended or forbidden by 18th-century medical writers, some of these were reflections of the personal prejudices or knowledge of only one or two people. For example, Hamilton (1792) disapproved of the use of his national dish for infants:

> The common preparation of oatmeal (called pottage or porridge) ... much used in this part of Great Britain, is undoubtedly too difficult of digestion for infants [28].

And Buchan (1769) thought that root vegetables should only be given sparingly:

> This caution is peculiarly necessary for the poor; being glad to get what will fill their children's bellies for a little money, they stuff them two or three times a day with potatoes and the like [7].

Since oatmeal (which cannot be used for loaf bread) and – after 1750 – potatoes were the staple fare of the Scots peasantry, Lowland and Highland alike, these strictures are of the order of Marie-Antoinette's 'let them eat cake!' These comments again illustrate that the condem-nations of physicians frequently offer much indication of what parents were actually feeding to their children, as well as of medical attitudes towards these habits.

The forbidding of certain foods to children was a feature of the period 1750–1800 (table 17.3). Although this reflects a more punitive and simplistic attitude towards the diet of older children, which dated at least from John Locke's *Some thoughts concerning education* (1693) [38], and was reinforced by William Cadogan (1748), it was also related to the earlier age of weaning. With some doctors advocating weaning as perfectly possible in the first 3 months of life if necessary [2,44], there had to be more emphasis on nourishing yet simple foods with which to feed them safely. Smith's (1774) recommended regime (above) from weaning to the second birthday, although nutritionally well-balanced [39], was scarcely varied enough for the second year of life [37]. Al-though his regimen may have been followed in the nurseries of richer families, Brouzet's (1755) statement that women, especially mothers, gave children most of the foods which they themselves ate probably portrays a truer picture for the majority.

Eighteenth-century children were apparently beginning to be weaned in a way similar to those of today, beginning with puréed or minced foods containing milk or broth, progressing to the foods eaten by the rest of the family, firstly mashed then cut into small pieces as the child became older. This graduated weaning diet (which to some extent merged with mixed artificial feeding) was necessary because of the earlier weaning age.

Fourteen writers recommended a drink to replace breastmilk, including animal milk, buttermilk, water, ale or smallbeer, wine, and barley water (table 17.4). Eleven writers proscribed certain drinks, specifically wine, liquors, ale, milk and tea (table 17.5). Alcoholic drinks were advocated by 8 authors and forbidden by 9 [20]. In many cases the proscription applied to the type only, some writers condemning one while recommending another.

Although today it would be unthinkable to recommend or to give a child as young as 6 to 12 months alcoholic drinks on a regular basis, the situation was very different in pre-industrial Britain. Because the water was widely known to be contaminated, it was very rarely drunk by any part of the population [14]. Most of the authors who recommended it came from France, where it was apparently drunk either alone or with wine. This was emphasised by the anonymous English translator of Guillemeau's work in 1612. When Guillemeau recommended water, his translator added the footnote 'that is in France where they have not ale or beere' [27]. The common drink of most people in Britain was ale, beer or smallbeer [14,71]; ale had a fairly high alcoholic content but smallbeer was much weaker [14]. Therefore, once a child was weaned and ate similar food to the rest of the family, it was natural for him to have the same drink. Grape wine was drunk only by the wealthier sections of society, but home-made wines were common [14]. Disapproval of the use of wine in the 16th century was an echo of those ancient medical authorities who thought it was not good for children [22]. The fact that 18th-century physicians disapproved of wine indicates that it probably *was* given to the small children among their patients. It possibly had a higher alcoholic content than the beers and ale which some authors preferred [14].

The lower weaning age in this period meant that milk was ideally given for longer than previously and, added to the increased scientific knowledge after 1761 about its value and composition, explains why milk products were increasingly recommended [66,73].

A main concern of all authors, especially in the 18th century, was that spirituous liquors should not be administered to babies and young children. This was the period in which gin was very cheap and easily accessible even to the very poor and was a social problem to all age groups [14,23,33,70]. Hogarth's *Gin Lane* (1751) shows even small babies being dosed with gin. Among the wealthy, brandy was a favourite spirit and was apparently administered to infants from birth by some nurses wishing to quieten them [14,29]. Thus forbidding strong liquors or spirits was related to contemporary social problems, and did not prevent physicians recommending a more commonplace alcoholic drink such as beer (whose virtue was compared favourably with gin by Hogarth in *Beer Street* and *Gin Lane* [25]). William Buchan (1769) illustrates the medical attitude to children's drinks in the second half of the 18th century, with preferences turning towards milk products or the weaker alcoholic drinks:

> All strong liquors are harmful to children. Some parents teach their children to guzzle ale, and others strong liquors at every meal; but such a practice cannot fail to do mischief. . . . Milk, water, buttermilk, or whey, make the most proper drink for children. If they have anything stronger, it may be fine smallbeer, or a little wine mixed with water [7].

Fourteen writers associated specific diseases with weaning [19,20] (see table 17.6). As Glisson (1651) was the only pre-18th century writer, and discussed only rickets, he is included in order to give a complete picture. The other diseases were gastro-intestinal upsets, leanness and stunted growth, and teething.

In the 16th and 17th centuries, with the exception of Glisson (1651), medical writers had not associated particular diseases with weaning, although the constant mention of sudden change being dangerous, and the necessity for the period of teething to be over before weaning began, implies that it was frequently accompanied by some degree of illness. The Bills of Mortality consistently showed a large number of deaths from 'teething', long before some 18th-century writers linked it directly with weaning [3,32,40]. Teething was in fact believed to be a *disease* entity in the 16th and 17th centuries, and was still regarded as such by many physicians until the 19th century [53,56]. It has been shown, throughout, that weaning and teething were inextricably linked; the numbers of infant deaths attributed to teething (and, by implication, to weaning) in the Bills of Mortality are shown in the following extract for 1740:

Total number of infants christened	15,231
Total deaths age 0–2 year	10,765 (71%)
Cause of death age 0–2 years:	
a) convulsions	8,479 (79%)
b) teeth	1,708 (16%)
c) fevers, smallpox, etc.	578 (5%)

The reference to 'teeth' may be all but synonymous with weaning. Some deaths attributed to convulsions may also have been due to teething [55,56].

These figures can be used as a rough indication only, since the Bills of Mortality recorded only infants christened in the established church, and the cause of death was not normally given by a medical practitioner but by a paid 'searcher' who would have given the cause most immediately obvious to them (or accepted what the parents told them [26]). Since, in infants, convulsions may appear at the beginning of some infectious diseases, accompany severe rickets, and be present in the terminal stages of most untreated diseases of infancy [55,62], the causes of the deaths attributed to 'convulsions' were manifold.

Thomas Mantell (1787) said that, of the great numbers of infants who die in teething, those who were healthy and lived abstemiously 'generally suffer little' and the 'greatest sufferers from dentition' were those already debilitated by disorders before teething began [40]. The stress of teething which may (like other stresses) lower the body's resistance to infection temporarily [15], could have resulted in increased susceptibility to disease from unclean feeding vessels and unsuitable food during weaning; the healthy older child being likely to overcome this much more easily than an infant of only a few months old, or one already debilitated by disease or malnourishment.

Rickets was a prevalent disease of young children in the 17th and 18th centuries and has been discussed in connection with wet nursing and mixed feeding, but in this period it was a condition particularly associated with weaning. Glisson (1651) specifically linked the onset of rickets at 9–18 months of age with the loss of breastmilk:

So long as they are conveniently nourished with it, they incur the fewer errors of diet, and are rendered the less obnoxious to this disease. . . . After the ninth month, children are usually fed with other aliment besides breastmilk or other milk, and from that variety there easily resulteth some errors in the point of diet [24].

William Hunter (1775), after recommending weaning at 8–9 months, said 'Rickets usually happen to children at 10 months old' [31]. Young (1780) said rickets were rare before weaning [72] (plate 17.1).

This age of onset was undoubtedly related to which foods were given at and after weaning, and to the partial or total loss of milk from the diet of young children. It may also have been related to the fact that this is the approximate age at which children first stand up and begin to walk [37,46], and thus bowing of the legs and other skeletal deformities would become apparent. Although the age of first walking in the 17th and 18th centuries may have been different from today, the little evidence available [12,52] shows the range of walking ages to be similar.

The 'weaning illness' or 'weaning brash' was a gastro-intestinal

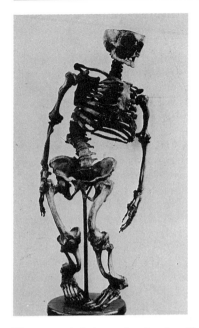

Plate 17.1. A skeleton showing the effect
of rickets. 'Bowed Joseph' was an Edinburgh character of the late 18th C., and
his skeleton is in the Anatomy Museum,
University of Edinburgh.

disorder which occurred when children were weaned from the breast
[19,20]. It was regarded as normal and inevitable and was associated with
the change in diet [1,6,72]. The Scottish surgeon John Aitken described
it in 1786:

> This is a violent purging, frequently attended with vomiting,
> wasting, etc.
> Causes: i) early weaning; ii) improper food.
> Cure: Removal of causes [1].

This condition was obviously a form of the weanling diarrhoea observed
in areas such as India, Africa and Central America today [34,43] (cf.
chapter 10).

Leanness, wasting and small growth were particularly associated with
early weaning [3,32,58], and with improper foods and too sudden change
of the milk for solid foods at weaning [30]. As we have seen, wasting was
part of the weaning illness described by Aitken (1786) and inevitably
would have been associated with conditions such as diarrhoea and
vomiting. Poor or inadequate feeding after leaving the breast would

have resulted in an undernourished and therefore underweight child and, since the quality of the diet in the first few months of life has been found to be a vital determinant in human growth [67], weaning in early infancy could have resulted in stunted growth.

¶ The most popular weaning foods recommended by medical writers were chicken broth, minced or pre-chewed meat, and meat gravies with breadcrumbs or rice. Weaning foods were usually different from those recommended and probably used, for mixed feeding, in particular they contained meat because the child was judged capable of digesting meat once he had teeth with which to chew. The increased concern about the pre- and post-weaning diet in the late 18th century was probably related to the earlier age of weaning at this time.

The recommended weaning diet of mainly meat and bread was related to the normal diet of the wealthy classes and, if given regularly and as recommended, children would have suffered lack of vitamins A, D and C, and some deficiency of calcium. Resultant diseases would have included scurvy, rickets, bladder stone, a degree of night blindness, and lowered resistance to infection, all of which occurred among the adult population during the period 1500–1800. Children in poorer families, weaned on to their normal diet, would probably have received a more balanced nutritious diet than that of wealthy families although in certain periods the former were more likely to have insufficient quantity of food.

Physicians recommended smallbeer, water or forms of milk to replace breastmilk but most condemned wine and strong liquors. Since the most usual drink of the adult population was smallbeer, beer or ale, most children would have been weaned on to the family's usual drink. The more frequent recommendation of milk drinks in the late 18th century was probably related to the earlier age of weaning.

Specific diseases began to be associated with weaning in the 18th century, possibly because of the earlier age of weaning and the increased interest in childhood diseases. Conditions particularly connected with weaning included rickets, gastro-intestinal upsets, leanness and small growth, and teething (which throughout this period was regarded as a disease entity).

REFERENCES
1. Aitken, J. (1786) *Principles of midwifery*, London, 3rd ed.
2. Armstrong, G. (1771) *An essay on the diseases most fatal to infants*, London, 2nd ed.
3. Astruc, J. (1746) *A general and complete treatise on all the diseases incident to children from their birth to the age of fifteen*, trans. anon., London.

4. Baudelocque, J-L. (1790) *A system of midwifery*, trans. Heath, J., London.
5. Beaver, M. W. (1973) Population, infant mortality and milk, *Popul. Stud. 27*, 243-54.
6. Brouzet, N. (1755) *An essay on the medicinal education of children; and the treatment of their diseases*, trans. anon., London.
7. Buchan, W. (1769) *Domestic medicine; or The family physician*, Edinburgh.
8. Burton, J. (1751) *An essay towards a complete new system of midwifery*, London.
9. Cadogan, W. (1748) *An essay upon nursing and the management of children, from their birth to three years of age*, London.
10. Culpeper, N. (1676) *A directory for midwives; or, A guide for women in their conception, bearing and suckling their children. Corrected from many gross errors*, London.
11. Davis, C. M. (1928) Self-selection of diet by newly-weaned infants, an experimental study, *Am. J. Dis. Child. 36*, 651-79.
12. De Mause, L. (ed.) (1976) *The history of childhood. The evolution of parent-child relationships as a factor in history*, London.
13. Downman, H. (1788) *Infancy or, The management of children. A didactic poem in six books*, London.
14. Drummond, J. C. & Wilbraham, A. (1957) *The Englishman's food. A history of five centuries of British diet*, London.
15. Dubos, R. (1969) *Man adapting*, New Haven and London.
16. Ellis, H. (1969) *A history of bladder stone*, Oxford and Edinburgh.
17. Elyot, Sir T. (1534) *The castel of helth*, London.
18. Fildes, V. A. (1980) Weaning the Elizabethan child, part 2, *Nurs. Times 76*, 1402-3.
19. Fildes, V. A. (1980) On the bottle again. The diseases of weaning 1600-1800, *Nurs. Mirror 151*, 18-21.
20. Fildes, V. A. (1982) *The history of infant feeding 1500-1800*, Unpublished PhD thesis, Dept. Human Biology and Health, University of Surrey.
21. Furnivall, F. J. (ed.) (1868) *Early English meals and manners*, London.
22. Galen (2nd century AD) *A translation of Galen's 'Hygiene' (De sanitate tuenda)*, trans. Green, R. M., Springfield, Illinois, 1951.
23. George, M. D. (1966) *London life in the eighteenth century*, Harmondsworth.
24. Glisson, F. (1651) *A treatise of the rickets, being a disease common to children*, trans. Armin, P., London.
25. Gowing, L. (1971) *Hogarth*, London.
26. Graunt, J. (1676) *Natural and political observations on the Bills of Mortality. Much enlarged*, London, 5th ed.

27. Guillemeau, J. (1612) *Childbirth or The happie deliverie of women. . . . To which is added a treatise of the diseases of infants, and young children: with the cure of them*, trans. anon., London.

28. Hamilton, A. (1792) *A treatise on the management of female complaints and of children in early infancy*, Edinburgh.

29. Harris, W. (1689) *A treatise of the acute diseases of infants*, trans. Martyn, J., London, 1742.

30. Hoffmann, F. (c.1740) *A system of the practice of medicine, vol.2*, trans. Lewis, W., London, 1783.

31. Hunter, W. (1775) *Lectures anatomical and chirurgical by William Hunter 1775*, Library of the Wellcome Institute for the History of Medicine, MS 2966. Also dated 1783.

32. Hurlock, J. (1742) *A practical treatise upon dentition*, London.

33. Jarrett, D. (1976) *England in the age of Hogarth*, Frogmore, Herts.

34. Jelliffe, D. B. & Jelliffe, E. F. P. (1978) *Human milk in the modern world. Psychosocial, nutritional and economic significance*, Oxford.

35. Jones, J. (1579) *The arte and science of preserving bodie and soule in healthe, wisedome, and catholicke religion: physically, philosophically and divinely devised*, London.

36. Lara, B. (1791) *An essay on the injurious custom of mothers not suckling their own children; with some directions for chusing a nurse, and weaning of children, etc.*, London.

37. Leach, P. (1974) *Babyhood. Infant development from birth to two years*, Harmondsworth.

38. Locke, J. (1693) *Some thoughts concerning education*, London.

39. *McCance and Widdowson's The composition of foods* (1978), revised and extended Paul, A. A. & Southgate, D. A. T. (eds), London, 4th ed.

40. Mantell, T. (1787) *Short directions for the management of infants*, London.

41. Maubray, J. (1730) *The female physician containing all the diseases incident to that sex . . . together with the diet and regimen of both the mother and child*, London.

42. Mears, M. (1797) *The midwife's candid advice to the fair sex; or The pupil of nature*, London.

43. Morley, D. (1973) *Paediatric priorities in the developing world*, London.

44. Moss, W. (1781) *An essay on the management and nursing of children in the earlier periods of infancy*, London.

45. Muffet (Moffet), T. (1584) *Health's improvement: or Rules comprising the nature, method, and manner of preparing all sorts of food used in this nation. Corrected and enlarged by Christopher Bennet*, London, 1655.

46. Musson, P. H. (1963) *The psychological development of the child*, New Jersey.

47. Nelson, J. (1753) *An essay on the government of children*, London.

48. *Nurses guide: or The right method of bringing up young children. By an eminent physician,* London, 1729.
49. Paré, A. (1575) *The workes of that famous chirurgion Ambrose Parey,* trans. Johnson, T., London, 1634.
50. Pechey (Peachey), J. (1697) *A general treatise of the diseases of infants and children,* London.
51. Pemell, R. (1653) *De morbis puerorum, or a Treatise of the diseases of children,* London.
52. Pollock, L. A. (1983) *Forgotten children: parent-child relations from 1500-1900,* Cambridge.
53. Radbill, S. X. (1965) Teething in fact and fancy, *Bull. Hist. Med. 39,* 339-45.
54. *Recommended intakes of nutrients for the United Kingdom* (1973), DHSS reports on public health and medical subjects, no.120, London.
55. Rendle-Short, J. (1955) The causes of infantile convulsions prior to 1900, *J. Pediat. 47,* 733-9.
56. Rendle-Short, J. (1955) The history of teething in infancy, *Proc. R. Soc. Med. 48,* 132-8.
57. Roesslin the Elder, E. (1540) *The byrth of mankynde,* trans. Jonas, R., London, first published 1512.
58. Rosenstein, N. R. von (1776) *The diseases of children and their remedies,* trans. Sparrman, A., London.
59. Sainte Marthe, S. de (1584) *Paedotrophiae: or The art of bringing up children,* trans. anon., London, 1710.
60. Sennert, D. (1657) *De mulierum et infantum morbis,* trans. in Johnston, J. (1657) *Idea of practical physick,* London. Partially trans. in Still, G. F. (1931) *The history of paediatrics,* London.
61. Sharp, J. (1671) *The midwives book or The whole art of midwifery discovered,* London.
62. Shaw, J. C. L., of University College Hospital, London, Personal communication.
63. Smith, H. (1774) *Letters to married women on nursing and the management of children. The 3rd edition, revised and considerably enlarged,* London.
64. Spence, D. (1784) *A system of midwifery,* Edinburgh.
65. Spock, B. (1973) *Baby and child care, revised English edition,* London.
66. Still, G.F. (1931) *The history of paediatrics,* London.
67. Tanner, J. M. (1981) *A history of the study of human growth,* Cambridge.
68. Trusler, Rev. Dr J. (1786) *The London adviser and guide,* London.
69. Underwood, M. (1784) *A treatise on the diseases of children,* London.
70. Watney, J. (1976) *Mother's ruin. A history of gin,* London.
71. Wilson, C. A. (1976) *Food and drink in Britain. From the stone age to recent times,* Harmondsworth.

72. Young, G. (1780) *A treatise on opium*, London.
73. Young, T. (1761) *De lacte*, Inaugural dissertation, University of Edinburgh. Cited in Still, G. F. (1931) *The history of paediatrics*, London.

CHAPTER EIGHTEEN

Epilogue

"A little child born yesterday,
A thing on mother's milk and kisses fed."
Shelley, *Homer's hymn to Mercury*

THIS investigation into infant feeding practices has shown that, during the 300-year period principally under review, there were two main points in time when changes in theory and practice occurred. The more obvious of these was the mid-18th century, when William Cadogan's widely-read and influential *Essay upon nursing and the management of children* was published. Many changes, in some cases quite radical, date from this time. In some instances, Cadogan appears to have been an initiator of ideas (e.g. the theory of not boiling milk for infant foods); in others, he consolidated the theories of earlier writers such as John Locke (1693), in his pleas for simple, wholesome food [12], and continental physicians such as Ettmueller (1699) and Hoffmann (c.1740), in his belief that the newborn child should be put to the breast early on, and receive colostrum rather than purges [6,10]. The fact that he put both these new and old ideas into book form, in a fresh, positive and refreshing way, makes him appear to have been the originator of them, in advance of his contemporaries; but other events occurred in the 1740s which had an equal influence on feeding practices.

In 1741, the Foundling Hospital opened in London [8], and initially experimented with dry nursing [11]. The high mortality which resulted, and the consequent change to, mainly, wet nursing in the surrounding countryside [13], was the first demonstrable experiment, on a relatively large number of children, to show the populace that dry nursing was a dangerous method of feeding in comparison to breastfeeding. As the Foundling Hospital was a fashionable place to visit, and was initially supported by subscriptions from wealthy patrons, the results of this experiment were published and were well known. This would surely have been taken into account when wealthy families were deciding upon the method of feeding for their own babies.

In 1747, the first lying-in wards were opened in London, closely followed in the next five years by several lying-in hospitals [5]. Concern about the high incidence of milk fever and breast disease among their newly-delivered women led to experiments and changes in neonatal feeding, and the consequent dramatic reduction in the incidence of milk fever [15]. Again, these were the first relatively large-scale experiments in putting infants to the breast within a few hours of birth; the results were, again, published and available for the populace to consider, in decisions about maternal breastfeeding (for example, *The Gentleman's Magazine* and other journals regularly carried reports about both the Foundling Hospital and the lying-in hospitals).

The timing of such changes in ideas in the mid-18th century was almost certainly related to three things: i) The consolidation of changes in medical ideas which had probably originated in continental medical schools where British physicians and some surgeons were educated (particularly Leyden). Cadogan, a graduate of Leyden, put these down in a short readable form and thus acted as a 'springboard' or catalyst in passing them on to both general and medical readers for the next 60 years. He was aided by the fact that the Foundling Hospital decided to adopt his suggested methods of infant care, thus further publicising these methods; ii) The visible and published experiments, with their results, of different infant feeding methods at the Foundling Hospital; iii) The experiments in early maternal breastfeeding at the Lying-in Hospital, Brownlow Street, which demonstrated the positive effect of this practice on the health of the mothers.

Major changes after c.1748 included decreased popularity of wet nurses accompanied by increased incidence of maternal breastfeeding among the wealthy; allowing the child to suck colostrum rather than discarding it; changes in the preparation of infant foods, particularly the non-boiling of milk; the adoption of handfeeding as the method of choice after maternal breastfeeding; medical discussion of handfeeding and the development of better substitute foods, and more suitable vessels for administering them; and a significantly earlier weaning age.

Rousseau's ideas about infant care, feeding and education, first published in *Émile* in 1762 [16], appear to have played little part in the change in Britain, since the major changes were well under way at least a decade before his text appeared. However, the popularity of this work probably reinforced the effects mentioned above.

An earlier period of change, which is much less easily defined, occurred about the year 1670. This again coincided with publication of a major work, a definitive midwifery text by the French surgeon-midwife Francois Mauriceau. His *Accomplisht midwife* (1668) was first translated into English in 1672/73, and within ten years, and for the first time, several publications appeared by English writers on midwifery. For example, James Wolveridge (1671) [18]; Jane Sharp (1671) [17]; new and expanded editions of Nicholas Culpeper in 1675 and 1676 [3,4]; and the anonymous *Compleat midwife's practice, enlarged* (1680), all of which dealt at some length with infant feeding. As has been shown throughout, Mauriceau and these English contemporaries were often at the forefront of new ideas, no longer giving credence to the ancient writers whose theories had dominated paediatric publications before the 1670s.

This change in emphasis in the medical literature was undoubtedly linked to the general changes occurring in other branches of medicine and science in the late 17th century, when empiricism was replacing the ideas of the Greeks and Arabs. Differences were also evident in practice, as was seen with the upper classes and their experimentation with handfeeding, and the beginnings of dissatisfaction with wet nursing. Different theories were beginning to be voiced concerning the weaning of children, and the food they were given. The first suggestions that early maternal breastfeeding was good for the child also date from this period, as does the beginning of diversification of feeding vessels [7]. Whether or not Mauriceau's book was the spur for British practitioners to put pen to paper, or was coincidental in a period of scientific enquiry and activity, is not clear but, like Cadogan's book, it is a marker, although less obvious, of a time of change in British infant feeding practices.

Theory and practice in infant nutrition between 1500 and 1800 therefore can be divided into three broad periods:

c.1500–c.1670 A period of little change in ideas or practice, where the principal criteria were unchanged from those of the Greeks. The main concern was for the child.

c.1670–c.1748 A period of experimentation, of rejection of old ideas, and the real beginning of publications dealing with infants and their care by English and Scottish writers. Concern was still for the child but, towards the end of this time, attention began to focus on the mother.

c.1748–1800 Major changes in infant feeding practices and ideas. The period when books of advice for mothers began to appear, and attention and concern was less for the child and much more for the mother. This was the era of early industrialisation, when modern ideas of infant feeding began to be voiced and practised.

The principal medical trend between 1500 and 1800 was a decreasing concern for the health and well-being of the infant. This was replaced in the 18th century by increased attention to that of the mother, from which infants benefited indirectly. There was also an apparent decline of the husband's influence in decisions about how his children were to be fed.

There remains much work to be done in this period; perhaps the most stimulating query is the reasoning behind the various changes, in the context of attitudes to infancy and childhood, and to wives and mothers. Although the majority of British women probably breastfed their babies as a matter of course, the changes in the habits of the wealthier families could well have influenced the women that they employed. The manufacture of feeding vessels in materials that the poor could afford meant also that they had the means with which to handfeed their babies.

It has been shown in this book that form often followed function. For example, an increased incidence of artificial feeding resulted in increased production of diverse feeding vessels. Similarly, the increased incidence of maternal breastfeeding among the educated classes resulted in a steady stream of 'advice books' instructing women how to be mothers. Changes of this nature also affected the employment opportunities of women wanting to become wet nurses. Although plenty of women were still employed as wet nurses by the beginning of the 19th century, enclosures, industrialisation, the spread of workhouses, and changing concepts of child care represented the beginning of the end of wet nursing as a lucrative and continuing occupation for women.

Finally, this book has shown how great were the similarities between pre-industrial British and European infant-feeding practices and those of Third-World countries today. Like the latter societies, all aspects of feeding, other than maternal breastfeeding and some conscientious wet nursing, were associated with increased risk of morbidity and death. The errors in infant nutrition made during industrialisation of western societies are being repeated today. Even though we have the knowledge and expertise to prevent the diseases associated with malnutrition, and to correct the ignorance of health measures that could prevent them, the infant mortality in Third-World societies today is identical to that of 18th-century London: up to 70 per cent of infants born did not survive to their second birthday.

REFERENCES

1. Cadogan, W. (1748) *An essay upon nursing and the management of children*, London.
2. *Compleat midwife's practice, enlarged* (1680), London.
3. Culpeper, N. (1675) *A directory for midwives*, London.
4. Culpeper, N. (1676) *A directory for midwives or, A guide for women, in their conception, bearing and suckling their children. Corrected from many gross errors*, London.

5. Donnison, J. (1977) *Midwives and medical men. A history of interprofessional rivalries and women's rights*, London.
6. Ettmueller, M. (1699) *Etmullerus abridg'd: or A compleat system of the theory and practice of physic*, trans. anon., London.
7. Fildes, V. A. (1982) *The history of infant feeding 1500-1800*, Unpublished Ph D thesis, Dept. of Human Biology and Health, University of Surrey.
8. Foundling Hospital (1749) *An account of the hospital for the maintenance and education of exposed and deserted young children*, London.
9. *Gentleman's magazine*, London, 1730-1800.
10. Hoffmann, F. (c.1740) *A system of the practice of medicine*, vol.2, trans. Lewis, W., London, 1783.
11. Lloyd Hart, V. E. (1979) *John Wilkes and the Foundling Hospital at Aylesbury 1759-1768*, Aylesbury.
12. Locke, J. (1693) *Some thoughts concerning education*, London.
13. McClure, R. K. (1981) *Coram's children. The London Foundling Hospital in the eighteenth century*, New Haven and London.
14. Mauriceau, F. (1673) *The accomplisht midwife, treating of the diseases of women with child, and in childbed... with fit remedies for the several indispositions of newborn babes*, trans. Chamberlen, H., London.
15. Nelson, J. (1753) *An essay on the government of children. Under three general heads: viz Health, manners and education*, London.
16. Rousseau, J-J. (1762) *Émile*, trans. Foxley, B., London, 1911.
17. Sharp, J. (1671) *The midwives book or The whole art of midwifery discovered*, London.
18. Wolveridge, J. (1671) *Speculum matrices; or The expert midwife's handmaid*, London.

Statistical Appendix

Table 2.1. The proportion of 46 medical authors who recommended a first food for neonates before and after 1748.

First food	1500–1747 (n = 21)	1748–1800 (n = 25)	Total (n = 46)
Purge and/or colostrum	0.33	0.44	0.39
Colostrum only	0.05	0.36	0.22
Purge only	0.43	—	0.20
Purge/colostrum + food	—	0.20	0.11
Purge + medicinal substance	0.10	—	0.04
Medicinal substance	0.05	—	0.02
Breastmilk, not colostrum	0.05	—	0.02

Table 2.2. The proportion of 21 medical authors who said the following first foods were commonly given, before and after 1748.

First foods	1500–1747 (n = 8)	1748–1800 (n = 13)	Total (n = 21)
Purge	0.75	0.31	0.48
Purge + food	—	0.31	0.19
Purge + medicinal substance	0.25	0.08	0.14
Food only	—	0.23	0.14
Purge + food + medicinal substance	—	0.08	0.05

To assess the frequency with which each substance appeared, all references to the first food given after delivery, whether a recommendation or a substance said to be commonly given, were examined with the results shown in table 2.3.

Table 2.3. The proportion of 49 medical authors who recommended and/or said that the following first foods were commonly given, before and after 1748.

First foods	1500–1747 (n = 21)	1748–1800 (n = 28)	Total (n = 49)
Purge and/or colostrum	0.33	0.39	0.37
Purge only	0.57	0.11	0.31
Colostrum only	0.05	0.32	0.20
Purge/colostrum + food	—	0.29	0.16
Purge + medicinal substance	0.19	0.04	0.10
Food only	—	0.11	0.06
Purge + food + medicinal substance	—	0.04	0.02
Medicinal substance	0.05	—	0.02
Breastmilk, not colostrum	0.05	—	0.02

Table 2.4. The proportion of 20 medical authors who stated reasons for administering purges/medicines, 1500–1800.

Reason	16th century (n = 3)	17th century (n = 7)	18th century (n = 10)	Total (n = 20)
To remove meconium	0.67	0.71	0.90	0.80
To prevent diseases	0.33	0.57	0.20	0.35
To clear mouth/throat/lungs	—	0.29	0.30	0.25

Table 2.5. The interval between birth and the first breastfeed.

When child first put to the breast	Period during which recommended or said to be common
3–4 weeks	1612–1673
8–9 days	1612–1730
5–7 days	1575–1682
4 days	1579
Not immediately;	
several days	1540–1550
2–4 days	1752–1781
within 24 hours	1699–1790

Table 2.6. The proportion of 11 medical authors who gave
reasons for not feeding colostrum to neonates, 1500–1800.

Reason	16th century ($n = 2$)	17th century ($n = 4$)	18th century ($n = 5$)	Total ($n = 11$)
Reasons affecting child	1.00	0.75	1.00	0.91
Reasons affecting the mother	0.50	0.75	0.40	0.55

Table 2.7. Total (0–12 months) and endogenous
(0–28 days) infant mortality and percentage
change, 1680s–1875. (From figures provided by
Schofield, pers. comm. 1979, and the Registrar
General's figures for 1840 and 1875.)

Date	Overall mortality ‰	% change	Mortality 0–28 days ‰	% change
1680s	204		88	
1730s	181	−11	74	−16
1780s	165	−9	51	−31
1840	150	−9	23	−55
1875	169	+13	22	−4

Table 2.8. Infant mortality
(0–12 months) of the British
aristocracy, 1650–1824
(from Hollingsworth 1957).

Date	Mortality ‰	% change
1650–74	210	
1675–99	196	−7
1700–24	169	−14
1725–49	166	−2
1750–74	102	−39
1775–99	85	−17
1800–24	82	−4

Table 2.9. Maternal mortality rate in a group of
13 English parishes (compiled from Wrigley and
Schofield 1983) and the percentage change
1600–1799, compared with those for 1850–54
and 1870–74 from the Registrar General.

Years	Mortality rate ‰ Actual	Corrected*	% change
1600–49	14.4	15.3	
1650–99	17.5	18.8	+ 22.8
1700–49	12.9	13.6	− 27.7
1750–99	8.7	8.8	− 35.3
1850–54	5.3	—	− 39.8
1870–74	5.4	—	+ 1.9

* For method of obtaining a correction factor,
and the reason for applying it, see Wrigley and
Schofield 1983.

Table 3.1. The proportion of 32 authors who stated some
common reasons why women did not breastfeed their own
children, 1500–1800.

Reason	16th century ($n = 6$)	17th century ($n = 10$)	18th century ($n = 16$)	Total ($n = 32$)
Mother's health/shape/dress	0.33	0.60	0.44	0.47
Husband's influence	0.33	0.50	0.25	0.34
The fashion or custom	0.33	0.20	0.38	0.31
Mother's (social) pleasures	—	0.50	0.31	0.31
Religious factors	—	0.50	—	0.16
Mother's lack of skill/care/ motherliness	—	0.30	0.06	0.13
Persuasion of others	—	0.20	0.06	0.09
Contraception	—	0.10	—	0.03
Other factors affecting mother*	0.17	0.50	0.56	0.47
Others†	—	0.20	0.19	0.16

* These included: laziness; because it was troublesome;
to ensure undisturbed nights; and want of luxury.
† Included: gain, because it was cheaper to put a child out to
nurse than to breastfeed at home and hire help; ignorance of the
harm it caused; because it was considered indelicate; and that
taking a nurse into the home justified the mother not feeding.

Table 3.2. The proportion of 34 authors who stated acceptable reasons for mothers not breastfeeding, 1500–1800.

Reason	16th century ($n = 7$)	17th century ($n = 11$)	18th century ($n = 16$)	Total ($n = 34$)
Factors affecting mother	0.71	0.91	0.88	0.85
Factors affecting breasts/ nipples/milk	0.57	0.64	0.44	0.53
Factors affecting child	0.14	—	—	0.03
Others*	0.29	0.09	—	0.09

* These included: another pregnancy immediately; if the parents were in a hurry to have another child; any natural impediment.

Table 3.3. The proportion of 65 medical and religious writers who stated opinions about maternal breastfeeding, 1500–1800.

Opinion	16th century ($n = 12$)	17th century ($n = 16$)	18th century ($n = 37$)	Total ($n = 65$)
Mother is the best nurse	1.00	0.94	1.00	0.99
Mother not always the best nurse	0.08	0.06	0.11	0.09
Mother not the best nurse	—	0.06	—	0.02

Table 3.4. The proportion of 29 medical and religious writers who recommended alternatives to maternal breastfeeding, 1500–1800.

Alternative	16th century ($n = 4$)	17th century ($n = 8$)	18th century ($n = 17$)	Total ($n = 29$)
Wet nurse	1.00	1.00	0.59	0.76
By hand at home	—	—	0.24	0.14
By hand if no wet nurse	—	—	0.18	0.10
By hand if the child is strong	—	—	0.06	0.03

Table 3.5. The proportion of 29 authors who gave examples in support of maternal breastfeeding, 1500–1800.

Examples	16th century (n = 8)	17th century (n = 11)	18th century (n = 10)	Total (n = 29)
From Nature	0.75	0.45	0.40	0.52
From the Bible	0.50	0.55	0.10	0.38
Breastfeeding peoples	0.25	0.36	0.50	0.38
Classical and legendary	0.13	0.64	0.20	0.34

Table 3.6. The proportion of 42 medical and religious writers who stated the reasons why mothers should breastfeed their own children, 1500–1800.

Reasons	16th century (n = 6)	17th century (n = 11)	18th century (n = 25)	Total (n = 42)
Qualities of mother's milk	0.50	0.55	0.64	0.60
Related to mother's health	—	0.09	0.60	0.38
Related to child's health	0.17	0.27	0.48	0.38
Mother/child relationship	0.17	0.36	0.24	0.26
Quality of mother's care	0.50	0.45	0.12	0.26
Religious factors	—	0.18	0.08	0.10
Others*	0.33	0.27	0.16	0.21

* These included: because women have breasts for the sole purpose of feeding children [16,87,209]; because the lower classes who breastfed were healthier than the rich [31]; because mothers could bring up their children as they wished [93]; to obey the laws of nature [164]; to make amends to her own children because she had not suckled them herself [36].

Table 3.7. The proportion of 11 writers who listed the benefits of maternal breastfeeding, 1500–1800.

Benefits	16th century (n = 2)	17th century (n = 4)	18th century (n = 5)	Total (n = 11)
For mother	0.50	1.00	1.00	0.91
For mother/child relationship	0.50	0.50	0.20	0.36
For child	—	—	0.40	0.18

Table 3.8. The proportion of 25 authors who described the adverse consequences of mothers not breastfeeding their own children, 1500–1800.

Consequences	16th century ($n = 7$)	17th century ($n = 7$)	18th century ($n = 11$)	Total ($n = 25$)
On mother/child relationship	0.71	0.71	0.73	0.72
On the mother	0.43	0.43	0.64	0.52
Problem of nurse/child relationship	0.29	0.29	0.36	0.32
On the child	0.29	—	0.09	0.12

Table 3.9. The proportion of 46 medical, religious and moralist authors who discussed the advantages of maternal breastfeeding with the relative benefits to maternal and child health, and to the maternal/infant bond, 1500–1800.

Advantages/benefits	16th century ($n = 9$)	17th century ($n = 12$)	18th century ($n = 25$)	Total ($n = 46$)
Mother/child relationship	0.67	0.83	0.44	0.59
Health and well-being of mother	0.33	0.42	0.76	0.59
Health and well-being of child	0.44	0.58	0.60	0.57

Table 3.10. The proportion of 46 medical, religious and moralist authors who discussed the advantages of maternal breastfeeding and child health, and the maternal/infant bond, before and after 1748.

Advantages/benefits	1500–1747 ($n = 29$)	1748–1800 ($n = 17$)
Mother/child relationship	0.76	0.29
Health and well-being of mother	0.45	0.82
Health and well-being of child	0.59	0.53

Table 3.11. The proportion of 23 medical authors who recommended the times at which infants were to be breastfed, before and after 1748.

Recommendation	1500–1747 (n = 13)	1748–1800 (n = 10)	Total (n = 23)
On demand	1.0	0.40	0.74
At stated times	—	0.60	0.26

Table 4.1. The proportion of 19 medical writers who prescribed methods for increasing the supply of breast milk, 1500–1800.

Method	16th century (n = 4)	17th century (n = 6)	18th century (n = 9)	Total (n = 19)
Internal remedies	1.00	1.00	0.78	0.90
Local applications	0.50	0.50	—	0.26
Drawing the breasts	0.25	—	0.22	0.16
Other treatments	0.25	—	0.11	0.11

Table 4.2. The proportion of 17 medical writers who prescribed the following major ingredients of internal remedies for a poor milk supply, 1500–1800.

Ingredient	16th century (n = 4)	17th century (n = 6)	18th century (n = 7)	Total (n = 17)
Fennel	0.75	1.00	0.43	0.71
Aniseed	1.00	0.50	0.14	0.47
Powdered crystal	0.75	0.83	—	0.47
Products of cows	0.50	0.33	0.43	0.41
Powdered earthworms	0.25	0.67	—	0.29
Dill	0.50	0.50	—	0.29
Parsnip	0.50	0.33	—	0.24
Lettuce	0.75	0.17	—	0.24
Rocket	—	0.50	—	0.18

Table 4.3. The proportion of 12 midwifery writers who gave
methods for drying up breastmilk, 1500–1800.

Method	16th century (*n* = 2)	17th century (*n* = 6)	18th century (*n* = 4)	Total (*n* = 12)
Local applications*	1.00	1.00	0.50	0.83
Purging or cleansing	—	0.33	0.50	0.33
Reducing food and drink	—	0.17	0.50	0.25
Bleeding or cupping	0.50	0.33	—	0.25
Drawing the breasts	—	0.17	0.50	0.25
Stop drawing the breasts	—	0.33	—	0.17
Internal remedies	—	—	0.25	0.08
Other†	—	0.17	—	0.08

* Includes ointments, plaisters, cataplasms, fomentations,
a major ingredient of which were mintes.
† Includes wearing the husband's shift straight after he takes it off
and wearing it until the milk has gone; apply the linen covers of
salt-butter pots to the breasts.

Table 4.4. The proportion of 27 medical writers
who described problems of the breasts and nipples
in nursing women, 1500–1800.

Problem	16th century (*n* = 2)	17th century (*n* = 10)	18th century (*n* = 15)	Total (*n* = 27)
Sore or infected nipples	0.50	0.70	0.87	0.78
General problems of breasts	0.50	0.50	0.47	0.48
Hard and swollen breasts	1.00	0.60	0.20	0.41
Curdled/clotted milk in breasts	0.50	0.80	0.13	0.41
Inflammation of breasts	0.50	0.50	—	0.22
Ulcers or abscess of breasts	1.00	0.20	0.13	0.22

Table 6.1. The proportion of 58 medical authors who gave
the qualities to be looked for when choosing a good wet nurse,
1500–1800.

Qualities	16th century ($n = 11$)	17th century ($n = 13$)	18th century ($n = 34$)	Total ($n = 58$)
Behaviour/way of life	0.91	1.00	0.91	0.93
Health	0.55	0.85	0.88	0.81
Age	0.46	0.69	0.71	0.66
Breasts and nipples	0.36	0.69	0.62	0.59
Complexion/colour/hair colour	0.73	0.85	0.27	0.48
Body size/stature	0.36	0.62	0.29	0.38
Facial appearance	0.27	0.46	0.35	0.36
Speech/education	0.36	0.62	0.06	0.24
General appearance	0.18	0.31	0.21	0.22

Table 6.2. The proportion of 31 medical authors who described
the qualities required in a nurse's breast milk, 1500–1800.

Qualities	16th century ($n = 6$)	17th century ($n = 7$)	18th century ($n = 18$)	Total ($n = 31$)
Correct consistency	1.00	0.86	0.94	0.94
Good colour/appearance	1.00	1.00	0.83	0.90
Pleasant sweet taste	1.00	0.86	0.72	0.81
Good smell	0.67	1.00	0.33	0.55

Table 6.3. The proportion of 21 medical writers who
described conditions* that precluded employment as
a wet nurse, 1500–1800.

Condition/characteristic	16th century (n = 3)	17th century (n = 7)	18th century (n = 11)	Total (n = 21)
Pregnancy	0.67	0.71	0.27	0.48
Menstruation	—	0.57	0.46	0.43
Red hair/freckled face	0.33	0.57	0.27	0.38
Hereditary disease	—	0.29	0.27	0.24
'The whites'	—	0.29	0.27	0.24
Diseased or sickly	—	0.18	0.18	0.14
Not having had smallpox or measles	—	—	0.18	0.10
Addiction to tobacco/alcohol	—	—	0.18	0.10

* The 'pox' or venereal infection, if detectable, was also a forbidden condition. This is discussed later in chapters 7 and 11.

Table 7.1. The proportion of 26 medical authors who described
infantile diseases caused by the nurse's milk, 1500–1800.

Diseases	16th century (n = 3)	17th century (n = 8)	18th century (n = 15)	Total (n = 26)
Gastro-intestinal conditions*	0.67	0.75	0.53	0.62
All or most infant diseases	0.33	0.25	0.27	0.27
Thrush; mouth & gum infections	0.33	0.50	0.07	0.23
Scabs, ulcers, scales, etc. on head	0.33	0.38	0.07	0.19
Watchings/startings/fears/ nightmares	—	0.38	0.13	0.19
Leanness, failure to thrive	—	0.25	0.07	0.12
Infections & fevers (including meningitis, tonsillitis)	—	0.38	—	0.12
Convulsions & falling sickness	—	0.13	0.13	0.12
Others†	0.33	0.13	0.27	0.23

* Includes colic, gripes, diarrhoea, vomiting, costiveness.
† Includes cough, hiccoughs, excessive urination, suppression
of urine, red gum, yellow gum or jaundice.

Table 7.2. The proportion of 23 authors describing infantile diseases said to be contracted from contact/exposure to a diseased wet nurse, 1500–1800.

Disease	16th century ($n = 3$)	17th century ($n = 6$)	18th century ($n = 14$)	Total ($n = 23$)
'The Pox' (venereal infection)	1.00	1.00	0.29	0.57
Rickets	—	—	0.57	0.35
Consumption	—	—	0.21	0.13
Epilepsy/convulsions	—	—	0.21	0.13
Thrush/aphthae	—	—	0.14	0.15
Others*	—	—	0.29	0.17

* Includes convulsive cough, jaundice, King's Evil, lice.

Table 7.3. The proportion of 44 mainly medical authors describing infantile diseases transmitted by, or contracted from, the wet nurse, 1500–1800.

Disease	16th century ($n = 6$)	17th century ($n = 13$)	18th century ($n = 25$)	Total ($n = 44$)
Gastro-intestinal conditions	0.33	0.69	0.40	0.48
'The Pox' (venereal infection)	0.50	0.46	0.16	0.30
Rickets	—	—	0.38	0.20
Thrush; mouth & gum infections	0.17	0.31	0.12	0.18
All or most infant diseases	0.17	0.15	0.20	0.18
Convulsions/epilepsy	—	0.08	0.20	0.14
Scabs/ulcers/scales on head	0.17	0.23	0.04	0.11
Watching/starting/fear/ nightmares	—	0.23	0.08	0.11
Infections/fevers	0.17	0.23	—	0.09
Leanness/failure to thrive	—	0.15	0.04	0.07
Consumption	—	—	0.12	0.07
Others*	0.17	0.15	0.28	0.23

* Includes cough, hiccoughs, excessive urination, suppression of urine, red gum, yellow gum or jaundice, bladder stone, convulsive cough, King's Evil, lice.

Table 7.4. The proportion of 24 medical authors who discussed the treatment of diseases in infants at nurse, 1500–1800.

Treatment	16th century (*n* = 3)	17th century (*n* = 11)	18th century (*n* = 10)	Total (*n* = 24)
Treat the nurse	0.67	1.00	0.80	0.88
Adjust the nurses diet and thereby her milk	1.00	0.55	0.40	0.54

Table 7.5. The proportion of 27 medical writers who gave reasons for changing a wet nurse, 1500–1800.

Reasons	16th century (*n* = 4)	17th century (*n* = 11)	18th century (*n* = 12)	Total (*n* = 27)
Illness or defect in nurse or her milk	1.00	0.82	0.92	0.89
Illness in the child	—	0.64	0.33	0.41

Table 8.1. The derivation of 73 infant food recipes, 1565–1807.

Century	No. of authors	No. of recipes given
16th	4	9
17th	7	14
18th	27	50
Total	38	73

Table 8.2. The proportion of 40 pap recipes that contained the following main groups of ingredients.

Ingredients	16th century ($n = 4$)	17th century ($n = 12$)	18th century ($n = 24$)	Change with time
Milk or milk + water	1.00	0.67	0.42	decrease
Broth	—	—	0.04	—
Other liquids*	—	0.33	0.54	increase
Flour or meal†	0.75	0.58	0.37	decrease
Forms of bread or breadcrumbs	0.25	0.42	0.63	increase
Sugar or honey	0.50	0.33	0.50	—
Spice	—	0.50	—	—
Egg yolk	0.25	0.17	—	decrease
Butter/fat/oil	0.50	0.33	0.25	decrease

* Other liquids were water, ale, or wine and water.
† The flour or meal was wheat, barley or oats, depending on the common cereal used in the area at that time.

Table 8.3. The proportion of 14 panada recipes that contained the following main groups of ingredients.

Ingredients	16th century ($n = 4$)	17th century ($n = 1$)	18th century ($n = 9$)	Change with time
Milk or milk + water	0.25	—	0.11	decrease
Meat or pulse broth/ broth + water	0.50	—	0.44	—
Other liquids*	0.25	1.00	0.44	increase
Breadcrumbs	1.00	1.00	1.00	—
Sugar or honey	—	1.00	0.67	increase
Spice	—	—	0.22	increase
Egg yolk/egg	1.00	—	0.11	decrease
Butter/fat/oil	1.00	—	0.11	decrease

* Other liquids were smallbeer, milk of sweet almonds, and water.

Table 8.4. The proportion of 19 alternative infant food recipes that contained the following main groups of ingredients.

Ingredients	16th century ($n = 1$)	17th century ($n = 1$)	18th century ($n = 17$)
Milk or milk + water	—	—	0.58
Broth or bouillon	1.00	1.00	0.41
Flour	—	—	0.06
Bread/breadcrumbs/rusks/rolls	1.00	1.00	0.59
Rice, bread or farinaceous substance	—	—	0.29
Sugar or honey	—	—	0.18
Spice	—	—	0.06

Table 8.5. The proportion of 73 infant food recipes that contained the following main groups of ingredients.

Ingredients	16th century ($n = 9$)	17th century ($n = 14$)	18th century ($n = 50$)	Change with time
Milk or milk + water	0.56	0.57	0.42	decrease
Broth or bouillon	0.33	0.07	0.24	decrease
Other liquids*	0.11	0.36	0.34	increase
Flour or meal	0.33	0.50	0.20	decrease
Bread or breadcrumbs	0.67	0.50	0.68	—
Rice or bread or farinaceous substances	—	—	0.12	—
Sugar or honey	0.22	0.36	0.42	increase
Spice	0.44	0.43	0.06	decrease
Egg yolk/egg	0.56	0.14	0.02	decrease
Butter/fat/oil	0.33	0.29	0.14	decrease

* Other liquids were milk of sweet almonds, ale, smallbeer, wine and water, and water.

Table 8.6. The proportion of 40 pap recipes in which milk or other liquids were boiled at some point during preparation.

Century	Boiled	Sometimes boiled	Not boiled	Not specified
16th ($n = 4$)	0.75	—	—	0.25
17th ($n = 12$)	0.67	0.08	—	0.25
18th ($n = 24$)	0.63	—	—	0.38

Those recipes containing milk ($n = 22$) were then examined to discover whether the milk itself was boiled (table 8.7).

Table 8.7. The proportion of 22 pap recipes containing milk in which the milk was boiled.

Century	Boiled	Sometimes boiled	Not boiled	Not specified
16th ($n = 4$)	0.75	—	—	0.25
17th ($n = 8$)	0.63	0.13	—	0.25
18th ($n = 10$)	0.10	—	0.40	0.50

Table 8.8. The proportion of 14 panada recipes in which milk or other liquids were boiled at some point during preparation.

Century	Boiled	Not boiled	Not specified
16th ($n = 4$)	1.00	—	—
17th ($n = 1$)	1.00	—	—
18th ($n = 9$)	0.78	—	0.22

Of the two panada recipes that contained milk, one described in the 16th century was boiled, the other, from the 18th century, was not boiled.

Table 8.9. The proportion of 19 alternative recipes (similar to pap and panada) in which milk or other liquids were boiled during preparation.

Century	Boiled	Not boiled	Not specified
16th ($n = 1$)	1.00	—	—
17th ($n = 1$)	—	—	1.00
18th ($n = 17$)	0.59	0.12	0.29

Of these, ten recipes from the 18th century contained milk (see table 8.10).

Table 8.10. The proportion of 10 alternative eighteenth-century infant food recipes containing milk in which the milk was boiled.

Century	Boiled	Not boiled	Not specified
18th ($n = 10$)	0.20	0.40	0.40

Table 8.11. The proportion of all 73 infant food recipes in which milk or other liquids were boiled during preparation.

Century	Boiled	Sometimes boiled	Not boiled	Not specified
16th ($n = 9$)	0.89	—	—	0.11
17th ($n = 14$)	0.64	0.07	—	0.29
18th ($n = 50$)	0.64	—	0.04	0.32

Of these 73 recipes 34 contained milk (table 8.12).

Table 8.12. The proportion of 34 infant food recipes containing milk in which the milk was boiled.

Century	Boiled	Sometimes boiled	Not boiled	Not specified
16th ($n = 5$)	0.80	—	—	0.20
17th ($n = 8$)	0.63	0.13	—	0.25
18th ($n = 21$)	0.14	—	0.43	0.43

In addition, the 13 18th-century recipes that contained milk and water were investigated to see whether it was only the milk, or liquids in general, that were not boiled (table 8.13).

Table 8.13. The proportion of 13 eighteenth-century infant food recipes containing milk and water in which these ingredients were boiled.

	Boiled	Not boiled	Not specified
Water	0.69	—	0.31
Milk	0.15	0.62	0.23

NB The recipes in tables 8.6–8.13 have been strictly listed under 'Not specified' unless it was explicitly stated that boiling occurred, although it is clear from the context of some recipes that boiling probably took place at some point during the preparation. For example, where broths were used, the usual method of cooking would have included simmering for long periods over a fire [56]. Therefore the proportion of recipes boiled was possibly higher than shown in the tables above.

Table 9.1. The proportion of 5 sixteenth-century authors who recommended, condemned, or said foods were commonly used for mixed feeding.

Food	Recommended	Said to be common	Condemned
Pap	0.60	1.00	0.20
Broth	0.20	—	—
Bread in broth	0.20	0.20	—
Bread	—	0.20	—
Foods like milk	0.40	—	—
Meat	0.20	—	—
Pre-chewed foods	—	0.20	—
Sweet foods	—	—	0.20

Table 9.2. The proportion of 12 seventeenth-century authors who recommended, condemned, or said foods were commonly used for mixed feeding.

Food	Recommended	Said to be common	Condemned
Pap	0.68	0.33	0.33
Panada	0.08	—	—
Broth	0.08	—	—
Bread in broth	0.08	—	—
Bread	0.17	—	—
Gruel	0.17	—	—
Milk/milk + water	0.33	—	—
Milk mixtures	0.08	—	—
Foods like milk	0.08	—	—
Meat	0.17	0.08	0.08
Pulse	0.08	—	—
Fruit	—	0.08	0.08
Pre-chewed foods	—	0.08	0.08
Alcoholic drinks	—	0.08	0.08
Others	0.08	—	0.17

Table 9.3. The proportion of 35 eighteenth-century authors who recommended, condemned, or said foods were commonly used for mixed feeding.

Food	Recommended	Said to be common	Condemned
Pap	0.34	0.54	0.29
Panada	0.23	0.17	—
Foods similar to pap	—	0.23	0.20
Broth	0.29	—	0.06
Bread/rice in broth	0.17	—	—
Bread	0.17	0.03	0.11
Gruel	0.06	—	—
Milk/milk + water	0.09	—	—
Milk mixtures	0.17	—	—
Foods like milk	0.03	—	—
Meat	0.09	0.09	0.11
Fruit	0.03	—	0.03
Vegetables	0.03	—	—
Biscuits/cakes/ pastries/puddings	—	0.03	0.06
Sweetmeats	—	—	0.06
Sugar	—	0.11	0.14
Spice	—	0.03	0.09
Pre-chewed foods	—	0.06	0.09
Whatever mother/ nurse eats	—	0.09	—
Alcoholic drinks	—	0.14	0.14
Opiates	—	0.09	—
Other foods	0.17	—	0.17

Tables 9.1–9.3 show that although increasing numbers of foodstuffs were mentioned, there was no close relationship in the 16th, 17th or 18th century between the substances recommended by medical writers and those said to be in common use in the same period. Foods specifically recommended, said to be in common use, or condemned, over the whole period, are shown in tables 9.4, 9.5 and 9.6 respectively.

Table 9.4. The proportion of 40 medical writers who recommended particular foods for mixed feeding, 1500–1800.

Food	16th century ($n = 3$)	17th century ($n = 9$)	18th century ($n = 28$)	Total ($n = 40$)
Pap	1.00	0.89	0.43	0.58
Panada	—	0.11	0.29	0.23
Broth	0.33	0.11	0.36	0.30
Bread/rice in broth	0.33	0.11	0.21	0.20
Bread	—	0.22	0.21	0.20
Gruel	—	0.22	0.07	0.10
Milk/milk + water	—	0.44	0.11	0.18
Milk mixtures	—	0.11	0.21	0.18
Foods like milk	0.67	0.11	0.04	0.10
Meat	0.33	0.22	0.11	0.15
Pulse	—	0.11	—	0.03
Fruit	—	—	0.04	0.03
Vegetables	—	—	0.04	0.03
Other foods*	—	0.11	0.21	0.18

* Includes clear whey, gruels.

Table 9.5. The proportion of 35 medical writers who described the foods commonly given to infants for mixed feeding, 1500–1800.

Food	16th century ($n = 5$)	17th century ($n = 7$)	18th century ($n = 23$)	Total ($n = 35$)
Pap	1.00	0.57	0.83	0.80
Panada	—	—	0.26	0.17
Similar to pap	—	—	0.35	0.23
Broths and bread	0.20	—	—	0.03
Bread	0.20	—	0.14	0.06
Sugar	—	—	0.17	0.11
Spice	—	—	0.04	0.03
Wines/spirits	—	0.14	0.22	0.17
Opiates	—	—	0.13	0.09
Pre-chewed foods	0.20	0.14	0.09	0.11
Whatever mother/nurse eats	—	—	0.13	0.09
Meat	—	0.14	0.13	0.11
Fruit	—	0.14	—	0.03
Pastries/puddings	—	—	0.04	0.03

Table 9.6. The proportion of 33 medical writers who condemned particular foods as unsuitable for young infants, 1500–1800.

Food	16th century (n = 2)	17th century (n = 8)	18th century (n = 23)	Total (n = 33)
Pap	0.50	0.50	0.44	0.46
Similar to pap	—	—	0.30	0.21
Bread	—	—	0.17	0.12
Biscuits/puddings/cakes	—	—	0.09	0.06
Sweetmeats	0.50	—	0.09	0.09
Sugar	—	—	0.22	0.15
Spice	—	—	0.13	0.09
Broths, etc.	—	—	0.09	0.06
Meat	—	0.13	0.17	0.15
Fruit	—	0.13	0.04	0.06
Pre-chewed foods	—	0.13	0.13	0.12
Alcoholic drinks	—	0.13	0.22	0.18
Other foods*	—	0.25	0.26	0.24

* Includes tea, caudle, opiates.

Table 10.1. The proportion of 20 medical authors who recommended the age at which mixed feeding should begin, 1500–1800.

Age (months)	16th century (n = 2)	17th century (n = 4)	18th century (n = 14)	Total (n = 20)
2–3	—	0.75	0.21	0.30
3–4	—	—	0.36	0.25
4–5	—	—	0.14	0.10
5–6	—	—	—	—
6–7	—	—	0.07	0.05
7–8	0.50	—	0.07	0.10
8–9	0.50	—	0.07	0.10
Some months	—	0.25	—	0.05
Nearing a year	—	—	0.07	0.05

Table 10.2. The proportion of 29 medical authors who described the factors to be considered when beginning mixed feeding, 1500–1800.

Factors	16th century ($n = 3$)	17th century ($n = 7$)	18th century ($n = 19$)	Total ($n = 29$)
Age only	0.33	0.43	0.37	0.38
Teeth only	—	0.14	0.05	0.07
Age + teeth	0.33	0.14	0.11	0.14
Age + other factors*	—	—	0.26	0.17
Factors* other than age and teeth	0.33	0.29	0.21	0.24

* Occasions when food could be given regardless of the age of the child and whether or not he had cut his first teeth included, in order of importance: if the milk supply of the nurse or mother was insufficient; to get the child used to other foods early; if the child was particularly lusty and strong; if the child was unable to suck; if the nurse was menstruating.

Table 10.3. The proportion of 15 medical authors who discussed the problem of over-feeding, 1748–1800.

Statements	Proportion ($n = 15$)
Warned against over-feeding	0.73
Stated over-feeding was common	0.87
Gave adverse effects of over-feeding	0.60

Table 10.4. The proportion of 31 medical authors who associated particular disorders and diseases with mixed feeding in the 17th and 18th centuries.

Condition	17th century ($n = 8$)	18th century ($n = 23$)	Total ($n = 31$)
Gastro-intestinal disorders	0.38	0.61	0.55
Worms	0.38	0.17	0.23
Convulsions	—	0.22	0.16
Rickets	0.25	0.09	0.13
Thrush	—	0.13	0.10
Leanness	—	0.09	0.07
Fatness (bloatedness)	—	0.09	0.07
Other conditions*	0.38	0.13	0.19
Death	0.25	0.22	0.23

* Includes hiccoughs, swooning, lethargy, children's disorders generally.

Table 10.5. The proportion of 14 medical authors who associated particular disorders or diseases with the feeding of pap in the 17th and 18th centuries.

Condition	Proportion ($n = 14$)
Gastro-intestinal disorders	0.79
Rickets	0.07
Leanness	0.07
Hiccoughs	0.07
Lethargy	0.07
Children's disorders	0.07
Death	0.21

Table 12.1. Medical advice upon artificial feeding and its consequences, 1579–1800.

Advice	Date	No. of authors
Handfeeding advised	1706–1800	13
Handfeeding not advised	1579–1800	13
Dire consequences observed	1694–1800	12
Good consequences observed	1752–1800	4

Table 12.2. The proportion of 13 medical authors who gave circumstances in which they advised artificial feeding, 1706–1800 (some gave more than one).

Circumstances in which handfeeding advised	Proportion ($n = 13$)
When no breast milk available	0.46
As an alternative/superior to a bad wet nurse	0.46
When the infant is unable to suck	0.23
Only in dire necessity	0.16
As an experiment	0.16
When necessary to change nurse or mother suddenly	0.08
Better than milk of any kind	0.08

Table 12.3. The proportion of 13 medical authors who gave reasons for not advising artificial feeding, 1579–1800 (some gave more than one).

Reasons given	Proportion ($n = 13$)
Condemned outright	0.23
Dangerous, many ill-effects	0.23
No substitute for breast milk	0.23
When a child is unhealthy	0.23
Should not experiment	0.08
Further experiment is necessary	0.08

Table 12.4. The proportion of 12 medical authors who described conditions said to be a consequence of artificial feeding in the 18th century.

Condition	Proportion ($n = 12$)
Death	0.92
Illnesses in general	0.33
Griping, looseness, green stools	0.17
Wasting, inanition, starvation	0.17
Convulsions	0.08
Rickets	0.08
(possibly) the King's Evil	0.08

Table 12.5. Foods recommended, condemned, and said to be commonly given as substitutes for breast milk, 1700–1800.

Foods	Flour/ bread & water pap	Broths & gravies	Milk	Milk + water	Milk mixtures
Recommended (proportion of 18 recommendations)	0.22	0.39	0.72	0.17	0.72
Said to be commonly given (proportion of 10 such statements)	0.60	—	0.30	—	0.20
Condemned (proportion of 9 condemnations)	0.56	—	—	—	0.11
Dates when under discussion	1700-1800	1752-1792	1746-1800	1753-1781	1700-1792

Table 15.1. The age of weaning children from the breast
recommended by medical authors 1500–1800.

Author	Date	Age (months)	Source (where different from author)
E. Roesslin	1540	24	
A. Paré	1575	24	Paré 1634
Gordonius	pre 1579	36	Jones 1579
S. Ste Marthe	1584	24	Ste Marthe 1710
J. Guillemeau	1612	24	
D. Sennert	1657	21 (18-24)	Still 1931
J. Sharp	1671	12	
N. Culpeper	1675	12	
N. Culpeper	1676	21 (18-24)	
J. Pechey	1697	21 (18-24)	
M. Ettmueller	1699	12	
Nurses Guide	1729	19 (18-20)	
J. Maubray	1730	21 (18-24)	
J. Astruc	1746	21 (18-24)	
W. Cadogan	1748	12	
H. Sloane	1748	8	
J. Nelson	1753	9	
H. Smith	1774	12	
W. Hunter	1775	8.5 (8-9)	
W. Osborne & T. Denman	1776	9.5 (9-10)	
W. Moss	1781	7 (6-8)	
Practice of Midwifery	1783	8.5 (7-10)	
M. Underwood	1784	12	
T. Mantell	1787	12	
H. Downman	1788	9	
W. Cullen	1788	<9	
B. Lara	1791	8.5 (8-9)	
A. Hamilton	1792	10.5 (9-12)	
T. Young	late 18th	10.5 (9-12)	

Table 15.2. The age of weaning in the ancient world.

People: Author/work or region	Age (months)	Recommended, common or actual age	Source
Ancient Egyptian:			
Pharaonic Egypt	36	Common	Jonkheere 1955
Babylonians:			
Babylon	36	Common	Brim 1936
Hebrews:			
The Bible	36	Common	Maccabees 7:27
The Bible: Isaac	24	Actual	Rashi Gen. 21:8
The Bible: Samuel	36	Actual	1 Samuel 1:23
The Talmud	24	Recommended	Margalith 1968
Greeks:			
Greece	6	Actual (wet-nursing contract)	Garrison 1923
Romans:			
Roman Egypt 1	6-36	Common	Lindsay 1963
Roman Egypt 2	16	Actual (wet-nursing contract)	Lindsay 1963
Greeks in Rome:			
Soranus, 1st/2nd C. AD	18-24	Recommended	Soranus 1956
Galen, 2nd C.	36	Recommended	Galen 1951
Byzantine:			
Aetios of Amida, 6th C.	20	Recommended	Paulus Aeginata 1844
Paul of Aegina, 7th C.	24	Recommended	Paulus Aeginata 1844
Islamic:			
The Koran	24	Recommended	Pickthall 1948
Avicenna, 10/11th C.	24	Recommended	Avicenna 1966
Hebrews:			
Maimonides, 12th C.	24	Common	Maimonides 1971-72

Table 15.3. The age of weaning children from the breast said by medical writers to be common, 1500–1800.

Author	Date	Age (months)	Source (where different from author)
E. Roesslin	1540	12	
A. Paré	1575	19 (18-20)	Paré 1634
Mokerus	pre 1579	12	Jones 1579
J. Jones	1579	12	
J. Pechey	1697	11 (10-12)	
H. Sloane	1748	12	
J. Nelson	1753	3.5 (3-4)	
N. Brouzet	1755	15.5 (15-16)	
T. Denman	1777-78	12	Denman & Osborne 1777-78
W. Moss	1781	9 (8-10)	
W. Cullen	1788	9	
H. Tytler	1797	6	
T. Young	late 18th	13.5 (12-15)	

Table 15.4. The age at weaning from the breast of a sample of named children, 1500–1800.

Name	Date weaned	Season	Age (months)	Source
a) *16th and 17th centuries*				
Mary Tudor	1517	Winter	12	Waldman 1972
Elizabeth Tudor	1534	Autumn	12+	Tucker 1976
Jane Grey	1538	—	18	Pearson 1957
Charity Johnson	1545	Autumn	36	Winchester 1955
John Jones	pre 1550	—	36	Jones 1579
Arthur Dee	1580	Summer	13.5	Dee 1842
Katherine Dee	1582	Summer	14.5	Dee 1842
Theodore Dee	1589	Summer	18	Dee 1842
Madinia Dee	1591	Summer	15.5	Dee 1842
Francis Dee	1593	Winter	13.5	Dee 1842
Margaret Dee	1596	Spring	7.5	Dee 1842
John Evelyn	1622	Winter	14.5	Evelyn 1908
Mary Josselin	1643	Spring	12	Josselin 1976
Robert Sibbald	1643	Summer	26	Sibbald 1932
Thomas Josselin	1645	Winter	13	Josselin 1976
Mary Green	1646	Autumn	6	Greene 1929
Jane Josselin	1647	Spring	18	Josselin 1976
John Josselin	1653	Spring	19	Josselin 1976
Anne Josselin	1655	Autumn	16	Josselin 1976
Elizabeth Josselin	1665	Summer	12	Josselin 1976
Robert Thornton	1665	Autumn	36	Thornton 1875
— Josselin	1674	Winter	12.5	Macfarlane 1970
Robert Walpole	1677	—	18	Plumb 1975
— Josselin	1679	Summer	9	Macfarlane 1970
William Stukeley	1687	Winter	0.25	Stukeley 1882
b) *18th century*				
Jack Lovatt	1708		12	Verney 1930
— Marklew	1709		18	McHenry & MacKeith 1966
Samuel Johnson	1709		2.5	McHenry & MacKeith 1966
Case history 1	1733-42		10	Hurlock 1742
Case history 2	1733-42		24	Hurlock 1742
Case history 3	1733-42		6	Hurlock 1742
Lord Warkworth	1743		6	Hughes 1940
N. Brouzet	pre 1750		18	Brouzet 1755
George, Prince of Wales	1763		9	Hedley 1975
Prince Frederick	1764		8	Hedley 1975
Princess Royal	1767		6.5	Hedley 1975
William, Duke of Clarence	1767		4	Hedley 1975
— Armstrong	pre 1771		1	Armstrong 1771
— Armstrong	pre 1771		1	Armstrong 1771
— Armstrong	pre 1771		1.5	Armstrong 1771
Princess Sophia	1771		8	Hedley 1975
Case history 1	c.1781		37	Moss 1781
Case history 2	c.1781		21	Moss 1781

Table 15.5. The social composition of the sample of named children, 1500–1800.

Century	Royalty	Aristocracy	Gentry	Educated classes*	Merchants/ shopkeepers	Others	Total
16th	3	0	0	7	1	0	11
17th	0	0	3	11	0	0	14
18th	5	1	1	3	1	6	17
Total	8	1	4	21	2	6	42

* Includes physicians, lawyers, clergymen, etc.

Tables 15.6 and 15.7 — see pp. 433–4

Table 15.8. The method of feeding employed for the sample of 42 children.

Century	Wet nursed	Breastfed by mother	Uncertain
16th	11	0	0
17th	4	8	2
18th	8	7	2
Total	23	15	4

Table 15.9. The length of suckling (in months) in infants fed by their mothers and those fed by wet nurses.

Century	Wet nursed			Breastfed by mother		
	Range	Median	No.	Range	Median	No.
16th	7.5-36	14.5	11	—	—	0
17th	6.0-26	16.25	4	0.25-36	14.5	8
18th	2.5-10	7.25	8	1.0-37	18.0	7
Total	2.5-36	12.0	23	0.25-37	16.0	15

Table 15.6(a). The age of weaning in Britain, 1500–1799 (British writers and children only).

Weaning age (months)	1500–1599			1600–1699			1700–1799		
	Range	Median	No.	Range	Median	No.	Range	Median	No.
Recommended age	—	—	—	12–24	16.5	4	6–24	9.5	17
Actual age	7.5–36	14.5	11	0.25–36	13.75	14	1–37	8	17
Age reported to be common	—	12	1	10–12	11	1	3–15	9	7

Table 15.6(b). The age of weaning (using additional sources translated into English).

Weaning age (months)	1500–1599			1600–1699			1700–1799		
	Range	Median	No.	Range	Median	No.	Range	Median	No.
Recommended age	24–36	24	4	12–24	21	7	6–24	10	18
Actual age	7.5–36	14.5	11	0.25–36	13.75	14	1–37	8	18
Age reported to be common	12–20	12	4	10–12	11	1	3–36	10.5	8

Table 15.7(a). The age of weaning 1700–99 (British writers and children only).

Weaning age (months)	1700–1749			1750–1799		
	Range	Median	No.	Range	Median	No.
Recommended age	8-24	15.5	4	6-12	9	13
Actual age	2.5-24	10	7	1-37	7.25	10
Age reported to be common	—	12	1	3-15	9	6

Table 15.7(b). The age of weaning 1700–1799 (using additional sources translated into English).

Weaning age (months)	1700–1749			1750–1799		
	Range	Median	No.	Range	Median	No.
Recommended age	8-24	19	5	6-12	9	13
Actual age	2.5-24	11	8	1-37	7.25	10
Age reported to be common	—	12	1	3-16	9	7

Table 15.10. The age at weaning from the breast of children in three different families, fed under different circumstances.

Family	Class/occupation	Manner of feeding	Children	Date of weaning	Age of weaning (months)
John Dee of Mortlake, Surrey	Philosopher at court of Elizabeth I	Out to local wet nurse	Arthur	1580	13.5
			Katherine	1582	14.5
			Theodore	1589	18
			Madinia	1591	15
			Frances	1593	13.5
			Margaret	1596	7.5
				Range = 7.5–18, Median = 14.0	
Ralph Josselin of Earls Colne, Essex	Church of England clergyman	Breastfed by mother	Mary	1643	12
			Thomas	1645	13
			Jane	1647	18
			John	1653	19
			Anne	1655	16
			Elizabeth	1665	12
				Range = 12–19, Median = 14.5	
George III	King of England	Suckled by wet nurses in their own home	George, Prince of Wales	1763	9
			Prince Frederick	1764	8
			Princess Royal	1767	6.5
			William, Duke of Clarence	1767	4
			Princess Sophia	1771	8
				Range = 4–9, Median = 8.0	

435

Table 15.11. The weaning age in 12 rural and 10 urban societies from different parts of Africa (tabulated from information in Mondot-Bernard 1977).

Rural communities	Weaning age (months)	Urban communities	Weaning age (months)
Rural Gambia	21 (18-24)	Abidjan	13.5
Rural Guinea	36	Lagos	12
Rural Ivory Coast	42 (36-48)	Ibadan	14 +
Rural Nigeria	21 (20-22)	Dakar	18.7
Inesis, rural	23.2	Brazzaville	18 (12-24)
Sine, rural	24.3	Leopoldville	18 (12-24)
Burundi (suburb)	24 (18-30)	Kinshasa (I)	16.8
Bambara, rural	30 (24-36)	Kinshasa (II)	19 (11-27)
Highland tribes	27 (18-36)	Baganda, Kampala	14 (12-16)
Kenya Masai	36	Algeria, urban	11.3
Somalia (shepherds)	24		
Algeria, rural	14.4		
Median	24.1	Median	15.6

Table 15.12. The proportion of 22 medical authors who considered factors other than age when weaning a child from the breast.

Factor	16th century ($n = 2$)	17th century ($n = 8$)	18th century ($n = 12$)	Total ($n = 22$)
Health of the child	1.00	0.75	0.92	0.86
Number of teeth	0.50	0.50	0.75	0.64
Season of the year	—	0.63	0.17	0.32
State of the moon	—	0.63	0.08	0.27
Health of nurse/mother	—	—	0.50	0.27
State of nurse's milk	—	—	0.17	0.09
State of infant's bowels	—	—	0.17	0.09
Ability to digest variety of foods	—	0.25	—	0.09

436

Table 15.13. The proportion of 9 medical authors who stated factors to be considered when weaning a child early.

Factor	17th century (n = 2)	18th century (n = 7)	Total (n = 9)
Health of nurse/mother	1.00	0.86	0.89
State of the milk	—	0.57	0.44
Health of the infant	—	0.29	0.22

Table 16.1. The proportion of 11 medical authors who described abrupt methods employed in weaning, 1500–1800.

Method	16th century (n = 2)	17th century (n = 2)	18th century (n = 7)	Total (n = 11)
Painting breasts/nipples with bitter substance	0.50	1.00	0.86	0.82
Hiding the nurse	0.50	0.50	0.43	0.45
Disgusting/frightening child from breast	0.50	0.50	0.14	0.27
Calling breast by foul names	0.50	—	—	0.09

Table 16.2. The proportion of 25 medical authors who recommended gradual methods of weaning and/or said that they were commonly practised, 1500–1800.

Method	16th century (n = 4)	17th century (n = 3)	18th century (n = 18)	Total (n = 25)
Giving food beforehand	0.75	1.00	0.89	0.88
Increasing food & decreasing the amount of breast milk	—	0.33	0.28	0.24
Begin by suckling only at night	—	—	0.11	0.08
Getting child used to someone other than the nurse	0.25	—	—	0.04

Table 17.1. The proportion of 17 medical writers who recommended the following weaning foods, 1500–1800.

Food	16th century (n = 2)	17th century (n = 2)	18th century (n = 13)	Total (n = 17)
Chicken broth	0.50	0.50	0.69	0.65
Minced or pre-chewed meat	0.50	1.00	0.31	0.41
Meat broths/gravies & breadcrumbs or rice	—	—	0.46	0.35
Bread & butter and/or sugar	1.00	—	0.15	0.24
Panada	—	0.50	0.31	0.29
Pap	0.50	0.50	0.08	0.18
Milk mixtures	—	0.50	0.15	0.18
Foods like milk	—	—	0.15	0.12
Cereal/porridge	—	—	0.08	0.06

Table 17.2. The proportion of 7 medical writers who recommended suitable foods for children after weaning, 1500–1800.

Food	16th century (n = 1)	17th century (n = 1)	18th century (n = 5)	Total (n = 7)
Meat gravies, beef tea, etc.	—	—	0.80	0.57
Minced or pre-chewed meat	1.00	1.00	0.20	0.43
Bread or rusks	—	—	0.80	0.57
Milk mixtures/puddings	—	—	0.80	0.57
Panada	—	—	0.40	0.29
Cereals in water	1.00	—	0.20	0.29
Pulses	1.00	1.00	—	0.29
Fruit	—	—	0.40	0.29

Table 17.3. The proportion of 9 medical authors who listed foods forbidden to the newly weaned child.

Food	17th century (n = 1)	18th century (n = 8)	Total (n = 9)
Meat	—	0.50	0.44
Pastry/biscuits/sweetmeats	—	0.38	0.33
Sugar	—	0.38	0.33
Spice	—	0.38	0.33
Porridge	—	0.13	0.11
Stone fruits/almonds	—	0.13	0.11
Too many root vegetables	—	0.13	0.11
Fish	1.00	—	0.11
Fats	1.00	—	0.11

Table 17.4. The proportion of 14 medical writers who recommended suitable drinks for newly weaned children, 1500–1800.

Drink	16th century (n = 2)	17th century (n = 5)	18th century (n = 7)	Total (n = 14)
Milk/buttermilk/whey	—	0.20	0.57	0.36
Water	0.50	0.20	0.43	0.36
Ale/beer/small beer	0.50	0.20	0.43	0.36
Wine	—	0.40	0.29	0.29
Barleywater	—	—	0.14	0.07

Table 17.5. The proportion of 11 medical writers who listed drinks forbidden to newly weaned children, 1500–1800.

Drink	16th century (n = 2)	17th century (n = 1)	18th century (n = 8)	Total (n = 11)
Wine	1.00	—	0.63	0.64
Strong liquors	—	—	0.38	0.27
Ale	—	—	0.13	0.09
Milk	—	1.00	0.13	0.18
Tea	—	—	0.13	0.09

Table 17.6. The proportion of 14
medical writers who associated specific
diseases with weaning in the
eighteenth century.

Disease or condition	Proportion ($n = 14$)
Rickets	0.29
Gastro-intestinal upsets	0.29
Leanness and small growth	0.29
The weaning disease	0.29
Teething	0.21
Scrofula	0.07

Aetiology: Study of the causes and origin of any disease.

Agnus Castus: A tree, also called chaste tree or Abraham's balm.

Aloes: Drug with a nauseous odour, bitter taste, and purgative properties.

Amenorrhoea: Absence of menstruation during the time of life at which it should ooccur.

Anis(e), Anys: Plant cultivated for its seeds; has carminative properties.

Aphthae: Small white specks seen on the mouth and tongue in infantile thrush.

Balia (balie): Italian for wet nurse(s).

Beestings: Colostrum; the milk which is secreted for up to 4 days after parturition. Usually applied to animals but occasionally used when referring to women's first milk.

Biberon: Vessel used for drinking; alternative word for feeding bottle or other infant sucking vessels.

Bigge: Hare.

Bouillie, Bouillon: Broth or soup.

Bubby: Woman's breast.

Calculus(calculi): Stone(s); concretions occurring in the animal body, particularly bladder and kidney.

Casein: Protein occurring in milk and cheese.

Castile soap: Fine, hard soap made with olive oil and soda.

Cataplasm: Poultice, formerly also a plaister.

Caudle: A warm drink of thin gruel mixed with wine or ale, sweetened and spiced; given to sick people, especially women in childbed.

Chous: Small Greek jug for children, usually figured with scenes of early childhood. Said to be associated with the Athenian festival of Χδες.

Churching: The first public appearance of a woman at church to offer thanks after childbirth; particularly used as a service in the Anglican church.

Clout(s): Piece of cloth; particularly swaddling clothes or form of napkin or diaper (tail-clouts).

Clyster: Enema, injection or suppository.

Colocynth: Plant of the gourd family with an extremely bitter-tasting fruit (the bitter-apple) from which is made a purgative drug.

Colostrum: The first milk secreted by a mammal after parturition. Also known as 'beestings' or 'green milk'.

Consumption: Wasting disease, particularly pulmonary tuber-culosis.

Cordial: Medicine, food or beverage which stimulates the heart and circulation.

Costive: Constipated.

Diascordium: Medicine made from the dried leaves of *Teucrium scordium.*

Dry nursing: A woman who takes care of and attends to a child but does not suckle it. The opposite to a wet nurse.

Dug(ge): Pap or udder of female mammals; also the teat or nipple.

Durra: A type of corn; Indian millet.

Electuary: Medicinal conserve or paste consisting of a powder or other ingredient mixed with honey, preserve, or syrup of some kind.

Epilepsie: Epilepsy or epileptic-like convulsion.

Erysipelas: Disease in which there is fever and diffuse inflammation of the skin, producing a deep red colour. Also known as 'St Anthony's Fire' or 'The rose'.

Falling sickness: Epilepsy.

Fomentation: Application of flannels, etc, soaked in hot water, sometimes medicated.

Furmentie, Frumenty: A dish of hulled wheat boiled in milk, spiced and sweetened.

Gall: Bile; the secretion of the liver. Intensely bitter substance.

Gith: Name of plants in genus *Nigella.*

Gripes: Intermittent spasmodic pain in bowels; colic.

Gruel: Liquid food made by boiling oatmeal in water or milk.

Hartshorn: Substance obtained by rasping or scraping the horns of harts, formerly the chief source of ammonia.

Hectick: The kind of fever which accompanies tuberculosis or other wasting diseases in which the patient has flushed cheeks and hot dry skin.

Horehound: Herb; juice is used as a remedy for coughs.

Hydromel: Mixture of honey and water; when fermented is known as vinous hydromel or mead.

Incunabulum (-a): Book(s) produced in the infancy of printing, i.e. before 1500.

Itch: Scabies.

King's evil: Scrofula; supposed to be curable by the King or Queen's touch (until 1714).

Lisbon sugar: Type of soft sugar.

Lochia: Discharge from the uterus which follows childbirth.

Manchet bread: Finest wheaten bread.

Manna: Mild laxative obtained from juice of the bark of the Manna-Ash tree.

Meat(s): Food(s).

Meconium: Black tarry substance present in the intestine of newborn infants.

Milk fever: Feverish attack occurring in women (and other mammals) 2 – 3 days after childbirth particularly in women not breastfeeding; often accompanied by distended painful breasts.

Morbidity: Prevalence of disease; the extent of illness or disease existing in a given community.

Mump: Munch, nibble, chew.

Must: Juice or liquor undergoing, or prepared for undergoing, alcoholic fermentation.

Neonatal mortality: Refers to death of infants in the first month of post-natal life.

Ointment: Preparation of soft consistency mixed with medicament and applied to the skin.

Panada: Semi-liquid dish for invalids or infants in which bread is boiled in water or other liquid, and various ingredients added for sweetening and flavouring.

Pannikin: Small metal drinking vessel.

Pap(pe): 1) Teat or nipple of a womans's breast; occasionally breast giving suck. 2) Soft semi-liquid food for infants or invalids.

Passions: Moods or feelings in which the mind is powerfully affected or moved; e.g. avarice, desire, love, hatred, grief, anger.

Pathogen(s): Micro-organism(s) which cause disease.

Perinatal mortality: Refers to death of the foetus after 28 weeks of pregnancy and the death of infants in the first week of life.

Phlegm: In the humoral theory of disease this was one of the 4 bodily humours, described as cold and moist. When predominant it was thought to cause indolence or apathy.

Phthisis: A progressive wasting disease, especially pulmonary tuberculosis.

Physic(k): 1) Medical; medicinal. 2) To dose or treat with physic or medicine, especially with a purgative. 3) To treat with remedies; relieve; alleviate.

Pipkin: Small earthenware or metal pot or pan used for cooking.

Plaister: Solid or semi-solid substance spread upon a piece of muslin, skin, or other material and of such a nature as to be adhesive at body temperature. Used for local application of a medicament, for closing a wound, and sometimes for mechanical support.

Porringer: Small basin of metal, earthenware or wood from which broth, porridge or children's food is eaten.

Pottage: 1) Soup, particularly a thick soup of meat, vegetables and seasoning. 2) Oatmeal porridge made from oatmeal, water and salt, often eaten with milk.

Poultice: Soft mass of a substance such as bread, bran, linseed, usually made with boiling water and spread upon muslin, linen, or other material; applied to the skin to supply moisture or warmth, as an emollient for a sore or inflamed part, or as a counter-irritant; a cataplasm.

443

Pox: Syphilis.

Primipara: A woman who gives birth for the first time.

Proteolytic: Having the action of decomposing or splitting up proteins.

Ptisan: Drink of nourishing and slightly medicinal quality; originally made with barley water and sometimes flavouring.

Puerperium: The period from the birth of a child until the mother is restored to her ordinary health. Generally considered to last for one month.

Pulses: Edible seeds of leguminous plants, i.e. beans, peas, lentils.

Purge: 1) Aperient or purgative medicine. 2) Cleanse. 3) To issue forth, evacuation (of bowel).

Rachitic: 1) Rickety. 2) Affected with rickets. 3) Connected with, referring to, rickets.

Red gum: Rash affecting infants particularly during dentition; consisted of red pimples and patches distributed irregularly over the skin; possibly infantile excema.

Relief: Raised or embossed part of a design from a plain surface in order to give it a natural and solid appearance.

Rocket: Type of cabbage.

Sack: White wine imported from Spain and the Canaries.

Scrofula: Disease characterised by chronic enlargement and degeneration of the lymphatic glands; particularly tubercular infections of the neck glands.

Smallbeer: Beer of a weak, poor, or inferior quality.

Spelt: 1) Species of grain related to wheat. 2) To husk or pound grain.

Stele: Upright slab bearing sculptured designs or inscriptions.

Teat: 1) Nipple. 2) Whole breast.

Tops and bottoms: Type of rusk.

Tup(pe): Male sheep.

Venice treacle: Electuary composed of many ingredients and supposed to possess universal curative and preservative qualities.

Watery gripes: Diarrhoea; probably form of *Cholera infantum.*

White meats: Dairy foods.

Wormwood: Plant *Artemisia absinthium,* proverbial for its bitter taste. Leaves and tops are used in medicine as a tonic and anthelmintic.

Yellow gum: Jaundice.

IMPORTANT AUTHORS AND WORKS
on infant feeding in English
1500–1800

16th century

John Jones (of Bath) fl.1562–79. Welsh physician, practised at Bath and Buxton. *The arte and science of preserving bodie and soule in healthe, wisedome and the Catholicke religion: physically, philosophically and divinely devised.* London, 1579. One edition.

Ambroise Paré 1510–90. French surgeon, one of the great medical figures of the renaissance; practised in Paris and as an army surgeon. Made many innovations in surgical treatment. *The workes of that famous chirurgion Ambrose Parey,* trans. T. Johnson, London 1634. At least 16 editions in French, Latin, English, Dutch, German and Japanese 1575–1841.

Eucharias Roesslin the Elder ?–1526. German physician, practised at Worms and Frankfurt. *The byrth of mankynde,* trans. R. Jonas, London 1540. At least 40 editions in German, Latin, French, English and Dutch 1512–1730.

Scévole de Sainte Marthe 1536–1623. French lawyer and poet; his medical knowledge was acquired during the serious illness of his son. *Paedotrophiae: or The art of bringing up children,* trans. anon., London 1710 and H. Tytler, London 1797. At least 20 editions in French, Latin and English c.1584–1797.

Luigi Tansillo ? 1510–?69. Italian soldier and poet. *The nurse. A poem,* trans. W. Roscoe, Liverpool and London 1798. At least two English editions 1798–1800.

17th century

Robert Barrett fl.1699. English surgeon and man-midwife. *A companion for midwives, childbearing women and nurses. Directing them how to perform their respective offices,* London 1699. One edition.

Elizabeth Clinton, Countess of Lincoln fl.1584–1622. English wife of the 3rd Earl of Lincoln. *The Countesse of Lincolnes nurserie,* Oxford 1622. One edition.

Nicholas Culpeper 1616–54. English apothecary, practised in London. Wrote and translated many medical and astrological works, many published posthumously. *A directory for midwives; or, A guide for women in their conception, bearing and suckling their children. Corrected from many gross errors,* London 1675 and 1676 (2 different texts bound together). At least 11 English editions 1651–1777.

Michael Ettmueller 1644–83. German physician, Professor of Medicine, Botany and Surgery and midwifery at Leipzig. *Etmullerus abridg'd: or A compleat system of the theory and practice*

445

of physic, trans. anon., London 1699. At least 5 editions in Latin, French and English 16?–1708.

William Gouge 1578–1653. English puritan clergyman and writer, Rector of St Anne's, Blackfriars, in London. *Of domestical duties. Eight treatises,* London 1622. At least 2 English editions 1622–1626.

Jacques Guillemeau 1550–1613. French surgeon, pupil of Ambroise Paré; surgeon at Hôtel Dieu, Paris, and surgeon to three Kings of France. *Childbirth or The happie deliverie of women.... To which is added a treatise of the diseases of infants, and young children: with the cure of them,* trans. anon., London 1612. At least 3 editions in French and English 1609–1635.

James McMath ? 1649–?94. Scottish physician and surgeon-apothecary, practised in Edinburgh. *The expert midwife: a treatise of the diseases of women with child, and in childbed... with fit remedies for the various maladies of newborn babes,* Edinburgh 1694. One edition.

François Mauriceau 1637–1709. French surgeon and man-mid-wife, practised in Paris. The dominant figure in 17th-century obstetrics. *The accomplisht midwife, treating of the diseases of women with child, and in childbed... with fit remedies for the several indispositions of newborn babes,* trans. H. Chamberlen, London 1672–73. At least 21 editions in French, English, German, Dutch, Italian, Flemish and Latin 1668–1755.

Henry Newcome 1627–95. English non-conformist clergyman, preached in Manchester and Cheshire. *The compleat mother or, An earnest persuasive to all mothers (especially those of rank and quality) to nurse their own children,* London 1695. One edition.

John Pechey (Peachey) 1655–1716. English physician, practised in London. He translated the works of Thomas Sydenham. *A general treatise of the diseases of infants and children. Collected from the best practical authors,* London 1697. One edition.

Jane Sharp fl.1671. English midwife, lived in London. *The midwives book or The whole art of midwifery discovered. Directing childbearing women how to behave themselves in their conception, breeding, rearing and nursing of children,* London 1671. At least 4 English editions 1671–1724.

Johannes Baptista Van Helmont 1577–1644. Belgian chemist and physician. *Oriatrike or, Physick refined* (Chapter 'On the nourishment of the infant'), trans. J.C., London 1662.

Anonymous. *The compleat midwifes practice, enlarged,* London 1680.

Anonymous. *The English midwife Enlarged... containing two new treatises.... Of the diseases of little children, and the conditions necessary to be considered in the choice of their nurses and milk,* London 1682.

18th century

George Armstrong 1719–89. Scottish apothecary and physician, practised in Hampstead. Opened the first public dispensary for sick children in Europe in 1772. *An essay on the diseases most fatal to infants. To which are added rules to be observed in the nursing of children: with a particular view to those who are brought up by hand,* 2nd edition, London 1771. At least 4 editions in English and Italian 1767–1808.

Jean Astruc 1684–1766. French physician, Professor of Medicine at Paris and chief physician to the king of France. *A general and complete treatise on all the diseases incident to children from their birth to the age of fifteen,* trans. anon., London 1746. At least 6 editions in French and English 1745–70.

Jean-Louis Baudelocque 1745–1810. French man-midwife, head of the midwifery school at the Maternité in Paris. *A system of midwifery,* trans. J. Heath, London 1790. At least 11 editions in French, German, Dutch, English and Italian 1781–1844.

Edward Baynard 1641–fl.1719. English physician and poet, practised in Preston, Lancashire, Bath and London. *The history of cold bathing: both ancient and modern, Part 2,* 2nd edition, London 1706. At least 5 English editions 1706–32.

Henry Bracken 1697–1764. English surgeon, man-midwife and writer on farriery, practised as a surgeon in Lancaster. *The midwife's companion or, A treatise of midwifery,* London 1737. At least 2 English editions 1737–51.

N. Brouzet ?–c.1772. French physician to the hospitals at Fontainbleu, and physician to the King of France. *An essay on the medicinal education of children; and the treatment of their diseases,* trans. anon., London 1755. At least 2 editions in French and English 1754–55.

William Buchan 1729–1805. Scottish physician to the Foundling Hospital at Ackworth, Yorkshire, later practised in Sheffield, Edinburgh and London. *Domestic medicine; or The family physician,* Edinburgh 1769. At least 45 editions in English, French, Italian, Portuguese, Spanish, Russian and American 1769–1805. It earned Buchan a tomb in Westminster Abbey.

William Cadogan 1711–97. English physician, practised in Bristol, later became physician to the London Foundling Hospital. His views on children, outlined in the *Essay* were adopted by the Hospital Governors. *An essay upon nursing and the management of children, from their birth to three years of age,* London 1748. At least 11 editions in English and French 1748–92.

Daniel Defoe ?1661–1731. English journalist and writer, lived in London. *The compleat English gentleman* (1728–29), edited K. D. Bülbring, London 1890. One printed edition.

Hugh Downman 1740–1809. English physician and writer, practised in Exeter. *Infancy or, The management of children. A didactic poem in six books,* London 1774. At least 7 English editions 1774–1809.

Alexander Hamilton 1739–1802. Scottish surgeon, physician and man-midwife, Professor of midwifery at Edinburgh. *A treatise on the management of female complaints and of children in early infancy*, Edinburgh 1792. At least 9 editions in English, French, Italian and American 1792–1824.

Friedrich Hoffmann 1660–1742. German physician, Professor of Medicine and Natural Philosophy at Halle; physician to the King of Prussia. *A system of the practice of medicine, vol.2*, trans. W.Lewis, London 1783. At least 2 editions in Latin and English 1715/1740–83.

William Hunter 1718–83. Scottish surgeon, physician and man-midwife, practised as a physician in London, and surgeon-accoucheur to the Middlesex and Lying-in Hospitals; physician-extraordinary to Queen Charlotte. *Practice of midwifery by a pupil of the late Dr W. Hunter*, London 1783. One edition. An obstetric diary of William Hunter. edited J.N.Stark, *Glasgow Medical Journal 70*, 167–77, 241–56, 338–56.

Benjamin Lara fl.1788–1814. English physician, surgeon and man-midwife; a naval surgeon, later practised as a physician. *An essay on the injurious custom of mothers not suckling their own children; with some directions for chusing a nurse, and weaning of children etc.*, London 1791. One edition.

Sir Thomas Mantell 1751–1831. English antiquarian and surgeon, practised in Dover, Kent. *Short directions for the management of infants*, London 1787. One edition.

John Maubray ?–1732. English physician and man-midwife, practised and taught in London; generally regarded as the first public teacher of midwifery in England. *The female physician . . . containing all the diseases incident to that sex . . . together with the diet and regimen of both the mother and child*, London 1724. At least 2 English editions 1724–30.

Martha Mears fl.1797. English midwife, practised in London. *The midwife's candid advice to the fair sex; or The pupil of nature*, London 1797. Possibly 2 English editions 1797.

William Moss fl.1781. English surgeon, practised in Liverpool; surgeon to the Liverpool Lying-in Charity. *An essay on the management and nursing of children in the earlier periods of infancy*, London 1781. At least 2 English editions 1781–94.

James Nelson 1710–94. English apothecary, practised in London. *An essay on the government of children. Under three general heads: viz. health,manners and education*, London 1753. At least 3 English editions 1753–63.

Nicholas Rosén von Rosenstein 1706–73. Swedish physician, Professor of medicine at Uppsala; physician to the King of Sweden. *The diseases of children and their remedies*, trans. A.Sparrman, London 1776. At least 6 editions in Swedish, English, French, Italian and German 1765–98.

Jean Jacques Rousseau 1712–78. French philosopher. *Émile*, trans. into English, London 1763. Numerous editions in French, English and other languages since 1762; still in print 1985.

Sir Hans Sloane 1660–1753. Irish physician, practised in London; physician to Christ's Hospital and to Royalty. His collection of books and specimens, left to the nation, formed the basis of the British Museum. *MS letter to the Governors of the Foundling Hospital*, 28 October 1748. Quoted in full in J. Brownlow, *Memoranda; or Chronicles of the Foundling Hospital*, London 1847.

William Smellie 1698–1763. Scottish physician and man-midwife, practised and taught midwifery in London. *A treatise on the theory and practice of midwifery*, London 1752. At least 12 editions in English, French and Dutch, 1752–90.

Hugh Smith ? 1736–89. English physician with fashionable practice in London. *Letters to married women on nursing and the management of children. The third edition, revised and considerably enlarged*, London 1774 (contains the first description of the 'bubby-pot'). At least 11 editions in English, French, Dutch, German and American 1772–92.

Michael Underwood 1737–1820. English physician, surgeon and man-midwife, practised in London at the Lying-in Hospital; physician to the Princess of Wales. *A treatise on the diseases of children. With directions for the management of infants from the birth: especially such as are brought up by hand*, London 1784. At least 20 editions in English, French, Italian, German and American 1784–1848.

Anonymous. *The nurses guide: or The right method of bringing up young children. By an eminent physician*, London 1729.

Anonymous. *The ladies physical directory by a physician 7th edition with large additions, alterations and amendments*, London 1739.

Anonymous. *The ladies dispensatory or, Every woman her own physician*, London 1740.

SELECT LIST OF MUSEUMS/COLLECTIONS
holding good examples of infant feeding vessels
and associated material from antiquity to
the end of the 18th century

MANY small museums in Western Europe contain one or two examples of pre-19th century feeding vessels, especially those dating from the Roman Empire. German museums occasionally possess a wooden sucking bottle, dating from the 15th century onwards. Feeding vessels, breast pumps and nipple shields are often included in pharmaceutical museums. Companies which manufacture feeding bottles or baby foods frequently have a collection of infant feeding vessels; for example, CIBA and Nestlé in Europe and the Mead-Johnson Company in the USA. These tend to include relatively few examples from earlier than c.1700. After 1800, surviving feeding bottles are much more numerous and most folk museums, pharmaceutical and medical collections, and museums of childhood hold 19th- and 20th-century specimens.

There follows but a select list of known larger collections worth visiting. Where a museum has a large collection from one or more particular periods this is shown in brackets. This is not claimed to be a comprehensive listing and, of course, does not include private collections.

Canada
T. G. H. Drake Collection, Museum for the History of Medicine, Academy of Medicine, Toronto. (A large, comprehensive collection with examples from antiquity to the 20th century.)
England
Wellcome Collection at the Science Museum, The Science Museum, London. (Large, comprehensive collection with examples from antiquity to the 20th century.)
Cow & Gate Collection of Feeding Bottles, Cow & Gate Ltd, Trowbridge, Wiltshire. (Examples from early 18th to 20th century.)
Fitzwilliam Museum, Cambridge. (Egyptian, Cypriot, Greek and Roman examples.)
British Museum, London. (Egyptian, Cypriot, Greek and Roman examples.)
Museum of London, London. (Examples from the Roman and Tudor periods.)
Ashmolean Museum, Oxford. (Egyptian, Greek and Roman examples.)

Colchester and Essex Museum, Colchester, Essex. (Has a large
number of Roman examples excavated from infant burials and
in good condition.)
France
Louvre, Paris. (Large collection from antiquity, particularly
Egyptian and Roman examples.)
Musée de L'Enfance du Docteur Dufour, Musée Municipal de
Fécamp, Fécamp. (Large and comprehensive collection from
antiquity to 20th century; includes examples from many parts of
the world in addition to European specimens.)
Germany
Staatliche Museen, Berlin. (Examples from antiquity.)
Switzerland
Museum des Medizin-Historischen Institutes der Universität,
Zurich.
USA
The Eisenberg Collection, University of New Mexico Medical
Centre, Albuquerque, New Mexico. (Comprehensive examples
from early Christian era to 20th century.)
Howard Dittrick Museum, Cleveland Medical Library, Cleveland,
Ohio. (Has several examples of the rare tin nursing cans used by
German immigrants in Pennsylvania in the late 18th century.)

The publisher is indebted to the following institutions and individuals for kind permission to reproduce the illustrations listed below.
Ashmolean Museum, Oxford: 1.1a, 1,1b, 1.1c, 1.2b, 1.7a. British Museum, London: 9.2, 9.3. Castle Museum, York: 9.1. Colchester Museum, Essex: 13.App.10. Cow and Gate Ltd, Trowbridge, Wiltshire: 4.6d, 4.6e, 13.App.17, 13.App.31, 13.App.45. Anatomy Museum, University of Edinburgh: 17.1. H. Dittrick Museum, Cleveland Medical Library, Cleveland, Ohio: 13.App.15. Dover Books, New York: 12.2. Joan Drage: 1.17, 1.20, 1.21, 3.2, 3.3, 7.3, 13.App.3, 13.App.20, 13.App.28. Drake Collection, Academy of Medicine, Toronto: 3.6, 5.2, 5.3, 6.2, 7.5, 11.6, 13.App.16, 13.App.18, 13.App.19, 13.App.23, 13.App.32, 13.App.33, 13.App.35, 13.App.36, 13.App.42, 13.App.43, 13.App.46. Edinburgh University Library: 1.15. Louvre, Paris: 1.2c, 13.App.1. Museo Nazionale, Taranto: 1.9. Museo del Vetro, Comune di Altare: 4.3. Museum für Kunst und Kulturegeschichte der Hansestadt Lübeck: 13.3, 16.1. Museum of London: 1.11, 1.12, 13.App.11, 13.App.26. Nestlé Company Ltd: 4.8, 13.App.29, 13.App.37, 13.App.38, 13.App.39, 13.App.41, 13.App.44, 13.App.47. Reading Museum, Berkshire: 13.App.9. Romische-Germanische Museum der Stadt Koln: 1.11. Staatliche Museen, Berlin: 1.6, 13.5. Thomas Coram Foundation for Children, London: 11.7. Victoria and Albert Museum, London: p.151, p.211. Wellcome Institute Library, London: 1.4, 1.5, 1.7b, 1.7c, 1.8, 1.18, 1.22, 1.23, 2.2a, 2.2b, 2.2c, 3.1, 3.5, 3.7, 4.2, 4.4a, 4.4b, 4.5, 4.6a, 4.6b, 4.6c, 4.7, 5.1, 5.4, 6.1, 6.3, 10.1, 103, p.260, 11.1, 11.2, 11.3, 11.4, 11.5, 11.8, 13.1, 13.4, 13.6, 13.App.5, 13.App.6, 13.App.7, 13.App.8, 13.App.12, 13.App.13, 13.App.14, 13.App.24, 13.App.25, 13.App.27, 13.App.30, 13.App.34, 13.App.40, 14.1. Yale Medical Library, Clement C. Fry Collection, New Haven, Connecticut: 3.8.

breastfeeding
  in ancient Greece, 17-20
  in ancient Rome, 27
  forbidden by husbands, 102, 104-5, 290
  frequency, 118
  instruments to facilitate, 141
  Islamic regulation, 41
  maternal benefits, 112-17, 408
  in maternal-infant bonding, 90, 409
  in medieval Europe, 48
  and mortality reduction, 89
  postures, 118
  reasons for avoidance, 100-7, 406-7
  size of feed, 121
  and social responsibilities, 119
  techniques, 117; learning problems, 90
  time change by late 18th century, 368
  well-known women practitioners, 111-12
  see also maternal breastfeeding
breast milk
  drying-up methods in 16th and 17th centuries, 138
  drying-up, 1500-1800, 411
  expression: in ancient India, 14-15; to discard colostrum, 85; to reduce engorgement, 138
  glass container for excessive, 147
  ideal colour, 174
  ideal consistency, 173-5
  ideal qualities recorded in Graeco-Roman, Byzantine and Arabian periods, 64-5
  ideal quantity, 175
  lack and handfeeding, 266
  overfeeding problems, 121
  oversecretion, 137-9
  pleasant smell, 175
  pleasant taste, 175
  reasons for declining supply, 134-5
  supplementation age, 248
  supply, and mixed feeding, 245-8
  as treatment for sore eyes, 174
  treatment to increase supply, 135-6, 410
  see also human milk
breasts
  damage by breastfeeding, 101, 138-47, 411
  engorgement, 138
  of ideal wet nurse, 171
  preparation for feeding, 117-18
breast pumps, 141
  see also sucking glasses
bromocryptin to dry up milk, 139
broth, in panada, 214
  in recipes, 417
  as substitute for breastmilk, 428

broth for weaning, 385-6
Brouzet, N., *Essay on the medicinal education of children*, 299
ewe nursing, 271
frequency of mixed feeds, 250
handfeeding benefits, 264-5
on pre-chewed food, 239
recipe for panada, 231
recipe for pap, 227
on sucking bottle, 347
weaning diet, 388
Brown, Sarah, on breastfeeding technique, 118
bubby-pot, 309, 312-13, 326
  description, 346
Buchan, William, 233
  on alcoholic drinks, 236, 390
  on weaning diet, 388
Burton, Robert, *Anatomy of Melancholy*, 111, 380
buttermilk, 389-90
Byzantium, infant feeding in, 37-9
  medical literature, 37-9

Cadogan, William, dry-nursing mortality, 301
  changes in theory and practice, 398-9
  Essay upon Nursing . . ., 1748, 82, 115
  infant diet, 216, 233
  infant nursing position, 118
  milk boiling, 218
  mixed feeding, 248-8; frequency of demand, 250
  scheduled breastfeeding, 121
  on suckling several children, 178
  wet nurse wages, 162
Caligula, Emperor, and bloodthirsty wet nurse, 189
Caraka Samhita, 13-14, 16
Cardigan, 3rd Earl of, on wet nurse's injury, 192
Catherine of Siena, St, 48
cereal in pap, 214
changelings, 159
chicken panada, 232
child, meals after weaning, 386
Cholmeley, Hugh, wet nurse experience, 158, 178-9
Christ's Hospital, high infant foundling mortality, 277
cleanliness, desirability, 217
  of feeding vessels, 348
cleft palate and sucking problems, 267
climate and successful artificial feeding, 265
colostrum, chronology of changes in ideas, 86